FANTASY ISLAND

ISLAND

WAKING UP TO THE INCREDIBLE ECONOMIC, POLITICAL AND SOCIAL ILLUSIONS OF THE BLAIR LEGACY

Larry Elliott and Dan Atkinson

CONSTABLE · LONDON

Constable & Robinson Ltd
3 The Lanchesters
162 Fulham Palace Road
London W6 9ER
www.constablerobinson.com

First published in the UK by Constable,
an imprint of Constable & Robinson Ltd, 2007

A copy of the British Library Cataloguing in
Publication Data is available from the British Library.

ISBN 978–1–84529–605–6

Printed and bound in the EU

3 5 7 9 10 8 6 4 2

Contents

Preface

Trinculo: The folly of this island! . . . the state totters.
William Shakespeare, The Tempest

Every summer since 2003, Tony Blair has accepted an invitation to spend August at Sir Cliff Richard's holiday home in the Caribbean. Pictures of the Prime Minister striding from the white sands of Barbados into the clear blue water have appeared in the papers at home, normally under headlines such as: 'Blair's bargain break on Fantasy Island'. It is the contention of this book that the press has got it wrong: the real Fantasy Island is not the former British colony in the West Indies but the country the Prime Minister leaves behind.

From start to finish, there has been an element of fantasy about Mr Blair. Back in the glory days of 1997, he talked of remaking Britain as a young country and of New Labour as the 'political arm of the British people'. In 2003, this 'pretty straight guy' convinced himself that the necessity for Britain to help the United States topple Saddam Hussein from power justified deceiving the British public about the reasons for war. And even as he faced the unparalleled indignity of being questioned by the police about Downing Street's involvement in the sale of peerages to Labour's financial backers, Mr Blair was said to be reluctant to leave office while there were still concerns about his legacy.

Mr Blair was right to be concerned. He may have been the most spectacular election winner in modern British political history, but he leaves behind him a seedy dream world mired in debt and bankruptcy, facing a looming crisis of employment and employability, trying to find the money for a diplomatic and military role that it cannot afford. Meanwhile, its inhabitants revel in the fact that increasing numbers of goods and services seem to be getting ever cheaper, but make no connection between this and their parallel belief that their own earnings ought to rise briskly year by year. Furthermore, few see any contradiction between limitless growth and saving the planet from extinction.

We are told repeatedly that the public sector is being transformed by taxpayer cash and private-sector management expertise and that just round the corner we will enjoy a radiant future in which everyone (or at least most people) will work in the creative economy.

Welcome to Fantasy Island

This book is a companion volume to one we wrote almost a decade ago, *The Age of Insecurity*,[1] a critique of both the market-orientated world order and the apparent over-eagerness of Mr Blair to buy into the new consensus. It is now considered by some to be a cult classic, which is a polite way of saying it is hard to get hold of and not many people have read it. Britain was still infatuated with Tony Blair and New Labour in 1998; the warnings in *The Age of Insecurity* and similar books went unheeded. Almost a decade later, the love affair between the British public and the longest-serving Labour prime minister was over. With his own backbenchers clearly concluding that the three-times election winner was a liability, Mr Blair has booked the removal vans for Downing Street. Now seems a good time to assess his record.

There are some at either end of the political spectrum who view the Blair premiership as a decade of unmitigated failure – or worse. To leftist critics, the Prime Minister is a war criminal who enjoys rubbing the noses of the poor into the dirt while he hangs out with the super-rich, a class he patently admires; to those on the right, he is a supine incompetent who has allowed violent louts out of prison and on to the streets and who has taken the economy to the brink of the abyss. Indeed, it is a measure of Mr Blair's once-wide political appeal that former admirers from all political viewpoints are rushing into print, denouncing his failure to use his vast parliamentary majorities variously to sign Britain up for the euro; to dismantle the welfare state; to introduce proportional representation in general elections; to reunify the island of Ireland; to liberate big business; to restore the prestige of the trade unions; and either to halve or double the prison population, according to taste. In all cases, the theme is the same: the 'great betrayal'.

We reject the notion of 'betrayal', although we believe it is a hallmark of the Blairite fantasy that Mr Blair was able to persuade so very many people with so very many different and contradictory beliefs for such a very long time that he was so very firmly on their side.

So this is a critique of New Labour's record, but, we hope, a fair one. Indeed, the first two chapters make the case *for* Mr Blair and New Labour. He was the dominant political force of his era, the prime minister who managed to rid Labour of its reputation for economic incompetence, the investor in the public services, the anti-appeaser in foreign policy. Nor is it fair to say that he simply got lucky; as with all successful politicians, he had his fair share of good fortune when it mattered, but one does not dominate the political landscape in the way Mr Blair has done, and for as long as he has, on luck alone.

Thus our first chapter, 'Forever Summer', makes the maximum case for Mr Blair and his colleagues. Neither of us is a member of a political part, and our later criticisms of the New Labour years are not motivated by partisanship. Yet it is precisely because we believe there are gaping flaws in Mr Blair's legacy that we are unafraid to start the book by making the sort of expansive list of claimed achievements that would be assembled by a diehard supporter, or perhaps even by Mr Blair himself. It is not so much a case of playing devil's advocate as of pre-empting criticism that we are merely ranting away at Mr Blair and New Labour in a self-indulgent fashion.

At the end of this first chapter, we sift out from this maximum list a rather more modest schedule of what could be considered solid accomplishments for a centre-left government. The balance, we will argue, is made up not of achievement but of a series of dangerous fantasies. How the Labour Party came to believe in these fantasies, and then found itself in power and able to act upon them, is the subject of our second chapter. Thus those who still count themselves Blair sympathizers might like to stop reading at the end of chapter 2. The next seven chapters outline the fantasies of Mr Blair's Britain, and they are bookended by the two we consider the most serious – the belief that the economy can be sustained on ever-higher levels of debt and the belief that the environment can be sustained with ever-higher levels of growth.

In between, the five other chapters look at the fantasy that the decline of manufacturing does not really matter; that prices can continue to fall while wages continue to go up; that the public sector is on the verge of becoming 'world class' rather than being on the edge of meltdown; that the labour market can be both flexible enough to beat off the challenge from China and India but cosy enough to attract more people back to work; and that Britain can play the part of the world's policeman on the cheap. Our view is that Fantasy Island is rapidly approaching a reality checkpoint, and the final chapter gives our view of what may need to happen if crisis is to be averted – or, failing that, if its impact is to be cushioned. In every case other than debt and the environment, we ask simply that a genuine choice be put to the electorate, in place of the current dreamy notion that such an unpleasant, discordant activity as making a choice can be subsumed in the 'third way'. With regard to debt and the environment, we are rather more prescriptive, believing there is little room for manoeuvre if disaster is to be averted. Like someone with a heart condition, there is no real choice between a diet of cream cakes and one of healthy, nutritious foodstuffs.

That said, fantasies are not the same thing as policy failures. So, for example, New Labour's difficulties over public safety and criminal justice are not, in our opinion, the evidence of a fantasy. To be 'tough on crime and tough on the causes of crime' are entirely respectable objectives for a Labour government. That it seems to have been ineffectual in realizing these aims does not make the aims themselves fantastical.

Nor is Fantasy Island merely shorthand for what has been happening in our country for very many years, the process whereby politicians promise to bring back, *inter alia,* the bobby on the beat, the traditional hospital matron and old-fashioned teaching methods, while also protecting the Post Office, the branch railway network, the car industry and the green belt. Once safely elected, confronted by vested interests opposed to these pledges, they promptly choose not to deliver. Furthermore, British governments may well have been kidding themselves about the country's 'post-industrial' future since at least 1987, but never has an administration believed quite so fervently that this future was so bright.

By the same token, the New Labour fantasy is quite different from the routine duplicity practised by the likes of French president Jacques Chirac, pledging at one and the same time free-market reform, an end to social 'fracture', a strong, independent France and a united Europe. Mr Blair and his colleagues have not only signed up to a much wider range of fantasies, but they seem genuinely to believe in them.

A last word: we are writing about Fantasy Island, not Hypnotism Island; about Tony Blair, not Franz Mesmer. For the most part, many millions of people have been more than happy to go along with the fantasies. This will not, of course, stop them from blaming Mr Blair and his lieutenants when it all goes wrong, the moment that, we predict, will resemble the ending of a dream of riches in which the sleeper, on waking, scrabbles in vain among the bedclothes for the million pounds given them just seconds earlier.

We thank our families for their patience while we have been engrossed in this project and thank also the staff of the Gay Hussar restaurant in London's Greek Street, where the book's themes were explored over plentiful supplies of roast duck and Hungarian potatoes.

Larry Elliott and Dan Atkinson
London, February 2007

1

Forever Summer

For the air force pilots taking part, it may have seemed like the opening gambit of a coup d'etat. Hurtling through the sky towards the nation's capital, they had left the nondescript buildings and stubbly grass of their provincial air base far behind and now had just one objective ahead of them: London. With a muffled scream, the jet aircraft lost height rapidly as Europe's largest city came into sight, a city for whose eight million people a blameless and routine lunch break on an ordinary day in the middle of an ordinary working week had just started.

As the aeroplanes swooped above their heads, the defence-less populace looked up . . . in delight. For these jets belonged to the Red Arrows, the much-loved display team of the Royal Air Force. Patriotic red, white and blue smoke belched from the rear of the aircraft, trailing the colours of the Union Jack across the summer sky. Nobody who had been tuned into television, radio or internet news services during the previous half-hour needed to ask the reason for the sudden appearance of the Red Arrows. For word had been flashed halfway round the world from Singapore that the International Olympic Committee had decided, after much cogitation, that the 2012 Games should be awarded to London.

The date was 6 July 2005.

Few had expected it, least of all Tony Blair.

The Downing Street switchboard broke the news to him on his mobile. 'We have won! We have won!' the official screamed. According to his own account, the Prime

Minister punched the air, did a little jig and embraced his startled Chief of Staff, Jonathan Powell.[1]

Paris, with its superior infrastructure and allegedly superior ability to organize large-scale projects of this type, had been the clear favourite. The French capital's mayor, Bertrand Delanoë, in partnership with President Jacques Chirac, represented the sort of ruthless professionalism needed to hook a big fish such as the Olympic Games. London's front people, by contrast, looked, as a group, amiably amateurish, whatever their individual strengths, and doomed to defeat.

This group included, at different times, London Mayor Ken Livingstone; Barbara Cassani, formerly the chief executive of Go, an unimportant airline; Sebastian (now Lord) Coe, someone who had actually won Olympic medals for Britain before becoming a Conservative MP, and former Millennium Dome chief executive Pierre-Yves Gerbeau. London's daily paper, the *Evening Standard,* added its weight, but Paris looked unbeatable, particularly in light of the fact that, unlike London, it has not hosted an Olympic Games since the Second World War. Furthermore, one part of London's sales pitch – that the diversity of its population ought to tell in its favour – seemed a little odd. Few cities would suggest they ought to be awarded the Olympic Games on the grounds that their citizens had little in common with each other. A more upbeat interpretation of this, however, was that most visiting nations would have ready-made supporters here in the UK.

Joy was pretty well unconfined as the news spread, with even those sceptical about the project keeping their counsel. And it barely needs retelling that, 24 hours after the Olympic news broke, London was bombed by Islamist terrorists who left 52 innocent people dead. In a short period of time, 6 July and 7 July came to represent the Janus face of modern Britain – one cheerful, one tragic. But we would suggest that, even without the terrible events of 7 July, there was cloud enough to accompany the silver lining of 6 July.

Because the plain fact then, as has been confirmed since, is that for reasons best known to itself, the International Olympic Committee had decided to hand its 2012 Games to a country with a weak infrastructure, including highly erratic public transport, and with an abysmal record of large-scale construction projects. Just four of these ought to give a flavour: the Millennium Dome in east London (at least £200 million over budget and patchily received by the public); the Scottish Parliament building (ten times its original budget and more than three years late) and Wembley Stadium in Middlesex, the venue with as good a claim as any to be the home of the world's favourite sport, association football, and whose redevelopment was reportedly more than £100 million over its £757 million total budget. At the time of writing it had still not opened, having long since missed its original autumn 2005 deadline. Because of this, the 2006 FA Cup final was staged in the Millennium Stadium in Cardiff, our fourth example, which had cost £120 million against an original budget of £96 million.

From this perspective, the Red Arrows' display appears in a slightly different light: less the good-natured celebration of a piece of welcome but inessential news and more a somewhat desperate piece of staged enthusiasm ahead of inevitable bad news on the Olympic preparations front.

Needless to say, such thoughts were rarely expressed on the day. And indeed, it did seem as if Britain had come a long way in a very short time. Just ten years earlier, on the eve of another gloriously hot summer, there were doubts not as to whether the United Kingdom could host the Olympic Games but whether it could even organize a celebration of its defining national moment – VE Day, the triumphant ending of the Second World War in Europe 50 years earlier. But fears that public interest would be at a low ebb, that people would cavil at celebrating a military endeavour and that the whole thing would be an embarrassing damp squib were banished as crowds took to the Mall to cheer the Royal Family and the nation observed a two-minute silence. Keith Waterhouse noted: 'What the organisers couldn't possibly have foreseen was just how much the nation was in the mood for a party, and how hungry we were to have something to cheer about.'[2]

Another year, and another summer: in 1996, Britain was host to the European football championship. The England team made a disastrous start to the tournament, flying home to begin the series of games from Hong Kong on a Cathay Pacific airliner that they were later accused of damaging. Matters were not helped by the team's opening match of Euro '96, a performance of abject mediocrity against Switzerland (a one-all draw), but thrilling performances against Scotland and Holland and a narrow victory over Spain caught the public imagination. For the first time since the early 1970s, people with no interest in football were talking about the game. Generally peaceful behaviour from supporters and a good-natured shrug of the shoulders when England went down to Germany in the semi-finals made for a memorable ten days in June. Perhaps more importantly, it began the process of affixing major football matches and other top-level sporting events as features of an aspirational lifestyle, something to be enjoyed on costly and stylish television equipment with a glass of chilled white wine and some exotic nibbles. There was brief talk that Conservative Prime Minister John Major could call an 'Umbro election' (a reference to the sportswear manufacturer) in the hope of surfing back to office on the feel-good factor. But it was Tony Blair who showed the surer touch in exploiting the uncomplicated atmosphere of goodwill – 'Labour's coming home,' he declared, echoing the chorus of the official England song.

Figures of hate: the Old Guard out in the cold

So it was to prove when, the following year, on the edge of another summer, 1 May 1997 dawned, the day of the general election. Were the events and atmosphere of this day to have been presented in a script for film or television, any self-respecting producer would have thrown it back at the writer as hopelessly unrealistic: the wash of sunshine, the smiling policemen, the holiday atmosphere. Surely, our producer would ask, there ought to be a light drizzle or a bomb scare, just to add a touch of authenticity? As 1 May turned into 2 May, the mood became more extraordinary still, with the televised electoral decapitation of unpopular Conservative politicians, the crowds in Downing Street waving Union Jacks as Tony Blair came into his kingdom, and a Labour majority in the House of Commons that was actually larger than the entire Parliamentary Conservative Party.

It was like some grand climax to the period that had started with the modest and hesitant VE Day celebrations two years earlier, through Euro 96 to this extraordinary event, less a general election, more a national Spring festival, a vast fertility rite. The economic and industrial thunderstorms of the 1970s, the icy winter of the early Thatcher years, the mist and rain that had marked the opening of the 1990s – all had been banished, it seemed. Henceforth the British people would live in endless economic sunshine. To borrow the title of one of Nigella Lawson's cookery books, it would be 'Forever Summer'.

Needless to say, this phrase describes a longing that, given the realities of the British climate, can be fulfilled only by delusion, illusion or both. And there was indeed an element of fantasy right from the start of the Blair years. We are not referring merely to the fact that those flag-wavers in Downing Street were actually Labour supporters, bussed in for the occasion; even after the biggest landslide in nearly

175 years, Labour bosses were leaving nothing to chance. Rather, the fantasizing was encoded in New Labour's 1997 election pitch, which asserted simultaneously that exciting radical change would follow a Labour victory and that it was quite safe to vote for the party because things would stay much as they had before, with Mr Blair and his lieutenants committed to Tory levels of income tax and public spending.

This split personality ran through the party's first few months in office. It vowed never to be isolated in Europe while promising a bulldog defence of British interests. It loved big business but signed Europe's 'social chapter' on workplace rights. Scottish home rule was at one and the same time an urgent constitutional necessity, an exciting political innovation and something of no real importance – at one point Mr Blair rather infelicitously compared the proposed devolved administration to a county council. The National Health Service was to be 'saved' by Labour, but there would be no more money to do so than had been provided by the Tories, who had presumably been responsible for imperilling it in the first place. Thus, behind the frenetic presentational and media pyrotechnics ('spin') by which the hallucination was maintained were a number of contradictory or self-cancelling positions, the net effect of which seemed a recipe for immobility.

Fortunately for Mr Blair and his colleagues, large sections of the British public seemed only too happy to join in the fantasy in their own right. Indeed, the election result could be seen less as the process by which a mature democracy disposed of an unpopular government and more as a huge-scale piece of school-playground banter, with a child's escalating boast of 'I bet you a million, billion, squillion pounds' becoming an ever-more fantastical Labour majority as election night wore on, as if voters were daring each other to inflict more and more damage on the hated Tories.

A key element in this fantasy was that no one was quite sure what it was that Britain's Conservatives had done to deserve such hatred. Economic bungling? Certainly the devaluation of sterling had been a costly humiliation, but it was nearly five years in the past. The lie about not raising taxes, part of the 1992 election campaign platform, had caused widespread resentment. But the 1995 and 1996 Budgets had actually reduced income tax. House prices had kept falling right through to the end of 1995. Now, however, they were rising again. True, John Major and his ministers had presided over a return to recessionary conditions reminiscent of the early 1980s, with one million homes in negative equity, one million jobs lost and one million businesses going bust. But most of this had been quite obvious by the time of the 1992 general election, in which the Conservatives had been returned to office. Furthermore, it was now receding in the rear-view mirror as the employment scene returned to buoyancy.

What was their real crime, especially in light of Mr Blair's pledge to pursue much the same economic policy as they had done? What could justify the overblown rejoicing at the Tories' ejection from office, the ludicrous hint of a Czech-style quiet revolution, with the suggestion that there was something courageous about voters exchanging one collection of professional politicians for another? Why the sudden invisibility of the three people who had voted Conservative for every four who had voted Labour?

On the night of 30–31 August 1997, the answer was supplied by way of the French interior ministry. Diana, Princess of Wales, had been killed in a car accident in central Paris. Life in Britain seemed to seize up in the days that followed as floral tributes lay in great drifts outside Diana's home, Kensington Palace, while commentators suggested approvingly that the nation was unbuttoning at last and getting in touch with its emotions. In the days and weeks that followed, the Tories' real crime was exposed. They and those like them were not cool. They were not relaxed. They were not part of the New Britain. They were not 'in touch with their feelings'. Forget economic or social policy, or foreign affairs. The Tories were excluded from the fantasy because of the sort of people that they were. There was room for only two parties in this particular grand illusion – New Labour and its supporters in Middle Britain.

All that said, modishness alone could not explain the success of Tony Blair's Labour Party. Edward Heath did not eject Harold Wilson from Downing Street in June 1970 because Conservatism had suddenly become deeply fashionable. In 1992, the extrovert, rock'n'roll-loving curry fiend Neil Kinnock failed to winkle out of office the buttoned-down former bank employee John Major, whose 'grey' persona had long been the butt of jokes. There has to be a very strong case for Labour, an account that quite legitimately puts the best interpretation on the party's actions. This 'maximum' case would suggest a great rolling vista of achievement during the past ten years. Of course, there are 'buts'. Indeed, we believe this case to be so riddled with caveats that the only 'but-free' stretch of territory is a narrow strip of land rather than the above-mentioned rolling, sunlit uplands.

It is, however, only fair to present this maximum case, and we propose to do so by dividing it into five main areas: public sector and welfare policy; the economy; foreign policy (with special reference to what may be referred to as 'muscular multilateralism'); constitutional reform; and the miscellany of social policy and the general ambience that have gone towards creating the spirit of the times we live in. This last section, we hope, shows Mr Blair's Britain through the eyes of ordinary people, rather than grand personages such as economists, commentators and academics. To millions of Britons this is, for the time being, something of a golden age.

We considered a sixth area in the case for Labour: the party's apparent triumph in both electoral strategy and in the battle for ideas (or if not ideas, at least for control of the terms of debate). Labour has enjoyed its most successful period ever. It has never previously won two consecutive full terms in office, let alone three. The coalition between the working class and the liberal-minded middle class is similar to that which propelled Labour to power in 1945 and 1964, with the difference that those alliances fragmented in the face of economic adversity and this one has not – unsurprisingly, as there has yet to be much in the way of such adversity.

So great has been Tony Blair's electoral success that his entirely respectable 66-seat majority in the 2005 election seemed a comedown after the landslide victories of 1997 and 2001. So dominant have he and his party become that it is hard to recall that Mr Blair is only the fifth-ever Labour prime minister, and only the fourth to have won a general election. There were more Tory chancellors between 1960 and 1997 than there have ever been Labour chancellors. Until 1997, Labour had won six general elections since 1945; the Conservatives had won the remaining eight. Such facts grate on the ear in the Blair era; they come over as quite wrong, despite being entirely correct. And there is no greater symbol of Tony Blair's success than David Cameron, living proof that the Conservatives have been forced to compete on Labour's ground, or, to put it another way, to partake in the same grand illusion.

But we decided against devoting a section to the topic of Labour's electoral success. Even in our debased political culture, a proven ability to remain in power is not in itself an achievement worthy of public respect. Some of the parties around the world with the most impressive records of staying in office have also been among the least admirable: Japan's Liberal Democratic Party and Italy's Christian Democrats spring to mind. Conversely, some admirable, or at least likeable, politicians have been humiliated, if not pulverized, at the polls, such as George McGovern in the 1972 US presidential elections and Lionel Jospin in the 2002 French presidential race.

On the other hand, our attempt to present the maximum case for Tony Blair will take full account of the legitimate biases of the Labour Party. A centre-left government that has been freely elected is entitled to be judged by its own lights. Too much commentary and analysis in the British media in the decades since the breakdown of the post-war consensus in the late sixties has suggested that there is something illegitimate in governments of either colour pursuing policies true to their beliefs and their election pledges, whether privatizing the water authorities or dramatically increasing spending on the NHS. Attacking the Labour Party for failing to be guided by libertarian, rightist policies would be rather like criticizing the Rugby Football Union for failing to stage tennis matches.

Here, therefore, in its own terms, is the case for ten years of Tony Blair and New Labour.

Can we fix it? Public-sector investment and welfare policy

> [T]hat great contest which he intended to wage and to win, and by which he hoped to bring it about that plenty should henceforward be the law of the land at Groby Park.
>
> Anthony Trollope, *Orley Farm*

In August 1976, Britain's Foreign Secretary Anthony Crosland spent a fortnight in France, recharging his batteries. As his widow recalled, he jotted down some thoughts in his commonplace book about the apparent turn of the tide against his own brand of big-government social democracy. He noted the 'breeding of [an] illiterate and reactionary attitude to public expenditure – horrible'.[3] He had read the mood more accurately than he could have known. The following month, sterling plunged on foreign exchanges; a loan was sought from the International Monetary Fund (IMF) in order to stabilize the currency, and part of the price of that loan was a package of public-spending cuts that outraged Labour's rank and file. It appeared to draw the curtain on the 30 years of Keynesian economic management that had followed the end of the Second World War.

The events of that autumn, widely seen as the arrival of the bailiffs in Britain, had a profound effect on the outlook for public spending during the next two decades. In particular, they were to blight the prospects for public investment. Nurses and police officers still needed to be paid. But just as a family can make its car last a year or so longer, or patch up domestic equipment at the end of its useful life, so refurbishment of hospitals or police stations could usually be postponed. After all, it was not as if the existing ones were about to disappear. And any shortcomings with the infrastructure could be overcome by the dedication of the staff concerned. Were they not, after all, people with a vocation?

What went for hospitals and police stations also went for schools, libraries, social-services facilities and local and central government buildings. It was true also of roads, public housing and the railways – this last category providing a textbook example of how public investment worked (or did not work) during this period. The electrification of the east coast main line from London to Edinburgh via various important communities had been urged for years. Had the scheme been approved in the late 1970s or early 1980s, it would have had beneficial spin-off effects in terms of reviving some of those communities, the ones that had been badly hit by the recession – in particular those on Humberside, Teesside and Tyneside. As it was, electrification was given official clearance later, for the simple reason that some money had become available. The same *ad hoc* approach governed the building of a fast railway link from Central London to Heathrow Airport; not until 1998 did the Heathrow Express open for business, until which time those wishing to use public transport to reach the airport either took the bus or sat on a Piccadilly Line slow train through places such as Turnham Green or Northfields.

Mr Crosland's fears seemed to have been borne out. But what goes round comes round, and had he lived to see it he would surely have applauded the return of unabashed, large-scale public expenditure under New Labour. In 1996–7, total managed expenditure was £309.1 billion. By 2004–5, it had climbed to £491 billion and through the half-trillion pound limit in 2005–6 to reach £522.8 billion. In the 2006 Pre-Budget Report, it was estimated to reach £554.6 billion, and projected to reach £585.1 billion in 2007–8 – an 89 per cent increase on 1996–7, the last year of the Conservative government.

And within those figures, investment has increased steeply. In 1996–7, net capital spending was £6.7 billion. It was £20.7 billion in 2004–5 and is planned to reach £36 billion in 2010–11. As percentages of gross domestic product (GDP), the figures are equally striking. In 1996–7, total managed expenditure totalled 40.8 per cent of GDP. In 2005–6, it totalled 42.2 per cent. More striking still is that public sector investment net of asset sales was equivalent to 1.8 per cent of GDP in 2005–6, against a paltry 0.7 per cent in 1996–7.[4]

In light of these numbers, it is hardly surprising that every state school in England has been targeted for either complete rebuilding or major refurbishment, nor that examination results have improved (though see the discussion on p. 118), hospital waiting lists reduced and, on some measures, the rise in crime halted. Furthermore, New Labour has turned the tide in terms of rising income inequality. Whereas Mr Crosland believed growth to be a motor of equality, the experience from the 1970s through to the early 2000s had been that, in the absence of strong countervailing government action, boom conditions widened inequality – ironically, only recession seemed to have a compressing effect. But assorted measures, including tax credits – much abused for their complexity – have had an effect on household income. In 2001, once taxes had been deducted and benefits paid, the wealthiest 10 per cent of households enjoyed 6.5 times the final income of the poorest 10 per cent. By 2004–5, the figure was 5.15 times.[5]

Along with benefits and tax credits, the national minimum wage – bitterly opposed by the Conservatives as a sure-fire job-destruction measure – has also clearly had an effect. It is less certain that the modest rolling back of Tory trade union legislation has had any impact on living standards, but it has been an entirely proper legislative activity for a Labour administration.

Gordon Brown: Britain's one-man economic miracle

> I am the greatest, I am the king!
> Cassius Clay (later Muhammad Ali),
> speaking in Miami, 25 February 1964

Howard Davies, Chairman of the Financial Services Authority (FSA), the newly created finance regulator, had hoped for a quiet chat over wine and sandwiches with the relatively small number of journalists who reported on City supervision and similar subjects. He had summoned them to the FSA's Canary Wharf headquarters in the high summer, confident that there would be plenty of time for a relaxed and far-ranging discussion of the FSA's future.

It was Wednesday 19 August 1998.

Unfortunately for the FSA chairman, the Russian government had decided two days earlier to devalue the rouble and default on tens of billions of dollars of foreign debt. Coming on top of the meltdown in the Far East, as previously booming economies were plunged into turmoil by hot-money movements, the Russian crisis threatened a wave of turbulence that could engulf the City of London, Europe's premier financial centre.

For Gordon Brown, it seemed his Treasury honeymoon of just over a year's duration was over. Surely here was a nightmare in the making, an external shock that would, on cue, generate what had become a grand old Labour tradition – the sterling crisis? For those who had taken an interest in New Labour's takeover at the Treasury, it seemed nemesis had struck. Few could be confident that this gathering storm could be headed off by the likes of the Chancellor's wonkish economic adviser Ed Balls, his cheeky-chappie chain-smoking press officer Charlie Whelan, his link-man with the world of high finance, Paymaster General Geoffrey Robinson or even the man who, in some ways, was the ultimate obsessive student politician, Gordon Brown himself.

But then, perhaps it did not need to be. In Bank of England Governor Edward George and in the Governor's former deputy Howard Davies, Mr Brown had picked a formidable combination of experience (the Governor) and flair (the FSA chairman). The City was shielded from the rouble crisis and the economy continued to flourish. Indeed, it has continued to do so ever since, to the astonishment of connoisseurs of British economic management. The usual pattern of events (1964, 1974) would have seen an incoming Labour government trying to clear up the debris from a Tory consumer boom while being itself pledged to increased public spending. These contradictions would resolve themselves in a crash of the pound (1967, 1976), followed by the ejection of Labour in the next election.

This time round, what used to be called stop-go (more accurately go-stop), and which Mr Brown dismisses as 'boom and bust', has, apparently, been banished. The economy has grown in every quarter of Mr Brown's watch. If the growth rate itself has been higher under previous chancellors, that may be no bad thing. The Chancellor, often lazily depicted as having no understanding of the English suburbs and small towns in which so many voters live, seemed instinctively to grasp that, after the 1970s, 1980s and early 1990s, the last thing Middle England wanted was any more excitement on the economic front. And Mr Brown has delivered that welcome tedium in full measure.

There has been no 'Black Wednesday'. An IMF team has not arrived at Heathrow Airport with a prepared package of 'austerity measures'. Unemployment has been at its lowest level since the mid-1970s. The Chancellor has been a respected figure on the international stage, and has served for many years as the chairman of the IMF's ministerial committee, filling a vital space between the fund's full-time officials and the finance ministers of the member nations.

And whatever the Prime Minister's wishes and urgings may have been, Britain shunned the European single currency, the euro. In January 1999, UK membership was thought inevitable even by opponents. But by sitting out the initial launch, New Labour let the facts speak for themselves. By the end of 2006, even supporters of British membership had gone quiet. It was clear that the UK's best interests would not have been served by joining, whatever the arguments relating to those countries inside the euro-zone.

We may never know why Gordon Brown decided against membership when he had, at the start of New Labour's terms in office, been thought to be more in favour than Tony Blair. Doubtless there are many theories, not least of which being that the institutionally sceptical Treasury won him round – had Mr Brown presided over the Euro-enthusiastic Foreign

Office it could have been a different story. But it may also be that Mr Brown found the possible consequences for the British economy to be simply too exciting for his tastes.

Maintaining sterling and a national interest rate brings us, finally, to the first and perhaps most enduring of New Labour's economic legacies – operational independence for the Bank of England in setting interest rates to hit an inflation target set by the Chancellor. As the Bank's all-important 'credibility' has been established, so interest-rate movements have become less volatile and inflation has been controlled. Funnily enough, it was this reform that split banking supervision away from the Bank and required the establishment of the FSA, in the company of whose chairman, Sir Howard Davies, we opened this section on a hot August day all those years ago.

Beating up the right guy: New Labour's muscular multilateralism

> Jeff Tracy: Saving lives is a dangerous business, but it's what we do.[6]

Perhaps the oddest thing about the daring and successful mission to free British hostages in Sierra Leone was that it did not cause far more of a stir back home. The raid began at first light on Sunday 10 September 2000 as men from the 1st Battalion of the Parachute Regiment, along with RAF and Royal Navy forces, began their assault on the camp outside Freetown, capital of Sierra Leone. Their purpose was to rescue six British soldiers and a Sierra Leonean officer being held by so-called militiamen, and they succeeded. One British soldier was killed in the assault, as were 25 militiamen.

Had Margaret Thatcher, let alone James Callaghan or Harold Wilson, presided over such a dramatic mission, it could have swung the next general election. But after nearly three years of Tony Blair in Downing Street, the British had become used to their involvement in conflict round the world, conflict that was promoted as furthering humanitarian aims. In Kosovo, a province of Serbia, Mr Blair had sent British forces to fight alongside the Americans to drive out the Serbs who were seen as oppressing Kosovo's ethnic-Albanian majority. Then there was Sierra Leone itself, a purely British intervention against brutal rebels who had made life miserable for very many innocent people. After 11 September 2001, when the immediate target was the Taliban-run rogue state of Afghanistan, Britain was ready.

And, of course, in March 2003, when most of the rest of America's fair-weather post-11-September allies had melted away, Labour was shoulder to shoulder with the United States in the controversial and dangerous invasion of Iraq. It was still there more than four years later.

None of these conflicts involved the seizure of territory for Britain, along old-fashioned imperialist lines. None even involved the defence of existing British territory, in the manner of the 1982 Falklands campaign. Every one was fought for humanitarian reasons, for reasons of high principle. Those same principles, it could be argued, motivated Labour's foreign policy in general, as in Europe, where Mr Blair earned opprobrium at home for giving up £1 billion a year from the country's European Union budget rebate, a move he believed necessary to avert a budget crisis and to ensure the new EU members in Eastern Europe would have access to additional funds. And they have motivated New Labour's approach to global environmental negotiations, where Mr Blair has spelled out some uncomfortable truths to the US government and may even have played some part in pushing climate change and other ecological issues up the American political agenda. It is precisely because he has been prepared to send gunboats and soldiers on military missions that he has earned the right to push and preach on the environment.

Above all, perhaps, Tony Blair's muscular multilateralism bought him an advocate's licence at the highest bar of international opinion, rights of audience in the highest chambers of world affairs, which he has used to press the case of the wretched of the earth, those on the brink of starvation in Africa and elsewhere. With Mr Blair and his Chancellor in their corner, the world's poorest have had a huge weight of debt lifted from their backs and the richest nations have made pledges on development, education and access to the world trading system. This too is an aspect, or possibly a by-product, of muscular multilateralism.

Who can forget the Group of Eight summit in Gleneagles in Scotland in July 2005, in which Britain's G8 presidency yielded an historic agreement to double aid to Africa and to write off the debts owed by the poorest countries to the IMF, the World Bank and the regional development banks? Previous British politicians had talked a good game on helping the poor countries; only New Labour has carved out the sort of position in diplomatic and military affairs that makes this achievable. Tony Blair instinctively understood that only small countries such as Sweden and New Zealand can link neutralist foreign policy stances with moral influence in world affairs. For a medium-sized nation such as Britain, that option does not exist.

Iraq was the acid test of this understanding, and he passed it with flying colours. The sight of Tony Blair facing down bad poll numbers and a huge street demonstration to do the right thing and oust a regional troublemaker who happened also to be one of the most bloodthirsty tyrants on earth was more than inspiring to many. It finally consigned to history the toe-curling memories of the long, unprincipled period between Suez and the Falklands campaign in which Britain let others do the fighting, however just the cause; in which insufficient condemnation of US military policy, let alone support for it or (unthinkably) involvement in it, was enough to pull large numbers of potentially violent demonstrators on to the streets; in which quavering ministers would time even relatively anodyne announcements depending on whether or not the universities were 'up'; in which it was a sort of article of faith among the British intelligentsia that the South Vietnamese were under some sort of duty to be invaded; in which, above all, Britain would huddle behind the US nuclear shield and borrow American money but was never prepared to fight alongside its principal ally.

As he started, so he finished. Tony Blair bowed out on a pledge to renew the Trident submarine-launched ballistic missile. It was another principled decision in the service of muscular multilateralism, another rough ride with his own party, another piece of national and international statesmanship.

Devolution: hills of the north, rejoice

> We feel in England that we have treated you rather unfairly.
> It seems history is to blame.
>
> James Joyce, *Ulysses*

Before 1997, the extremities of Britain's ossified constitutional settlement resembled something out of the last days of the Austro-Hungarian Empire. Scotland enjoyed a venerable legal system all of its own but no legislature to adapt that system to the changing requirements of time and place; in other words, the very definition of parliamentary democracy. Indeed, the Conservatives had specifically campaigned against the creation of such a legislature in their successful 1992 election campaign. In place of a proper parliament was the cumbersome vice-regal Scottish Office, headed by a secretary of state and with wide powers over most internal Scottish affairs. Wales enjoyed its own linguistic autonomy and its own national government structure, centred on the Welsh Office and with authority over aspects of education and training, health, industry, environment, transport and agriculture. But from 1987 to 1997, all four Tory Welsh secretaries during that period sat for English constituencies: Peter Walker, David Hunt, John Redwood and William Hague. Nor was this executive power subject to any oversight by a Welsh legislature.

The House of Lords remained stuffed with hereditary peers, as successive governments had shied away from reform. Britain was subject to the European Convention on Human Rights but its own courts were unable to interpret it. MPs worked ridiculous, antiquated hours, Whitehall departments appeared reluctant to communicate and public procurement systems seemed almost guaranteed to waste money. Beyond this was an acceptance of, and over-reliance on, a seraglio of self-contained closed shops: the inns of court, the army regiments, the medical profession, accountancy, the Oxbridge colleges and the senior civil service.

From this ramshackle constitutional structure emerged two baleful consequences. There was the emphasis at the highest levels of government on process over results, on elegant midfield play as opposed to actually scoring goals. And there was a cavalier approach to the rights of the citizen, as seen in the miscarriages of justice that came to light in the 1990s and in the alleged 'institutional racism' of the Metropolitan Police identified in the early Blair years.

Tony Blair refused to be cowed by do-nothing talk along the lines of 'if it ain't broke, don't fix it', the motto of the placeman down the ages. He created, in Scotland and Wales, institutions that no one now suggests ought to be abolished. He ejected most hereditary peers from the House of Lords, and no one seems to think they should be brought back. In

Whitehall, he modernized the creaking machine, and Gordon Brown has brought some rationality to public procurement. He entrenched citizens' rights in law. And he threw open the windows in the corridors of power, encouraging freedom of information, the flow of ideas and the movement of personnel between the public and private sectors.

Finally, building on the early work of the Conservative government that preceded him, he worked tirelessly for peace in Northern Ireland, with the result that, in the latter part of his premiership, watchtowers were being pulled down and soldiers withdrawn from the province.

Whatever the short-term carping, Mr Blair and his colleagues will be remembered as great constitutional reformers.

All summer long: living the good life in Blair's Britain

> And when you
> Catch a wave you'll be sitting on top of the world
> The Beach Boys, *Catch a Wave*[7]

For Shannon Sickles and Grainne Close, the huge media attention given to their recent interaction with a public servant at Belfast City Hall was, in all honesty, less to do with they themselves than with the brief celebrity conferred on them by their historical status. Neither was especially glamorous; Ms Close could have passed as a middle-aged music teacher, while Ms Sickles exuded the jollity and charisma of the proprietor of a small but highly regarded restaurant. But on 19 December 2005 they became Britain's first gay married couple. Or rather, they didn't, because officially there was, and is, no such thing. Same-sex civil partnerships are available to any two unrelated or otherwise unmarried (or partnered) people of the same sex, and, in contrast to the law governing marriages, there is no requirement that the partnership be consummated. Thus the same legal structure was simultaneously a marriage and not a marriage and could be presented in the two different guises to two different groups of people – those campaigning for gay marriage and those resolutely opposed. It was a triumph of Blairite 'positioning', and none the worse for that, perhaps. There is a lot to be said for keeping everybody happy, if at all possible.

That said, many people without the inclination for legal niceties used (and use) the M-word. But for those with longer memories, there was a certain irony in the government's introduction of these partnerships (or marriages, if you prefer). In the 1960s, the party had become associated with freeing people from legalistic shackles, such as those binding one or other half of a couple into an unhappy marriage and, of course, the prohibition of homosexual activity. A.J. Davies noted that the reforms of the 1960s were

> the social equivalent of the welfare state and full employment, which were recognized by virtually everyone as achievements . . . Personal relationships and friendships were paramount and anything that came in the way of them, especially if it related to outdated legal constraints, was suspect.[8]

In the twenty-first century, Labour seemed eager to provide gay people with some legal constraints of their own, albeit voluntary.

But perhaps the oddest thing about the civil partnerships was how little fuss they caused. And perhaps that reflects what may have been the best part of Tony Blair's legacy: the laid-back, tolerant and gregarious society that has blossomed on his watch. New Labour ministers tried and failed to find a language to express this development, just as Harold Wilson and his colleagues had been unable fully to describe the social revolution over which they had presided. Mr Blair and his ministers said 'diversity', 'inclusion' and 'modernize' a lot, just as their 1960s predecessors kept talking about 'dynamism' and 'purposiveness'. But that does not matter very much; they are government ministers, not poets laureate. What is important is the economic and social climate they created, one in which this open-minded, indeed open-ended, society could flourish.

Of course, they can hardly take credit for the wide spread of gadgets that few had heard of in 1997 – wifi, iPods, DVD players and the BlackBerry. But no account of Tony Blair's time in office that failed to mention them would be complete. They are the material evidence of the good life in Mr Blair's Britain, just as the beaming smiles of those joined together in civil partnerships are the intangible evidence, and no less real for that.

That, then, is our 'maximum case'.

What of the minimum case, the list of achievements that withstand scrutiny and can be said to do credit to any social democratic government in our time? We stress that these achievements are judged to be such by the lights of a Labour government; assessing those of a centre-right administration would use different criteria.

Here, as may be expected, the tally is more modest. Yet for all that, it is entirely respectable. At home, there has been the minimum wage and redistribution of wealth through tax credits and other mechanisms. The Good Friday Agreement in Northern Ireland will probably go down as an indisputable achievement, while devolution to Scotland and Wales, along with changes to the House of Lords, were, at least, manifesto commitments that were honoured, regardless of one's enthusiasm for them. Abroad, the interventions in Kosovo and Sierra Leone would seem, at the very least, to have done more good than harm. As for the progress on

African development, that would have been a source of pride to any social democratic government.

But it was never enough for Tony Blair and his colleagues to lay claim to these modest, incremental achievements. Instead, they have said there has been a fundamental shift in the economy, the public sector, foreign policy and the battle against climate change. We do not believe that these extravagant claims can be justified. On the contrary, it is our view that they reflect a series of dangerous illusions that need urgently to be dispelled.

But before we do so, let us take a last lingering look on the bright side of the Britain that Mr Blair leaves behind. We genuinely believe that, for very many ordinary people, the Blair years will be remembered in the difficult times ahead as a golden age, as were the late 1950s and the 1960s during the dark days of the 1970s and early 1980s. Through the lens of nostalgia, our times will have been forever summer, with plenty of jobs and plenty of money, with friends always popping round for a barbecue, cheap flights to interesting destinations, white wine in the fridge and a flat-panel television on which to watch the latest British sporting triumph.

That the prosperity, like the sporting triumphs, has been largely illusory is the central theme of this book.

2

The Voyage of the *Dawn Treader*: Blair Takes Labour to the Edge of the World

Labour now has no leeway for mistakes. A crash course of learning the lessons of the past is essential. The prescription for what needs to be done is clear and straightforward.

Austin Mitchell MP[1]

Comrades, it seems to me lately that some of our number become like latter-day public schoolboys. It seems it matters not whether you won or lost, but how you played the game. We cannot take that inspiration from Rudyard Kipling. Those game players get isolated, hammered, blocked off.

Neil Kinnock, addressing the Labour Party conference, Bournemouth, 1 October 1985

But what has come home to me more than anything else is the utter futility of opposition. I did not join the Labour Party to protest. I joined it as a party of government and I will make sure that it is a party of government.

Tony Blair, addressing the Trades Union Congress, September 1995

British history is replete with voyages of discovery. Livingstone, Cook, Drake and Scott all embarked on great adventures, often at considerable personal danger, to put their country on the map. Not all of them returned safe and sound. Tony Blair might be thought an unusual name to be bracketed with those who sailed the seven seas, travelled to the heart of Africa and braved the polar wastes, since even in his gap year – when contemporaries were on the hippie trail to Kathmandu – the closest Mr Blair came to experiencing the thrill of uncertain travel was on the tube back to Kensington. That said, he deserves his place in Britain's litany of explorers, since in slightly longer than it took Odysseus to sack Troy and find his way back home to Ithaca, the most successful leader in Labour's history has taken his party and beached it on the shores of Fantasy Island. Despite the achievements rightly chronicled in the last chapter, and for which Mr Blair deserves his share of the credit, the fantasy is that Britain under his stewardship is well on its way to becoming 'this other Eden'.

The rest of this book outlines what we consider to be the seven main elements of this fantasy – an economy built on debt; the shrinking of the industrial base; the unfinished battle against inflation; the disastrous commercialization of the public sector; the looming crisis in the labour market; Britain's dangerously over-stretched armed forces; and the game of Russian roulette being played with the environment. This chapter explains the seven stages of Labour's epic voyage, a journey for which the party was laying in stores long before the future prime minister joined the ship. Indeed, by the time Mr Blair embarked in the early hours of 10 June 1983, the party was so traumatized by its soundest electoral thrashing in the post-war era that it took scant notice of the new MP for Sedgefield. Certainly, there was not the slightest inkling that the 30-year-old lawyer would one day be charting the course for Fantasy Island.

Mr Blair himself had reason to be pleased; he had been the last Labour candidate chosen for the election, only picked after Margaret Thatcher had named the date for the poll and selected after some traditional Labour Party back-room machinations. With less than a month to go before the election, Mr Blair expected to be trudging round the hopeless seat of Thanet North in Kent in support of his wife Cherie, rather than having a parliamentary seat for life.

For the party as a whole, however, the election result was a disaster. Despite unemployment at three million, despite the devastation of Britain's manufacturing base, despite the riots in the inner cities and the 17 per cent interest rates to bring down inflation, the Conservative government of Mrs Thatcher won a second term with a landslide victory (a majority of 144 seats). In terms of the popular vote, Labour had only just beaten off the combined forces of the Social Democratic Party (SDP) and the Liberals; indeed, so worried had Mrs Thatcher been by the prospect of the principal opposition party imploding in the final days of the campaign, thereby handing marginal seats to the centre-ground parties, that she took it upon herself to talk up Labour's chances, in the hope that the party's supporters would turn out and vote in seats where the Tories were being challenged by the Liberals or the SDP.

So, the state in which the party found itself in 1983 was the starting point for Labour's epic journey, which was to be the political equivalent of the voyage to the edge of the world in the *Dawn Treader* undertaken by C. S. Lewis' fictional inhabitants of Narnia.

Crawling through the wreckage: the emergence of the modernizers

At Oxford in the early 1970s, the future prime minister appeared to have the same low boredom threshold for the minutiae of student politics – the motions, the points of order, the late-night flights of rhetoric – that he displayed two decades later when faced with the Labour Party's National Executive Committee. In his last year at university,

Mr Blair could be found cavorting round a stage doing impressions of Mick Jagger as the lead singer in the student band Ugly Rumours rather than organizing rent strikes or sit-ins. 'He wasn't terribly interested in politics. He wasn't involved in politics, put it that way,' his fellow band member Mark Ellen was quoted as saying in a book linking the rise of New Labour to the arrival of Britpop in the mid-1990s. 'I can't remember having that conversation with him: I think he felt that side of it was irrelevant.'[2]

It was the mid-1970s before the future prime minister had his political baptism, and by then the political sands were shifting. When Mr Blair went up to Oxford in 1972, the post-war economic boom was in its final frenetic phase; by the time he left, Britain had been through a three-day week and inflation was running at more than 25 per cent. Harold Wilson's boast that Labour was the 'natural party of government' looked somewhat hollow by the end of the 1970s; the Winter of Discontent finished off James Callaghan's government and was the catalyst for a civil war in the Labour Party. Those on the left said that monetarism, incomes policies and spending cuts had led to a betrayal of the poor; those on the right said that Mr Callaghan and his Chancellor, Denis Healey, had done the best they could in the difficult circumstances bequeathed to them by a combination of Edward Heath and the oil sheikhs. Whatever the rights and wrongs of the argument, there was no doubt that the Labour Party had – for the first time since the Second World War – lost the political initiative. The 25-year boom from the late 1940s to the early 1970s had been based on social democratic principles – full employment, a mixed economy, investment in the welfare state and partnership between industry and unions. Yet the scale of the economic crisis in the 1970s shook Labour's confidence in its own beliefs; when it tried to tackle the unemployment caused by the oil shock of 1973 by reflating the economy, the result was not shorter dole queues but spiralling inflation. Even before Mr Callaghan's repudiation of Keynesianism at

Labour's 1976 conference, the government had been paying more attention to the growth in the money supply and the public sector borrowing requirement. Thatcherism was never really the monetarist new broom of Tory folklore; the new credo had already been quietly introduced by Labour some years before 1979.

Handbagged: the rise of the New Right

Messrs Callaghan and Healey were, however, reluctant monetarists. Neither would ever have said, as Norman Lamont later did, that higher unemployment was a price well worth paying for control of inflation. To the end they sought to reach an accommodation with the unions; incomes policy and the tax system were skewed towards those at the bottom, not those at the top. By no means could Margaret Thatcher be described as a reluctant monetarist; rather, she embraced the ideas coming out of the Institute for Economic Affairs (IEA) and the Centre for Policy Studies with gusto. The free-market think tanks had been biding their time. The IEA was founded in 1957 during the political hegemony of the cross-party movement loosely known as Butskellism (after two chancellors of the period, R.A. [Rab] Butler of the Conservatives and Labour's Hugh Gaitskell). Drawing heavily on the Austrian school of economists, and owing a particular debt to Friedrich Hayek, the thinkers on the right persuaded Mrs Thatcher that she had to give up the consensus policies that she had pursued as Education Secretary in the Cabinet of Edward Heath, her predecessor as Tory leader. Mr Heath had abandoned an early stab at the hard-edged economic policies that would later become known as Thatcherism when the dole queues hit one million; the IEA convinced Mrs Thatcher that price stability rather than full employment should be the focus of economic policy. If unemployment rose as a result of policies designed to keep inflation low, then the blame for that should be laid at the door of trade unions impeding the interplay of demand and supply in the labour market. More generally, the new right critique was that the post-war consensus had been a dangerous deviation from the tenets of classical liberalism and that the apparent success of the Golden Age was due to the pent-up demand in Western economies from a decade and a half of slump and war. The proper course was to roll back the state, stop feather-bedding inefficient parts of the public sector, create incentives for risk-taking by cutting taxes.

There was early evidence of the Thatcher government's intention to break with the past. The first decision taken by the new Chancellor, Sir Geoffrey Howe, was to abolish exchange controls, the means by which governments of both left and right had, since the Second World War, sought to prevent the domestic economic objective of full employment being torpedoed by hot-money flows in, and more often than not, out of sterling. Abandoning exchange controls was the harbinger of full-blown financial deregulation under the Conservatives, which included getting rid of credit controls, mortgage queuing and – ultimately – the rules governing ownership in the City of London under the process popularly known as Big Bang. Henceforth, demand for credit would be governed in the same way as the demand for anything else: through the price mechanism, which in this case meant interest rates. Even while Mr Blair was cutting his teeth in the internecine local politics of the Labour Party in the early 1980s, decisions were being taken that would lay the foundations for his government's first fantasy: growth artificially induced by debt.

Britain's record of devaluation and sterling crises in the first three-quarters of the twentieth century meant there were fears of investors stampeding for the exit once they were able to take their money out of the country unhindered. In fact, the opposite was the case: Mrs Thatcher's decision to use sky-high interest rates to control inflation, and the high price of the oil that had started to flow from the North Sea in the mid-1970s, meant the pound rose sharply in value. Already beset by dear energy and punitive interest rates, Britain's exporters now had to cope with an exchange rate that made their goods uncompetitive on world markets. For many it was a cocktail laced with hemlock, and they did not survive. By the time Mr Blair became an MP, Britain's uninterrupted run of annual surpluses in manufactured goods was already over. The country has not been in the black since 1982, forcing politicians to look for alternative sources of exports, productivity growth and prosperity. Never fear, said Nigel Lawson, Mrs Thatcher's Chancellor from 1983 to 1989: something else will take manufacturing's place. Here was the genesis of the second fantasy: that Britain can pay its way in the world through the efforts of the City of London, the drugs industry and the 'creative economy'.

The longest suicide note: Labour out of power

In the 1983 election, voters appeared to pay scant regard to the shut-down factories and the three million unemployed. By all the traditions of recent British political history, Labour should have been returned to power after four years out of office, just as Wilson had been in 1974. Sandwiched between Labour's spells in office, the three-day week and an ill-judged confrontation with the National Union of Mineworkers had cost Edward Heath the premiership in 1974. Pendulum politics dictated that Margaret Thatcher should suffer the same fate in 1983, particularly since she had presided over a rise in unemployment to levels not seen since the 1930s.

It did not work out that way. For one thing, Mrs Thatcher had no intention of repeating Mr Heath's U-turn. What's more, she was proud of the fact, boasting that 'the lady's not for turning' as the dole queues stretched to three million and the inner cities went up in flames. Michael Foot, Labour's honourable but ineffectual leader in 1983, expressed disbelief that the British public could give another term to a woman who seemed indifferent to the poverty caused by mass joblessness and de-industrialization. There were three factors accounting for Labour's defeat: the public, deep down, was ready for some tough medicine after the problems of the 1970s; the government's decisive action in sending a task force to recapture the Falkland Islands was seen as an example of that resolve; and Labour was seen as nasty, divided and extreme.

Labour's quest for ideological purity after the great Callaghan 'betrayal' over monetarism had not been an unalloyed success. The redrawn political map of Britain on the morning after the 1983 election showed that the party had been pushed back into its heartlands in the North, Scotland and Wales. South of a line drawn from the Wash to the Severn Estuary, there were only two Labour seats outside London – one in Oxford and one in Bristol. This was not lost on Mr Blair; the first lesson he took from 1983 was that divided parties lose and divided parties that lose touch with the voters are massacred. In a contest between a party that had appeared, with the victory in the South Atlantic, to draw a line under a quarter of a century of national decline and one that appeared only to know how to be at war with itself, there was only ever going to be one winner.

The Falklands could easily have gone badly wrong for Mrs Thatcher, but the gamble paid off both militarily and politically. Faced with a Labour opposition, including the card-carrying member of the Campaign for Nuclear Disarmament, Tony Blair, the Prime Minister exploited her advantage to the full, comparing her own defence of British sovereignty with Labour's one-sided nuclear disarmament. Not that defence was the only issue. Labour was also proposing withdrawal from the European Economic Community (now European Union), the nationalization of large chunks of industry and the City and increased borrowing to pay for a back-to-work programme. The left of the party was in control after the defection of the right to the SDP, and it had come up with a manifesto that was by equal parts radical, long, unreadable and deeply, deeply unpopular. It is unlikely Mr Blair believed in much if any of it, but like a good barrister he learned his brief, received the inevitable verdict from the jury and tried to work out how to do better next time. Addressing the Labour Party conference in 2006, Mr Blair said that when he came up from London to speak to party members in his constituency, a moderate seat in a generally moderate part of Britain, it was the first sensible political conversation he had experienced for some time. Mr Blair's analysis of Labour's defeat went deeper than Mr Foot's splenetic disbelief; Mrs Thatcher was doing some things that were necessary and popular as well as things that were brutal and damaging. She was also showing that sticking to policies – even unpopular policies – could pay off.

By the mid-1980s, the first leg of the voyage to Fantasy Island was complete; the intellectual underpinnings of the Britain of 1986 – tough on inflation, free capital markets, curbs on trade unions, increasing individualism – were altogether different from those pertaining to when Mr Blair had left Oxford in 1975. He quickly became convinced that the party had to reach out from its inner-city strongholds and connect with the millions of aspiring working-class voters lost to Mrs Thatcher. Mr Blair's belief, forged in the difficult days of the 1980s, was that Labour had a choice: either it could move with the times and recognize that Thatcherism was more in tune with the Britain of the 1980s or it could condemn itself to permanent opposition and increasing irrelevance. Indeed, in some ways the 1987 election – when Mrs Thatcher won again, this time with a majority of just over 100 – gave the first inkling of where British politics was heading. There was the re-branding of Neil Kinnock, the makeover of the party with the red rose and music by Brahms, the heavy emphasis on PR. Flush with success after privatizing British Telecom and British Gas, it was Britain's first post-industrial election; the manufacturing industry (or what was left of it) took a back seat as the government showcased the City of London, fresh from its radical overhaul a year earlier. Britain was no longer about making stuff; that was old hat. The new Britain was making programmes for the new era of multi-channel TV, then in its infancy; it was about deal-making and risk-taking. It was about creativity and enterprise. Or so it was said.

Another brick in the wall: the Cold War ends

There was, of course, no guarantee that the Labour Party would listen to the young member for Sedgefield. It was certainly true that the party had started to tack back towards the centre even before the 1983 general election, and this process was accelerated by the scale of Mrs Thatcher's triumph. Neil Kinnock jettisoned large chunks of the 1983 manifesto, including withdrawal from Europe and wholesale nationalization, but Labour was still a recognizably social democratic party, supporting a middle way between the two opposite poles of the Cold War, the harshness of free-market capitalism on the one hand and the cruelties and inefficiencies of communism on the other. For the entire post-war period, the fear that the working class in Western Europe might be seduced by the fool's paradise of the Soviet Union meant there was pressure for policy makers to interfere in the workings of the market. As such, productivity gains were shared between capital and labour; progressive taxation was used to fund public health and education programmes; unions were considered social partners. Mr Kinnock was very much part of this tradition; when he took over from

Mr Foot as leader he was considered a man of the 'soft left' and, as the challenge from the 'hard left' receded, he was in touch with the mainstream of the party. The so-called leadership 'dream ticket' was completed by Roy Hattersley, then considered to be on the right of the party but now seen as one of Mr Blair's most effective left-wing critics. It goes without saying that it is not Mr Hattersley who has changed in the intervening period.

The assumption, valid enough it seemed during the nuclear build-up of the early 1980s, was that the Cold War would continue indefinitely, but the sudden collapse of the Soviet Union at the end of the 1980s changed the nature of Western politics. Ever since, it has become fashionable to argue that the tearing down of the Berlin Wall was as grievous a blow to social democracy as it was to communism, yet the people of Norway, Sweden, West Germany, Austria, Britain, France and America all saw benefits from social democracy that were not evident to the citizens of the Soviet Union between 1917 and 1991, benefits which in many of those countries continue to this day. Indeed, it could be said that following America's victory in the Cold War, a robust defence of social democratic values was needed more than ever, since the impact was to reinvigorate capitalism and make those who supported a more overtly laissez-faire approach push back the boundaries of what had been acceptable under the post-war consensus. Put simply, there was less pressure to make concessions to the workers than there had been for the previous four decades; they now had nowhere else to go.

Going global: the free market goes on tour

The arrival of a unipolar world following the Kremlin's decision to hoist the white flag at the end of the Cold War was one aspect of the New World Order; the other was the series of technological, financial, economic and political changes bundled together under the catch-all term 'globalization'. For owners of capital in the West, the opportunity to produce in low-cost destinations meant higher profits; for consumers in the West, globalization meant cheaper imports and a higher standard of living, provided, of course, that they were still in a job. For the new breed of up-and-coming leaders on the centre-left, the Bill Clintons and the Tony Blairs, globalization meant the rules of the game had changed for ever. No longer could it be argued, as it was in the heyday of social democracy, that the market should serve the people; that was very much Old Labour and Old Democrat. Now, the people had to serve the market. Governments could no longer rely on companies being prepared to share the fruits of growth with their employees or to pay the business taxes that helped to fund welfare states. Instead, tax rates had to be competitive (i.e. lower) in order to prevent business from upping sticks and heading off to East or South Asia. As far as workers were concerned, the state could help through investment in education and skills, but the option of protecting citizens from the full blast of global competition was no longer available. Mr Blair, on many occasions, voiced the commonly held view that globalization was unstoppable; in vain did Keynesian critics such as Wynne Godley argue that the transformation of the global economy should not be seen as a natural phenomenon like a tsunami but rather a result of political decisions taken at the behest of vested interests in the West – principally, but not exclusively, the financial interests and those running trans-national companies.

The rise of social democracy in the West between 1850 and 1950 had been the response not only to the misery and inequity of the first epoch of industrialization but also a grudging acceptance by the rich and powerful that an ever-wider gap between rich and poor was incompatible with democracy. In the 1990s, however, the combined impact of globalization and the end of the Cold War engendered a sense of helplessness, almost despair, into social democratic parties, particularly those in the Anglo-Saxon countries. Mr Blair and Mr Clinton had the answer for their comrades: all was not lost if parties of the centre-left decided to jettison all the old ideological baggage and travel light. The solution to the left's problems was not to fight the global but to learn how to love it. Gradually, the central New Labour fantasy took shape: societies had to adapt to the essentially benign forces of globalization, and the way to bring about that transformation might be to take some of the policies normally associated with the right – privatization, competition policy, welfare reform – and pursue them with more vigour and urgency. Messrs Clinton and Blair, for example, have been far tougher on welfare reform than Mr Reagan and Mrs Thatcher ever were in the 1980s.

September song: the Tories' long goodbye

Bill Clinton won the race for the White House for the Democrats for the first time in 16 years in 1992, but there seemed scant chance of Labour's modernizers putting their new thinking into practice any time soon. Labour had just suffered its fourth straight electoral defeat. This had been inflicted by the Conservatives seven months before Mr Clinton's victory, despite the second big recession in a decade, with record numbers of people losing their homes and going bankrupt.

The two-year period between April 1992 and May 1994 was the making of Tony Blair. His views about where the Labour Party needed to go had been crystallized by its ability, once again, to snatch defeat from the jaws of victory, but the arrival of John Smith – a moderate social democrat of the old school – as leader of the Opposition meant there was little immediate prospect of Mr Blair winning over his party, let alone the country.

The Conservatives began their fourth term in good shape and inflicted another defeat on Labour at the local government elections a month after April's general election. In the early summer, Prime Minister John Major could be spotted in hospitality boxes at cricket matches, sipping a glass of champagne and exuding quiet self-confidence. The subliminal message was that Britain had had a fortunate escape; it could have fallen for Neil Kinnock and suffered higher taxes and higher mortgage rates, but in the end it had done the sensible thing, the right thing, and stuck with the man who liked to eat a full English breakfast at a Little Chef and knew his way round a B&Q superstore.

The post-election honeymoon, however, did not last long for Mr Major. When the Danes voted 'No' in the referendum on the Maastricht Treaty in early June 1992, the result unsettled the foreign exchange markets and left dealers anxiously awaiting the plebiscite in France in late September. The Maastricht Treaty was the blueprint for turning the Exchange Rate Mechanism (ERM) – a system whereby Europe's currencies borrowed credibility and strength from the German mark – into a single currency. Concern that the road to monetary union might be bumpy or, even worse, a dead end, affected sentiment towards sterling, which had joined the ERM in October 1990.

Barely five months after the 1992 election, in the seminal political event of the past three decades, concerted action by financial speculators led by George Soros saw the pound turfed out of the ERM, but not before a day of drama that cost the Conservatives their reputation for sound economic management. 'Black Wednesday' (16 September 1992) dawned with the Bank of England emptying the vaults of foreign currency reserves in an attempt to fend off the speculative attacks on sterling. It ended with Mr Lamont calling off a decision to raise interest rates to 15 per cent – up from 10 per cent when trading had started in London – and announcing that the ERM was history.

For Labour, Black Wednesday was a godsend. Financial crises were hardly uncommon in twentieth-century Britain; instead, they tended to arrive with uncanny regularity once a generation. In 1931, in circumstances akin to those in 1992, the onset of the Great Depression proved incompatible with the gold standard; in both 1949 and 1967, the pound had to be devalued in order to boost the competitiveness of British exports. There was one common factor to these events – and to Britain's appeal to the IMF for a loan in 1976: Labour was in government, and was accordingly blamed for all of them. It little mattered that it had been Winston Churchill who in 1925 foolishly put Britain back on the gold standard at its pre-First World War rate, nor that it was the Conservative Party's dash for growth ahead of the 1964 election that left Harold Wilson facing the prospect of devaluation for his first three years in power. Conservative political hegemony in the twentieth century was in part the consequence of never being in power when the crisis broke; Labour took the tough decisions, paid a high political price and then had to watch as the Conservatives reaped the benefits of the more benign economic climate created by the devaluation. In 1992, the tables were turned. The Tories presided over the devaluation and paid the political price.

Mr Blair's view of the post-Black-Wednesday political landscape was that Labour's modernization programme was incomplete and that Mr Smith was relying too heavily on voters being prepared to punish the Conservatives for the ERM fiasco. This was a view shared by Gordon Brown, who as the new Shadow Chancellor spent the two years after the 1992 election convincing voters that Labour no longer wanted to raise the taxes and National Insurance contributions of the rich in order to provide higher pensions and more generous child benefits. As one of Mr Brown's biographers put it:

> Brown was persuaded that Labour had simply not been rigorous enough in persuading the electorate that the economy was safe in its hands and that it wasn't a vindictive imposer of taxes on the successful and the aspirational. So he tore up Smith's shadow Budget. Gone were the explicit plans to raise taxes. He then proceeded to use his new authority to block any attempts by his front bench colleagues to come up with policies that had spending implications.[3]

Economics was never Blair's strongest suit but, in truth, he was better off shadowing first Kenneth Clarke and then Michael Howard at the Home Office during this period, since Brown's repudiation of 'tax and spend' led to a sharp fall in the Shadow Chancellor's popularity within the party, while Mr Blair attracted plaudits for his most memorable soundbite, that Labour would be 'tough on crime, tough on the causes of crime'.

Mr Smith had never really warmed to Mr Blair; there was, perhaps, too much distance between the two lawyers – the one from Oxford with little ideological baggage and the other with deep roots in a Scottish tradition of redistribution. Mr Smith thought Mr Blair a bit flash and self-serving; Mr Blair, according to his biographer, Anthony Seldon, considered Mr Smith lazy and complacent.[4] The Labour leader had made it clear, when Mr Blair flirted with the idea in 1992, that he wanted Margaret Beckett to be his deputy, and was suspicious of the ultra-modernizers. Given the choice, Mr Smith would have picked Gordon Brown as his successor, but when the Opposition leader died suddenly in May 1994, Mr Blair was in by far the stronger position to seize the leadership.

Cometh the hour, cometh the man

The seventh and final port of call on the voyage to Fantasy Island is the personality of Mr Blair himself: a brilliant communicator, a clear thinker and – behind the charm – utterly ruthless. He is not, and never has been, a crypto-Tory, nor is he devoid of principles. The fact that those principles are rooted in the moral teachings of the church rather than the traditions of the Labour Party has proved both an advantage, as he sought to reshape what it means to be on the left in modern Britain, and a curse, to the extent that Blairism has always had shallow roots in the party. What really has marked him out from other politicians, even other Labour leaders, is not his undoubted abilities but his abundance of the quality Napoleon looked for in all his generals – luck.

Securing Sedgefield at the eleventh hour was merely the start of a streak of good fortune. Mr Blair might easily have had to wait another four years to find a seat, and even then he might not have found one as safe as Sedgefield. Had it taken him until 1987 to find his way to Westminster, he would have had no prospect of becoming leader in 1994 on the death of Mr Smith. Other Labour leaders have been silver-tongued; Harold Wilson, for example, was a powerful public speaker, but inherited economic problems from the Tories in both 1964 and 1974. Other Labour leaders have had a ruthless streak; Clement Attlee was notorious for the brutal way in which he despatched ministers deemed not up to the job, but in 1945 Britain was bankrupt after six years of war and the new socialist government had to go cap in hand to the Americans for a loan. Labour had had but four prime ministers until the moment John Major left 10 Downing Street on the afternoon of 2 May 1997. All had been talented in their own way, but none could match Mr Blair's luck in a 20-year-streak that lasted from the night in May 1983 when he beat off the challenge of the left-wing MP Les Huckfield for the Sedgefield seat to the moment in March 2003 when he sent British troops into Iraq. Mr Blair, too, was gifted, yet in politics that is not always enough; those who succeed need good fortune, and Mr Blair had it. For those two decades, a stupendously long term in modern politics, he had the Midas touch.

Mr Blair was not a one-off, however, but rather a distinct type. There are generally two types of Labour leaders: those who come from humble backgrounds, like James Callaghan and Ramsay MacDonald, and haul themselves up by their bootstraps; and the middle-class progressives, like Clement Attlee (Haileybury and Oxford) and Hugh Gaitskell (Winchester and Oxford), who reject – up to a point – their privileged background. Tony Blair (Fettes and Oxford) is in the second group, although he was, in his own words, a politician from the rock'n'roll generation that grew up with the Beatles and the counter-culture. Mr Attlee had fought in the trenches in the First World War; somewhat ironically, he also saw service in what is now Iraq and was wounded planting a red flag on trenches abandoned by the Turks to prevent his men being shelled by their own artillery. He had seen poverty at first hand while working in the East End of London and been radicalized by it. Mr Blair's biographer recalls how he was scathing about the Combined Cadet Force at Fettes, but much enjoyed playing the part of Captain Stanhope in *Journey's End*, R.C. Sheriff's play set on the Western Front.[5] Mr Blair's first family home as a married man was in Hackney, one of inner London's less salubrious boroughs, and one where the scars of Mrs Thatcher's first term were deep and livid, but he was never seen as especially interested in politics at university and his background – father a Tory, public school, career in one of the professions – was more like that of the archetypal Conservative MP from the 1950s or 1960s, taking a seat on the green benches of the House of Commons out of a sense of duty rather than conviction.

Mr Blair's background shaped him, as it does all politicians. He had bucked against authority in a measured way at Fettes (breaking school rules but not the law; smoking but drawing the line at illegal drugs), but had not been radicalized by the street-marching 1960s. Mr Blair's lack of political conviction in the mid-1970s was a handicap early in his political career, for he was considered something of an upper-crust dilettante by the party faithful in Hackney and failed to be selected as a council candidate. Later, however, it proved something of a blessing, with the MP for Sedgefield able to see clearly that Labour would never recover as a serious political force until it stopped speaking to itself and talked to the voters instead. Mr Blair's 'blokeishness' – the interest in football, the lapses into estuary English – was as contrived as Harold Wilson's pipe and alleged fondness for HP Sauce, but one of his great strengths as Labour leader was that he appeared less weird than colleagues who had spent a lifetime involved in political intrigue. In 1975, when Mr Blair was belting out *Honky Tonk Woman* at Oxford balls, Gordon Brown was calling for the end of capitalism in the so-called Red Paper on Scotland; in later years, there was no doubt which of them was more embarrassed about their youthful indiscretions.

We're 2,000 light years from home . . .

By the time of John Smith's death, Labour held a commanding lead in the opinion polls. Black Wednesday had been the turning point for the economy; it was followed by a rapid reduction in interest rates from 10 per cent to 6 per cent and a hefty devaluation of the pound. Growth picked up and unemployment started to fall almost immediately, but the abundance of spare capacity in the economy meant inflation also continued to fall. Yet voters were not prepared to give the Major government any credit for a recovery based on policies that were the diametric opposite of those on which the Conservatives had won the 1992 election.

The mythology of New Labour is that only Tony Blair could have taken the party back to power in 1997; the contempt felt by the public from Black Wednesday onwards suggests otherwise. This was a Conservative Party besmirched by economic failure, riven by civil war over Europe, tainted with corruption and sleaze and facing a public that was convinced it was time for a change. John Smith would have won in 1997; Gordon Brown would have won in 1997; in all probability, Michael Foot would have won in 1997, although perhaps with a somewhat smaller majority than 179. Mr Blair had learned much from his study of the right. He knew that Labour had to be serious about how it presented its policies; he knew that it had to keep the largely right-wing press at bay; he knew that the centre of gravity of the British electorate was far more conservative than many of his party activists were willing to admit; he knew that he had to forge a coalition between the inner cities and the suburbs if he was to win. At the same time, he could not appeal to an electorate that by 1997 was utterly sick of the Conservatives on a platform that a vote for Labour was a vote for more of the same. That, in any case, would have suggested that Mr Blair was a secret Tory flying under a Labour flag of convenience, which he was not. Mr Blair believed in a fairer Britain rooted in the values of social justice. His fantasy was that Labour could graft Thatcherism and anti-Thatcherism into a coherent programme for government rather than deal in a measured, social democratic way with the policy failures of the previous 18 years, or, indeed, imitate previous Labour administrations in both Australia and New Zealand and press ahead with a full-blooded free-market programme.

Some might argue that Mrs Thatcher was as big a fantasist as Mr Blair. Yet Thatcherism was consistent and coherent, offering a return to the precepts of classical political economy, a smaller role for the state, price stability, defence of the realm and free markets. Even those critics who argue that Mrs Thatcher was misguided or plain wrong rarely accuse her of lacking clarity of thought. She never for one moment believed that the way to run a Conservative government was to take the prevailing welfarist orthodoxy and blend in some free-market ideology. Her conviction in 1979 was that Britain was in a rotten state and in need of radical change. Mr Blair's conviction in 1997 was that Britain was in reasonable shape, but could be made better once the rough edges of the free market had been removed. Both prime ministers used the credibility established in their first terms for radical action once they had been re-elected: Mrs Thatcher smashed the unions, turfed Ken Livingstone out of County Hall and de-nationalized large chunks of the economy. Mr Blair went to war in Iraq.

There are two views of the period of Conservative hegemony between 1979 and 1997. One is that Thatcherism saved Britain in the nick of time, reversing decades of decline by removing the dead hand of the state. The other is that the four Conservative governments witnessed two painful recessions and one uncontrollable boom, and that the price of setting capital free was a public sector starved of cash, an explosion in crime and a burgeoning underclass. Mr Blair's fantasy was that Mrs Thatcher had not gone far enough in terms of harnessing private enterprise to the common good, and that her opposition to the sort of limited social democratic reforms favoured by Mr Blair himself was the result of regrettable short-sightedness rather than a rock-hard political position. It seemed stunningly obvious to him that the answer to Britain's problems was an even bigger dose of market forces – especially in the public sector – backed by the minimum wage and some modest redistribution. In the first flush of New Labour, back in the 1990s, this was the

much-vaunted 'third way', hailed as a way of setting traditional social democratic values in a modern twenty-first
century context. The third way meant that you could believe
both in private firms running hospitals and in the National
Health Service, in the freedom of the individual to gamble in
'super casinos' and in compulsory parenting classes, in a
development strategy that demanded 'clean' government in
Africa while turning a blind eye to corruption at home.

Mr Blair's answer to criticism of the 'third way' was
similar to Mrs Thatcher's response to her critics – there is no
alternative. That may well seem to be the case for that generation of politicians to which Mr Blair (and Gordon Brown)
belong, given that they had their formative political years in
the period between the mid-1970s and 1980s. There is,
however, always an alternative to believing in a fantasy and
that is to stop believing in it. The next seven chapters will
explain in more detail the topography of Fantasy Island.

3

The Ever-Louder Tick: Blair's Britain and the Debt Timebomb

Man in a pub to drinking companion: 'Lend me ten pounds and I'll pay you back the fiver I owe you.'
Skol Lager television advertisement, c. 1980

What does a debt mean? Twenty years ago in our parents' generation it was something that people would naturally repay. Today advice is being given to students that the minute they graduate they should default. It is a huge societal change.
Eric Daniels, Chief Executive of Lloyds TSB, speaking on 2 August 2006

I was a money enemy. And the tab police were on my tail.
Martin Amis, *Money*[1]

Peter Mandelson, Trade and Industry Secretary, could hardly have spoken more plainly than he did on 2 November 1998. Appearing in Birmingham at the annual conference of the Confederation of British Industry, he declared:

We want a society that celebrates and values its business heroes as much as it does its pop stars and footballers. So we must remove the barriers to enterprise in this country, reward risk-taking, and encourage innovation and creativity.

So far, so much New Labour boilerplate. But he added:

> In the US some of the most successful entrepreneurs are
> those who have failed once or twice. Banks and society as a
> whole don't write people off as failures. They see them as
> people who have learned; people who are worth backing
> again. That is why the Government needs to carry out two
> reviews: one looking at corporate rescue procedures . . . and
> the second looking at whether the law can be changed to
> reduce the stigma of financial failure.

Cynics may have admired Mr Mandelson's apparently
remarkable ability to use the same proposal to please widely
different groups of people. To his immediate business audience, this suggested relaxation of the insolvency laws was all
about 'encouraging enterprise'. To the liberal-minded, it
involved reducing one of the remaining few Victorian-era
forms of social disapproval visited on unfortunates who had
fallen on hard times. To those in the Labour Party who
disliked banks and other moneylenders, this would have
seemed an excellent scheme that would make it harder for
them to get their money back from the oppressed masses to
whom they had lent it. And just to add to the appeal to business people was the suggestion that all this would, in some
unexplained way, bestow on them the celebrity status of 'pop
stars and footballers'.

Mr Mandelson had long since left the Department of Trade
and Industry by the time his proposals reached the statute
book under a title that was of interest in itself: not the
Insolvency Act 2002, as one may have expected, but the
Enterprise Act 2002. The message was clear. This was not
about debt, but about entrepreneurship. Far more upbeat,
you have to concede; much less gloomy and 'judgemental'.

It is possible that Mr Mandelson's fabled arts as a media
manipulator were behind this rebranding exercise, and that

he had taken a tip from his Tory opponents, who gave to assorted pieces of legislation to control the trade unions during their 18 years in office the unobjectionable label of 'Employment Act'. More worryingly, it could be that the Trade and Industry Secretary really believed that a lack of 'quickie' insolvencies was stifling British enterprise. If so, we wonder what he makes of the outcome. The 2002 act liberalized both corporate insolvency and individual bankruptcy in England and Wales. For companies in trouble, the grip of their banks on their affairs was weakened and firms were granted the right to appoint their own administrators – effectively, an insolvency practitioner charged with rescuing the business as a going concern.

So how have the corporate insolvency statistics changed since the turn of the century? The answer is – not much. In 1999, the total number of firms in the old-style receivership or in administration was 2,058. In 2004, there had been some increase, to 2,466. But looking at company liquidations (the corporate equivalent of bankruptcy, used for companies that have ceased to be going concerns) there has been a decline, from 14,280 in 1999 to 12,192 in 2004. More recent figures show that, in 2005, there was a further rise in the total of receiverships and administrations, to 2,851, and a modest rise in the number of company liquidations, to 12,893.[2]

In other words, Mr Mandelson's reforms seemed to be working as planned. Companies in trouble were more likely to be nursed in the sick bay of the receiverships and administrations category than to be buried in the graveyard of company liquidations. The 'corporate rescue procedures' of which he had spoken in Birmingham all those years before seemed to be functioning smoothly. Hats off to Mr Mandelson?

Not so fast. Company insolvency was just one half of the reform package. The other, personal insolvency (better known as bankruptcy), has produced rather different results. Here, the 2002 changes had cut from three years to one the length of time before a bankrupt was 'discharged' (i.e. had their debt written off, was allowed to return to a normal financial life and had various other restrictions lifted, such as those on holding certain public offices). Roughly coincident with the provisions of the 2002 act, although not resulting from it, was a much wider use of 'individual voluntary arrangements' (IVAs), an alternative to bankruptcy arising out of legislation passed in 1986 under which borrowers agreed to pay some of their debt and creditors agreed to write off the rest. This tied in with Mr Mandelson's 'enterprise' agenda because, at the time he was speaking, 60 per cent of bankruptcies were linked to a business failure, either because the bankrupt person was a sole trader, partner or similar or because they had given personal guarantees to underwrite the borrowings of a limited liability company, thus effectively voiding the limited liability of the firm concerned, something upon which lenders are apt to insist.

In 1999, there were 21,611 bankruptcies in England and Wales and 7,195 IVAs. In 2004, there were 35,898 bankruptcies and 10,752 IVAs. During the 12 months to the end of September 2006, there were 59,516 bankruptcies and 38,604 IVAs.[3] Did these quite staggering rates of increase reflect an upsurge in the sort of freebooting entrepreneurship lauded by Mr Mandelson? They did not. The ratio of 60 per cent business-related bankruptcies to 40 per cent personal debt-related of the late 1990s had, by 2003, been reversed. By 2006, it was estimated that the proportion of bankruptcies related to a business failure was down to about 30 per cent. In the years since Mr Mandelson's speech, British consumers, along with their government (of whose borrowings more later) had become not only hooked on debt but dependent also on legalistic and other devices to make the debt disappear. In the case of the consumer, these included IVAs and bankruptcy; in the case of the government, ever-more elaborate accounting methods would be used to show the national books were (or would be) in balance 'across the economic cycle'. Debt and New Labour are inextricably linked; heavy borrowing allows the public to plug the gaps in its finances caused by 'stealth' taxes and other imposts, and to compensate for sluggish growth in earnings, and it also permits the government to continue with its spending plans without raising those taxes even higher.

But while government borrowing has climbed steeply in recent years, and the accompanying attempts to stretch and squash the 'economic cycle' to fit the debt figures have invited ridicule, consumers were the first to arrive at the great debt party, and have drunk the deepest. Astronomical levels of personal indebtedness will, we believe, prove a millstone round the economy's neck in the decade to come, a blinding hangover that will hobble economic activity and consumer spending for years.

We explain later how we believe this will take effect (see p. 61). In the meantime, we simply point out that, while looking at personal borrowings and at government debt – which we shall examine next – we shall have very little to say about the borrowings of incorporated business firms. They, of course, were the great concern of Mr Mandelson, who was so anxious that their enterprising ambitions should not be hobbled by old-fashioned social disapproval. Because the great irony is that, for several years, of the three sectors of the economy – corporate, household and government – the corporate sector has been 'in the black'. That's right. Taken as a whole, incorporated businesses, the great engine of the economy, whom many vaguely assume to be thirsty for the fuel of credit, have actually been saving money.

'The windmills of your mind': public borrowing and Gordon Brown's 'economic cycle'

Somewhere, in a remote hermitage, perhaps, or a windswept monastery off the coast of Northumberland, there is someone who has never heard of Gordon Brown's 'golden rule'. This someone has never heard the Chancellor pledge to 'meet our fiscal rules', never heard or read economic commentators pondering the likelihood that Mr Brown will or will not achieve this objective and never heard a City analyst discuss what a breach of the rules would or would not do to Mr Brown's credibility.

Oh lucky someone.

For the rest of us, discussion of 'the fiscal rules' is a background drone, like the noise made by a fridge or an office ventilation system. But for the benefit of that 'someone', the rules are these. First, the 'golden rule' states that the budget for 'current' expenditure – the day-to-day running costs of government, including pay – should be in balance or surplus across the economic cycle as a whole. The second is that public sector net debt – covering both the current budget and the 'capital' (i.e. investment) budget – should never total more than 40 per cent of gross domestic product (GDP – the annual output of the economy).

These rules were thought to be an essential brick in the arch of Labour's new-found economic respectability in the early 1990s. While the party had traditionally been rather sniffy about personal indebtedness, as we shall see later, it suffered a somewhat-undeserved reputation for being only too happy to plunge the state itself into debt. The 1945 Labour government has been lambasted by, among others, historian Correlli Barnett for reliance on US handouts to create socialism: 'And so, with the successful cadging in Washington of the $3.75 billion loan, the construction of New Jerusalem could go ahead after all.'[4] True, Harold

Wilson in the 1960s made much of the need for 'a Britain that is paying her way in the world'.[5] But the events of September 1976, when Britain was apparently forced to accept humiliating terms from the IMF (in terms of reduced public spending in return for a loan to stabilize sterling), added weight to jibes that Labour produced spendthrift administrations that would end up borrowing money off more successful 'capitalist' countries once their grandiose spending plans and economic incompetence got the better of them.

For some on the left, British indebtedness in general as regards the rest of the world – whether in terms of government borrowing or the balance of payments – was a symptom of

> the requirements of an international economic, political and military system, which imposed constraints on Britain's freedom to act. To deal with the problems of debt and deficit in any radical way would have involved an immediate confrontation, not only with this international system but also with those elements of it – the British financial institutions and large firms.[6]

But the appetite for this sort of 'confrontation' had been in decline within Labour's ranks for some time before Gordon Brown became the party's eighth Chancellor of the Exchequer. Mr Brown's 'fiscal rules' did not make Labour into a party that wanted to be seen as fiscally orthodox, they merely confirmed this desire.

However, wanting to be something and actually being it are two quite different things. In the chapter on the public sector (chapter 6), we look at the extraordinary quantity of 'off balance-sheet' liabilities being piled up by the Treasury in order to bankroll huge public infrastructure projects without either putting up taxes or appearing to borrow. Here, our interest is in the Labour notion of the 'economic cycle', once a dry piece of economic thinking now transformed into the Indian rope trick of public finances. Thanks to the economic cycle, Labour can borrow while claiming not to be doing so. It is a masterly hallucination, a worthy addition to the landscape of Fantasy Island.

At the time of writing, the position is this: on the 'sustainable investment rule', the one that keeps the stock of debt below 40 per cent of GDP, the Treasury was comfortably inside the ceiling in 2004–5, with 35 per cent. This was forecast to deteriorate to 37.5 per cent in 2006–7, and to reach 38.4 per cent in 2010–11. By this last financial year, of course, Gordon Brown will be long gone from the Treasury; indeed, Labour may have left office. This may be seen as mighty convenient, as may the fact that the rot is forecast to stop just short of 40 per cent.

This, however, is nothing compared to the real fun to be had with the 'golden rule', the one that insists that the budget for current expenditure balances 'across the economic cycle'. How long is this cycle and when did it start? That, as you will have noticed, is a critical question, because only when we know what the cycle is can we judge whether or not the current budget is balanced 'across' it. The easiest-to-grasp definition would date the current cycle from the end of 1992, when Britain broke out of the straightjacket of the ERM and began a long economic upsweep. It will end when economic activity dips back below its 'trend' rate (or actually drops into negative territory in terms of growth, depending on your point of view). At that point, the commentators can judge.

Gordon Brown did not like that definition of the cycle and one possible reason is not hard to find. John Major's Conservatives had run up big borrowings in the early 1990s and these would have blotted Mr Brown's own record had he dated the cycle from 1992. Fair enough, one may think, but it does show already that the whole notion of the 'cycle' is already pretty flexible, not to say deeply politicized. Instead, the Chancellor and his team announced that an economic cycle had begun in 1997, the year of New Labour's first landslide victory. It ended, they declared, in 1999, and a new cycle began. The 'short' two-year cycle coincided with healthy public finances, thus balancing the current budget was not too challenging. And the new century appeared to promise more of the same, as Labour's Treasury reaped a rich harvest from taxes on dealings in a booming stock market and relieved a number of telecommunications companies of staggering amounts of money in the auction for the right to operate third-generation mobile-phone networks.

But the more sombre mood following the 11 September terrorist attacks, combined with the collapse of the 'new economy' bubble, took their toll of the public finances. The current budget went into deficit in 2002–3, and has stayed there ever since. Whether or not this matters, of course, depends on the 'cycle', and here Mr Brown has not been idle. In July 2005, he abolished the 1997–9 mini-cycle and declared 1997 to be the start point of the current cycle. This allowed him to load £12 billion of long-ago money back into his current accounts to make the books look better. Unsatisfied with this venture into the world of creative accountancy, the Chancellor popped up again in December 2005 to extend the cycle forward, claiming it would end not in March 2006, as originally forecast, but in 2009. More recently still, in December 2006, the Chancellor hinted that the cycle would end in March 2007 when, presumably, it seemed the numbers would come right.

It may seem puzzling that extending the cycle both backwards (into happier financial times) and forwards (into at-best uncertain times) can both help the Chancellor to make his borrowings go away. But the forward extension does at least give a chance for 'fiscal drag' to work its wonders. This is the process whereby earners drift into higher tax bands as a result of pay rises, promotion and general wage inflation, thus producing more revenue for the Chancellor.

Furthermore, for as long as the cycle was still running, no accounting needed to be made. Gordon Brown's supposedly flat or in-surplus current budget was £19 billion in the red in 2002–5 and forecast to be another £11.4 billion in the red in 2005–6. Officially, however, the overall figure was zero, because, adjusted for the 'cycle', that is what it will be. Only when all the ducks are in a row, however briefly, should the cycle be declared over, and the budget balanced.

Mr Brown seems to have taken a leaf out of one of the books by the late Anthony Buckeridge, writer of much-loved Jennings prep-school yarns. In one such, two boys in a tea shop realize neither has the money to pay their bill.[7] However, as long as they continue to order doughnuts and fizzy pop, they need make no reckoning and could hang on for something to turn up, which it duly did. Perhaps we should be grateful that 'Jen and Darbi' did not break off from their assorted japes to lecture us all on their 'prudence' and their 'long-term' planning horizons.

Public borrowing under Messrs Blair and Brown, however, is a model of sober, rational calculation compared to the explosion of private borrowing that has been seen during their time in office. As we shall see, their complaisance in this extraordinary accumulation of debt is in direct contradiction to the traditions of the Labour Party.

'No money down': high-mindedness and after in a time of affluence

Traditionally, the Labour movement has enjoyed an uneasy relationship with consumer credit, with individual borrowing in general and even with personal affluence itself, however financed. Here is Aneurin Bevan, speaking at the Labour Party conference in Blackpool in November 1959:

> The so-called affluent society is an ugly society still. It is a vulgar society. It is a meretricious society . . . I have enough faith in my fellow creatures in Great Britain to believe that when they have got over the delirium of the television, when they realise that their new homes that they have been put into are mortgaged to the hilt, when they realise that the moneylender has been elevated to the highest position in the land . . . then we shall lead our people to where they deserve to be led.

But this was not the only voice. In October 1956, Anthony Crosland published *The Future of Socialism,* the key 'revisionist' tract for Labour's modernizers. As his widow recalled: 'In the blood of the socialist, he asserted, "there should always run the trace of the anarchist and the libertarian, and not too much of the prig and the prude."'[8] True, Mr Crosland did not exactly urge Labour supporters to take out the hire purchase plans that helped define affluence in the late 1950s, but, as Susan Crosland noted, the acquisition by herself and her husband of a converted mill in Oxfordshire in 1975 required some quite steep borrowing. It would seem Mr Crosland took the not-unreasonable view that money was better used making people's lives more pleasant than languishing in a bank. It was an attitude that was to gain ground rapidly during the decades after the war. In 1957, American journalist Drew Middleton noted: 'The British have a streak of self-indulgence.'[9]

That said, it seemed Labour disapproval of easy credit and easy money in general was never far below the surface. Harold Wilson referred to the Conservatives' premium-bond proposal as 'a squalid raffle', adding: 'The Tory Party used to have the slogan *Land of Hope and Glory* . . . They will be fighting the next election on *Honest Charlie always pays.*'[10] Indeed, for Mr Wilson, Harold Macmillan became something of a symbol of the distractions of affluence. On one occasion, Mr Wilson declared: 'Under the right hon. gentleman, we are becoming a nation dedicated to striped toothpaste, soft-centred chocolates, and fabulous pink Camay.'[11]

Nor was this mere rhetoric. Tory chancellors (such as Anthony Barber) relaxed credit controls; Labour chancellors (such as Denis Healey) seemed keener to impose them. Labour paternalism drew a strict line between acceptable forms of borrowing, such as from credit unions, and indebtedness to 'capitalist' institutions – all, to a greater or lesser extent, practising a form of loan sharking. The moneylender and the bailiff were bad twins in the left-wing world-view, the loan being followed, as night follows day, by the sight of the sofa and other furniture being loaded on to the back of a lorry. For working people, borrowing money was no alternative at all to the real tools of personal improvement – the pay rise and the array of generous social benefits. Properly organized in trade unions to take a larger slice of the cake, the workers could indeed enjoy more and more of the good things in life. Properly organized politically, they could channel more of society's resources their way in terms of spending on health, education and welfare.

Indeed, the idea of going into debt was vaguely louche and un-proletarian, the behaviour of the sort of people described in 1956 by the organization Socialist Union as 'the top-salary earners with elastic expense accounts'.[12] After all, it was a Tory MP, the famously sleek-living Edward du Cann, who declared in 1967: 'I'm a great believer in borrowing money.'[13] It was another Tory MP, Jeffrey Archer, who resigned his seat in 1974 because of the threat of bankruptcy (in the event, he was not declared bankrupt). True, Labour MPs were not immune to financial difficulties. But the best-known, John Stonehouse, was on the right of the party, a pro-European who set up home with his secretary, confirming the worst suspicions among puritanical-minded leftists as to the links between a dubious lifestyle and 'unsound' opinions.

Of course, distaste at the idea of personal indebtedness was far from being confined to Labour's ranks. Few on the left could have matched the scorn felt by Margaret Thatcher for those who lived beyond their means. But this was a personal scorn, not reflected in the policies of her government. Indeed, it was her first Chancellor, Sir Geoffrey Howe, who lifted credit controls in 1982 for what was to be the last time. Shortly thereafter, the Building Societies Association announced that its single mortgage rate, which, as a cartel, it set every month, would henceforth be merely advisory. In 1986 it disappeared altogether. The 'mortgage queue' vanished, and with it the limits on multiples of income that lenders were prepared to advance. By the late 1980s, the unregulated personal-debt market that we know today was more or less in place.

A charitable view would hold that Mrs Thatcher was not prepared to impose her personal view of indebtedness on the population at large, believing people should be free to make their own mistakes. Less charitably, it may be that Sir Geoffrey and others explained to her that easy credit would help create what came to be known as the 'feel-good factor' at a time of severe economic difficulties. Or perhaps she simply did not understand what was happening, assuming that the old credit restrictions had been merely expressions of now-vanquished 'socialist controls'.

On the left, the voices opposing affluence and indebtedness became fainter. Tony Benn may have recorded the demise of the department store Biba thus in his diary on 19 July 1975 – 'You can see why it failed really because it was the final fling for the excrescences of Sixties' fashion, now all gone bust'[14] –

but many of his colleagues had learned to stop worrying and at least live with the credit society. By the early and mid-1980s, with recession ravaging working-class areas, 'affluence' hardly seemed a problem, more a land of lost content. As the decade advanced, those still sceptical were out of the mainstream:

> Of course, it [affluence] was really all about selling things to the previously poor. What happened was that the working class were delivered to the market-place, not as labour, but as consumers.[15]

> Emphasis on growth, materialism and consumerism has been a hallmark of Labour's electoral appeal since 1964, together with an increasing reluctance to mention income tax as an essential factor in the financing of public services.[16]

On 20 May 1988, in the wake of a giveaway Budget and low interest rates, Labour leader Neil Kinnock – whom one suspects harboured rather old-fashioned notions about the undesirability of personal indebtedness – tore into the Conservative government for having created 'a loadsamoney economy' that would bring in its wake 'loadsatrouble'. His demotic terminology may have been borrowed from the comedian Harry Enfield, but his attack on an economy that preferred consuming to investing ('It's fun while it lasts') was in a long tradition of Labour distaste for easy money and financial speculation, stretching back at least as far as post-war Chancellor Sir Stafford Cripps.

Neil Kinnock's successor John Smith, whose alleged resemblance to a 'typical' Scottish bank manager became one of the clichés of the early 1990s, was never likely to be accused of promoting a spendthrift approach to life, although his largely uncritical attitude towards the City as Shadow Chancellor from 1987 to 1992 would not have predisposed him to clamp down on the moneylenders. But Mr Smith's death in May 1994 brought not only a very different leader to the top of the party but a very different attitude to personal indebtedness, an attitude displayed by Tony Blair's rival Gordon Brown as much as by the future prime minister himself. The attitude in question was that there was no need to have any attitude at all. As personal debt mushroomed to extraordinary levels, no opinion was offered either way. For a government with a view on everything else, from 'sensible' drinking to desirable parenting, it was an extraordinary piece of self-denial. In terms of laissez-faire, it was hard to beat.

The sound of silence: Blair, Brown and the borrowing binge

Few panics are easier to start than those triggered by statistics for lending to individuals. The recipe is simple. First, compare like with unlike, then ignore the effects of inflation and finally stir in some homely references to the wisdom and prudence of our grandparents. A more responsible approach starts from the premise that only quite recently has it become possible to draw meaningful comparisons between one year and another, and this means that, on the surface at least, any changes are likely to look less spectacular than they would have done were we to place the modern age of multiple plastic cards with wide credit limits side by side with the era when *Dad's Army*'s Captain Mainwaring presided over the affairs of the bank branch at Walmington-on-Sea.

Below the surface, it is a different story – as we shall see. But first, a brief history of credit. Contrary to what some may think, yesteryear was not a debt-free age of innocence in which all of life's necessities could be met out of money saved in jam jars on the mantelpiece. A major difference between now and then was not the absence of borrowing but the absence of formal credit. Well into the early 1970s, large amounts of consumer credit would have been invisible as far as official statistics were concerned, being in the form of 'tick' or a 'slate' at a local shop or, for the better-off, the more respectable-sounding 'account' with traders from butcher and grocer to tailor, dressmaker or wine merchant. Prior to the 1974 Consumer Credit Act, those offering credit did not need a licence, nor did the pawnbrokers upon whom many had traditionally relied for loans. Door-to-door loan providers had long been in existence, as had other informal channels of credit, all the way down to the least desirable, loan sharks. On a smaller scale, private mortgages could sometimes be arranged through solicitors (as, presumably, they still can be, provided all the formalities are observed). Up until the mid-1970s, the majority of the population did not have bank accounts. For those who did, the overdraft was the conventional form of borrowing, a relatively cheap type of credit in that it was (and is) charged only for the time when the money is being used; the quid pro quo is that it is a 'demand' loan that can be called in at any time, unlike a personal loan, a generally more expensive fixed-term debt for a fixed amount.

Just as formal credit was extended to the population at large during the 1970s, so roaring inflation and (at times) negative interest rates clouded the picture. If people were effectively being paid to borrow (which they were, if the rate of interest was below the rate of inflation, particularly the rate of wage inflation), then who could blame them? Such a distortion made it difficult to judge the true state of demand. Similarly, the 'distress' borrowing of the early 1980s and early 1990s throws up statistical 'smoke', as belt-tightening and additional debt could be two sides of the same coin in troubled times, for those reasonably confident of a return to financial security.

So let us, for the moment, ignore not only the 1970s and 1980s but also the 1990s, given that the backwash from the house-price crash and sterling crisis early in the decade may have influenced the figures for years to come. Instead, let us look at this first decade of the twenty-first century and take a spin in the Tardis back to January 2000. According to the Bank of England, there was net lending in that month on consumer credit (after repayments were taken into account) of £1,308,000,000, in round terms £1.3 billion, and net lending secured on dwellings (effectively mortgages) of £3,375,000,000, in round terms £3.4 billion. These movements took the total outstanding on consumer debt to £115,992,000,000 (or £116 billion in round terms) and the total outstanding on mortgages to £497,573,000,000 (or £498 billion in round terms).

Come December 2005, and net lending on consumer credit was a little more modest than it had been nearly six years earlier, with £0.8 billion advanced. Net mortgage lending, however, more than compensated, rising by £7.6 billion. The amounts outstanding had risen to £192.3 billion on consumer credit and £965.2 billion on mortgage lending. In other words, the outstanding amount of consumer credit had risen by 65.8 per cent in six years and outstanding mortgage debt had soared by 94 per cent. Earnings are, unsurprisingly, the key to the affordability of credit. So what happened to earnings between 2000 and 2005? According to the Office for National Statistics, average earnings for the whole economy, seasonally adjusted and excluding bonuses, rose by 22.4 per cent.

That's right – just 22.4 per cent.

True, interest rates have been at historically low levels for most of the decade, bounded by 3.6 per cent Bank Rate at the bottom of the range and 6 per cent at the top. But then inflation, as measured by the all-items Retail Prices Index, has averaged just 3.6 per cent a year. Consumer debt may be known as 'revolving credit', but with sluggish earnings growth and little prospect of a surge in inflation that would painlessly shrink the burden of previous debts, this type of credit will be revolving rather slowly at the moment. Indeed, as we have seen in the figures above, there are signs of slowing in the rate at which people are adding to the stock of consumer borrowing, perhaps as they finally become aware of just how long it is going to take to pay it off. This is especially so for those opting to repay only the monthly minimum on their credit-card statements. It was calculated that someone paying only the minimum of 3 per cent of the balance would take more than 14 years to clear £2,000 of borrowings, according to the financial website www. thisismoney.co.uk in May 2005.[17]

In November 2006, Mike Gerrard, head of personal insolvency at accountancy firm Grant Thornton, said:

> The seemingly never-ending rise in the number of UK personal insolvencies continues apace, sustained by the side-effects of the buy-now-pay-later generation. Individuals with credit-card debts in excess of £50,000–£60,000 are not at all uncommon, while the overall age of those affected appears to be on the decrease with a larger proportion of women also noticeable.[18]

But the increase in consumer borrowing between 2000 and 2005 was dwarfed by the staggering increase in the amount outstanding on mortgage lending, a rise of almost 100 per cent in six years. It is a notable fact of each crazed house-price boom that there is always an excellent reason for whichever boom is currently under way; this is the bricks-and-mortar equivalent of that hoary old piece of reassurance touted about whenever stock-market values are defying gravity – 'it's different this time'. In the run-up to the financial crash of 1974, tax breaks and the notion of a 'hedge against inflation' were cited as evidence for the defence of the boom:

> By the early 1970s, most individuals felt it was foolish not to own a house, maybe even insane, since cheap mortgages were a-plenty, while mortgage interest payments were

deductible from tax . . . It was generally believed that house prices would rise faster than inflation.[19]

In the late 1980s, the excuse was the wonderfully circular piece of reasoning deployed by Chancellor Nigel Lawson, who suggested that mortgage debt did not matter because it was secured on the asset side, i.e. on the same house prices that the debt itself had helped to inflate. And in this decade, the 2000s, the reassurance is simpler still: there is a chronic shortage of houses. We need to build, oh, 1.4 million, 2 million, 5 million new homes (the figure varies) – and show no sign of getting anywhere near those figures; it is therefore entirely safe to assume that distended property values are here to stay.

At the start of November 2006, it emerged that the Abbey bank, Britain's second-largest home loans provider, was to make available mortgages of up to five times earnings, as against the more traditional three and a half times earnings limit. As Graham Turner, an economist at GFC Economics, put it, the move was symptomatic of a property market once again 'spinning out of control'.[20] Capital Economics, the organization run by distinguished economist Roger Bootle, said the Abbey's decision could have mixed effects: it would keep activity in the housing market strong, but if individuals were having to allocate more of their disposable income to paying off the mortgage they would have less to spend on other things. In other words, the end result might be slower growth, higher unemployment and, eventually, a weaker housing market.

Capital's own figures show that debt servicing costs, taking into account repayments of principal as well as interest, rose from 17.4 per cent of household income in 2000 to 22 per cent in 2006. Although interest rates are lower, the build-up of both secured and unsecured debts means that debt servicing costs are as high now as they were at the time of the property meltdown of the early 1990s. Initial mortgage repayments for first-time buyers are at their highest relative to take-home pay since 1991. This makes borrowers acutely sensitive to even small rises in borrowing costs. Capital said: 'A rise in interest rates to 5 per cent by the end of 2006 [this has since taken place] would leave households devoting the greatest share of their income to interest payments since 1992'.[21] This refers to interest only, not interest and capital combined.

Extraordinarily, as we stated earlier, Tony Blair's government, usually more than happy to give its opinions and even instructions on people's private conduct, has nothing to say about any of this beyond occasional references to the need for education in 'financial literacy' for our schoolchildren. Indeed, the decision to make 'financial exclusion' an issue on which ministers wanted to make progress has, paradoxically, put more poorer people in a position where they will be coming into contact with the banks and other institutions, the main channels of formal credit.

And as formal credit has been made available further and further down the income and social scale, the 'floor' beneath the average level of interest rates has been gently rising. This is because the likelihood of default rises as the income of the borrower declines or otherwise becomes less certain, and the lenders have to rebuild their profits by charging more to the better 'risks'. The lenders deny this happens. They denied it in February 2005, when asked by the *Mail on Sunday*, claiming that 'credit scoring' was now so sophisticated that each customer was priced pretty well individually in terms of risk; thus there was no question of a spillover effect from bad risks to better ones. In autumn of the same year, Barclaycard said it was raising its interest rate by two percentage points, citing bad debts. And in May 2006, the Bank of England said overall rates on unsecured debt had risen, as a result of rising insolvencies.

Ah yes, the Bank of England, whose stance on the soaring levels of debt and bankruptcy is that they are doubtless distressing for those involved but of no wider economic significance. A special article in its quarterly *Inflation Report* concluded: 'Some households face repayment difficulties, particularly for unsecured debt. That is serious for those households. But they are likely to account for a small proportion of overall consumer spending.'[22]

That's all right then.

Launching the report, Bank of England Governor Mervyn King said: 'All lenders and all borrowers should think carefully, very carefully, before they lend or borrow.'[23] But how carefully? When Mr King and his colleagues on the Monetary Policy Committee (MPC) cut the Bank Rate, it is presumably because they believe that, in order to get the economy to where they want it to be in terms of hitting the inflation target, it is necessary that more credit be created, i.e. that more economic actors, including individuals, will go into debt. By the same token, when the MPC raises the cost of borrowing it presumably hopes that there are some borrowers out there who will feel the pain that it is trying to inflict on them, again for the purposes of reaching the inflation-rate target. After all, there would be little 'traction' in raising the carrying cost of something that economic actors – people, firms and the government – are not holding. Given that the MPC's entire *modus operandi* is, in essence, that of a man playing a concertina, alternately encouraging and discouraging the accumulation of debt, just how careful can people be before they start to cause serious problems for Mr King and his colleagues? After all, the MPC is deeply implicated in having promoted the accumulation of debt during 'easing' phases of monetary policy in order to achieve its objective of holding inflation steady. Furthermore, it could be argued that the more successful it has been in doing this, the more likely it is to have encouraged into debt those less able to cope with it.

This may all be terribly unfair, but it would seem that a monetary model based on the notion of regulating the economy by easing and tightening the flow of funds to industry (thus choking off 'marginal' business projects during a tightening phase and cooling the economic position) is now operating through the coaxing into debt of individuals who are then clobbered with higher interest rates. Put simply, a game designed to be played between two professional sides (the central bankers and the business community) is now being played between the central bankers and the supreme amateurs – the British public. No wonder what is delicately referred to in official circles as an 'imbalance' has built up in terms of enormous consumer and mortgage debt. One imagines a similar imbalance would emerge in the scoreline in a match played between Chelsea or Manchester United on one hand and the Hare and Hounds pub side on the other.

Nor is the substitution of the rookie consumer for the hardened denizens of the boardroom the only violation of classic economic theory involved in Britain's debt bubble. Another relates to the respective identities of the borrowers and the lenders. Developed economies such as our own, with an ageing population, ought to be net savers and net investors, lending to less developed countries with younger populations. By doing so, we would ensure a stream of income from these developing countries to help fund our own pensions. But China and Russia, two countries that have known famine within living memory, have been net savers, helping to bankroll Britain's debt habit.

The brooding dark cliff of debt towers over the economy. Even were every over-borrowed consumer to start repayments right now, it could take years to wind down the mass of consumer credit and mortgage borrowing – perhaps decades for those making just the minimum monthly repayment on their credit cards. Sooner rather than later, we suspect, very large numbers of people are going to try to retrench, realizing that Britain's modest earnings growth is no basis for 'gearing up' on this scale. When they do so, those parts of the economy that have benefited from heavy personal indebtedness are going to find that the whole borrowing spree was more like a ghastly drug addiction than anything else, with ever-larger doses needed to keep things moving forward. With consumers going 'cold turkey', large tracts of the economy are going to get the shakes.

To end where we began, there is, of course, an alternative to the long, plodding straight and narrow path of debt repayment – insolvency, whether bankruptcies or IVAs. Surely liberal personal insolvency laws could give the whole economy an escape route from these years of depressed spending, allowing deeply indebted individuals to dust themselves down and start all over again, albeit a little more prudently? Alas, it seems highly unlikely that banks and other lending institutions will simply smile in an avuncular manner as their erstwhile customers just walk away from their obligations. As we saw earlier in this chapter, they are already increasing the cost of credit to help recoup money lost to default.

Either debt repayment will depress the economy, or default-driven interest rate rises will depress the economy. Either way, the economy seems certain to be depressed. The vast swamp of private debt will have to be drained. Debt – both public and, to a much greater extent, private – is the greatest domestic threat to the British economy. Funnily enough, however, a feature of this debt build-up has been the amount of official effort that has gone into pretending it never happened. We have seen already the terrible contortions through which the Treasury has bent the 'fiscal rules'. We have seen also the liberalization of personal insolvency rules. Indeed, by early 2007 traditional bankruptcies and IVAs were starting to look old hat as the government wheeled out proposals for a streamlined Simple IVA (SIVA) and, more sweeping still, a 'debt relief order' (DRO). This latter would be the ultimate in 'quickie' bankruptcies, available without a court appearance to anyone capable of persuading a member of the Official Receiver's staff that they were entirely unable to pay what they owed. Discharge would follow in 12 months.

Gordon Brown tries to draw the line on his borrowings only rarely and only when the moment is right; consumers are encouraged to draw the line constantly. These are two somewhat different versions of the 'great escape' from debt, but they are merely different aspects of one single fantasy – that borrowing does not really have to be repaid.

4

Bullshit Britain: Multiple Hallucinations of a 'Creative Economy'

In all our plans for the future, we are re-defining and we are re-stating our socialism in terms of the scientific revolution. But that revolution cannot become a reality unless we are prepared to make far-reaching changes in economic and social attitudes, which permeate our whole system of society. The Britain that is going to be forged in the white heat of this revolution will be no place for restrictive practices or for outdated methods on either side of industry.

> Harold Wilson, addressing the Labour Party conference,
> Scarborough, 1 October 1963

With the right long-term decisions Britain can lead in some of the fastest-growing and highest value-added sectors – City and business services, education and health, creative and science-based industries – once small, now one-third of our economy and exports, soon a much higher share of jobs and wealth.

> Gordon Brown, Budget speech, March 2006

'When I use a word,' Humpty Dumpty said in a rather scornful tone, 'it means just what I choose it to mean – neither more nor less.'

> Lewis Carroll, *Through the Looking Glass*

We all know what the Germans are good at. They do precision engineering: all those quietly humming washing machines and the cars with their gleaming chrome and sleek bodywork. We also know that Germany is a country in serious trouble, failing as it has to embrace the need for flexibility in the tough new global environment. We know this because Gordon Brown has told us many times over the past ten years that the European model is washed up.

Germany was so abysmally competitive last year that it ran a record trade surplus and was the biggest exporter of any country in the world.

We know what the Japanese excel at also. In Tokyo and Nagoya there are world-beating companies in the field of electronics, designing the latest consumer gizmos. We know, too, that despite Sony, Panasonic and Mitsubishi, Japan like Germany is a country in serious trouble. It, too, has tried to stick its head in the sand and persist with an industrial model heavy on manufacturing that might have worked in the 1960s and 1970s but is an anachronism in 2007. Poor, washed-up Japan ran a trade surplus of around £50 billion last year as it found a ready market in China for its exports.

And so it goes on. The French have an ultra-competitive manufacturing base that specializes in food and drink; the Scandinavians are a dab hand at mobile phones; the Americans do computers, aircraft and Hollywood; even the poor, benighted Italians have the world of upmarket designer clothes. So what is Britain good at? Where does the UK fit in this world of changing economic geography, in which nations will increasingly follow the dictates of David Ricardo and concentrate on the things they do best? The answer is simple. We count the money and we do the bullshit.

Britain, on the tenth anniversary of Tony Blair's arrival in Downing Street, was a place whose default mode for earning its crust was to employ the gift of the gab. The Germans may have the engineers, the Japanese may know how to organize a production line, but the Brits have the barristers, they have the journalists, they have the management consultants and the men and women who think that making up jingles and slogans in order to flog Pot Noodles and similar products is a serious job. It has the deal-makers in the City who make fat fees by convincing investors to launch bids for companies, and the corporate spin doctors who tell their former pals in financial journalism that tycoon X will make a better fist at running Ripoff PLC than tycoon Y. It has the publishers and it has the 'film development' companies, some of whom have actually been known to produce a film. The four iconic jobs in twenty-first century Britain, according to a think tank called the Work Foundation, were not scientists, engineers, teachers and nurses but hairdressers, celebrities, management consultants and managers. Before he came into politics, Tony Blair was a lawyer, as was his Industry Secretary Alistair Darling and the Transport Secretary Douglas Alexander. Gordon Brown's sole experience of the go-getting world of the private sector was as a journalist for Scottish Television. Not that the other parties are much different. David Cameron prepared for the task of repositioning the Conservative Party by acting as PR for Carlton TV in the 1990s. He was described by one business editor as a 'poisonous, slippery individual' and a 'smarmy bully who regularly threatened journalists who dared to write anything negative about Carlton – which was nearly all of us'.[1]

But, when you get down to it, this is a country that tries to make its living from talk, talk and more talk. Of course, there's pharmaceuticals, the one sector of manufacturing where Britain still retains a world-class sector, and the UK still makes a tidy sum from selling arms abroad, often to some pretty unsavoury regimes. Yet, the fact is that bullshit is what we do and, let's not cavil here, we are mightily good at it. Take this review of a London restaurant in the 2006 edition of the *Good Food Guide*:

> Presentations have readers reaching for aesthetic comparisons: a study in peas that involves whole pods, shoots, a minted mousse and a lake of soup (as well as a couple of slices of rabbit boudin), distantly suggesting an Arcimboldo composition, while Pollock seems the reference point for battered snails with chervil mousse, sorrel and roast leeks.[2]

Only in Bullshit Britain could somebody compare a pea to a sixteenth-century Italian renaissance painter with a straight face (unless the reference to Pollock was a misprint).

The bullshit industries capture all our best brains: our speculators in the City are more than a match for anybody else's speculators; our libel lawyers are feared in every corner of the globe; what used to be known as Fleet Street has a reputation for ebullience and flair, if not always for accuracy and propriety.

And how has Britain fared recently when it comes to paying our way in the world? Have the traders in the forex markets and the regulars at the Groucho Club earned enough to make the UK's age-long problems with the current account a thing of the past? Sadly not. The deficit in visible trade in goods – stuff we make, in other words – was more than £60 billion in 2006. That's around 5 per cent of GDP, far bigger than anything the UK has witnessed in the post-war period. Trade in services – accountancy, insurance, banking, architecture, advertising – brings the deficit down a bit, to around 4 per cent of GDP. But for the past decade, the only thing that has made the deficit manageable is that Britain has been earning more money on its investments abroad than foreign investors have made here. One way of looking at Britain is as one big offshore hedge fund churning speculators' money while asset-strippers draw up plans for the few remaining factories to be turned into industrial theme parks.

That is not the way the government sees it, naturally. Labour believes that Britain is at the cutting edge of the knowledge economy and that Britain's well-educated (*sic*), highly skilled (*sic*) and entrepreneurial (*sic*) workers are ready to kick German, American, Japanese and Chinese butt all round the global village. The essence of successful bullshit is that the really top-notch exponents not only manage to convince others but also manage to delude themselves. Some explanation has to be provided for Britain's increasingly lopsided economy, dominated as it is by those not-so-heavenly twins – the City of London and the housing market. And that explanation is that the UK's future lies not – as might seem apparent at first glance – in the drinking factories, the estate agencies and the clothing chains that make up Britain's monochrome identikit high streets, but in the knowledge economy. Even more laughably, some cling to the idea that the way ahead is the even-more nebulous 'creative economy'. This fantasy, a particular favourite of ours, is that while Britain may no longer carry the overt industrial clout it once did in the days when it was the workshop of the world, it can still be the world's creative hub (copyright T. Blair). The country of Shakespeare and Wordsworth, of Chaucer and Larkin, still has a literary tradition of which to be proud. Rock'n'roll is an English-language medium and there are billions to be made by our cutting-edge bands. Britain's television is a cut above the rest and always has been, and the only reason the film industry has declined since the days of *Passport to Pimlico* is because of a lack of government backing, now happily remedied, for the inspirational new film-makers emerging from their university courses.

Well, we did warn you that the bullshit merchants are good at what they do.

Take two: alternative reality in a call-centre economy

We'll return to the creative industries at the end of this chapter, but you have to admit that Britain as the world's creative hub sounds a heck of a lot more impressive than saying that Britain is at the cutting edge of the call-centre economy, even though the number of people answering phones and inputting data into computer terminals in white-collar industrial sheds now stands at just under one million. And it really would not do to say that Britain is a servant economy even though there are at least four million people 'in service' and the proportion of the population employed by the well-off to do their cooking, cleaning, childcare and gardening is as high as it was in the 1860s.

This, in the modern political jargon, is not the right sort of narrative. The idea that millions of people are toiling away in menial, low-paid, low-skill jobs jars with the impression Mr Blair and Mr Brown wish to convey; namely that Britain is an exemplar of how vigorous and committed Western nations can ready themselves to meet the challenge from Asia. This, though, has proved to be only a minor difficulty. In Bullshit Britain you simply come up with a different kind of reality that provides you with the sort of narrative you prefer.

The story as far as New Labour is concerned is that our failure in the second half of the twentieth century to exploit the potential of higher consumer spending on cars, washing machines, hi-fis and personal stereos has actually left us better placed to exploit the sunrise industries of the twenty-first century – biotechnology, robotics, environmental protection, pharmaceuticals. Successful economies will require brains more than brawn, and Britain is full of smart people. Some economic pundits have even argued that the reason countries such as Germany and Japan are struggling is that they have concentrated too much of their effort in manufacturing; they would have been better off had they expanded their service sectors and encouraged their consumers to borrow more. Trade surpluses and high levels of investment are, according to Anatole Kaletsky, now a sign of economic weakness, not strength.[3]

Even New Labour has so far proved unwilling to go quite this far, preferring to argue that Britain can make use of its areas of expertise to specialize in a de-materializing global economy. One of Mr Blair's favourite pundits is the former *Financial Times* journalist Charles Leadbetter, who provided the intellectual underpinning for New Labour's vision of a successful economy.

> We are all in the thin air business. Our children will not have to toil in dark factories, descend into pits or suffocate in mills, to hew raw materials and turn them into manufactured products. They will make their livings through their creativity, ingenuity and imagination.[4]

There is an element of smoke and mirrors in all this. It is undeniably true that as countries develop, the number of people employed in services tends to go up. The reason for this is that productivity growth in manufacturing is much faster than it is in services; it takes far fewer hours to make a car today than it did a hundred years ago, but the same time to cut someone's hair. It is also true that each wave of capitalism since the industrial revolution has been based on a distinctive technology: coal and steam, then railways and electricity, then mass transportation and consumer goods. Although the vast numbers of poor people in India and China (let alone Africa and Latin America) suggests that there will still be strong demand for consumer durables and machine tools for a good while yet, information technology and the human genome may well be at the centre of the next long upswing.

But how do you make this square with what's happening in Britain? It's simple: Britain has a long tradition of excellence in science, especially chemistry, and the government's commitment to the knowledge economy is evident from its target of ensuring that 50 per cent of young people go to university. New Labour, therefore, has a neat syllogism. Britain is turning out more and more graduates. These graduates are entering the workforce with the knowledge they have acquired through the education system. So, work is becoming more knowledge-based. The problem, though, is that the syllogism is false. Many graduates are doing fairly menial jobs for which they do not need a degree (or anything like it). Research by Essex University's Institute for Social and Economic Research in 2002 found that a third of men and 41 per cent of women were overqualified for the first posts they took up after graduating.[5]

The sleight of hand has not fooled everybody. In his riposte to Leadbetter, *Skating on Thin Ice*, Paul Thompson notes that the 'thin air' concept was held to embrace all the 'distinctive and benign features of the new economy' – for example the move towards networks and creativity and the break from control and hierarchy. This notion, that work in the knowledge economy is moving away from the regimentation of the traditional Taylor model, is explored in more depth in chapter 7. It is worth noting, however, that some definitions of the 'knowledge economy' include call centres, an occupation that is regimented and automated.

> A closer look at many jobs finds that only a small degree of manipulation and almost no creation of new knowledge is taking place. Financial services, for example, frequently require little more of workers than information transfer – the inputting of customer details on to pre-programmed screens and software. In call centres, customer service representatives work within context-specific and procedure-driven knowledge.[6]

Studies have shown that in the United States only about 20 per cent of those employed could really be described as 'knowledge workers' to the extent that they needed 'thinking skills' that required them to be able to manipulate symbols and ideas. The figure might be slightly higher in the UK, at about one-third of workers, but as one study found, most employment growth has been, and will continue to be, at the low-skill end of the service sector – in shops, bars, hotels, domestic service and in nursing and care homes.[7] The fastest-growing occupation in the UK between 1992 and 1999 was hairdressing.

According to Thompson:

> Underpowered and over-hyped, it (the knowledge economy) has a status of myth – an imaginary, yet heroic story . . . What has emerged is a marriage of convenience between policy makers with an enduring need to believe an optimistic story that legitimises smaller government in an age of globalisation and low taxes.[8]

Commentator James Heartfield puts it even more bluntly:

> The things that used to be cited as explanations of what was wrong with the old economy have now been changed into explanations about what is good about the New Economy: a large service sector; a declining manufacturing base; job insecurity (now called flexibility); and youth unemployment (now called expanding higher education).[9]

A matter of rust: how the productive economy was allowed to crumble

It is not our contention that 'braining up' is a bad strategy for the UK. Nor would we deny that there are areas of the knowledge economy where Britain excels. Our point is that the size and strength of this high-productivity, high-profit sector has been massively exaggerated, and that when you scratch below the surface the outlook is far less rosy. A case in point is spending on research and development, something that is seen as a vital ingredient in developing new product lines and is one of the government's economic priorities. Every year the Department of Trade and Industry publishes an R&D scoreboard to show how UK firms compare with those in the rest of the world. The findings are somewhat chastening, with just 25 companies accounting for two-thirds of all R&D spending in the UK, and Britain's presence virtually insignificant in seven of the 10 sectors measured.[10] More than half of the UK's effort in R&D is spent in just two sectors, pharmaceuticals and aerospace – two sectors, incidentally, where support from the government via the National Health Service and the Ministry of Defence has been considerable over many decades.

An analysis by the *Guardian* showed that one factor in Britain's poor performance was the higher cost of raising funds for investment in the UK,[11] a constant complaint from industry about the City for at least a century and probably longer. In all 10 sectors looked at – automobiles and parts, IT hardware, pharmaceuticals and biotechnology, electronic and electrical, software and computer services, chemicals, aerospace and defence, engineering and machinery, telecommunications, and health – the UK cost of funds was among the highest in the developed world. In four of the 10 sectors investigated, it was in line with the rest of Europe and in six it was significantly above the rest of Europe. Similarly, in four sectors it was in line with the United States and in six sectors it was significantly higher. Japan was the cheapest place in the developed world to raise money for innovation and in the electronic and engineering sector, where the country accounts for 47 per cent of global R&D spending;

the cost of funds was 1.1 per cent. Britain accounts for 1 per cent of R&D in electronics and engineering; here the cost of funds was 5.3 per cent.

Yet, not for nothing is Bullshit Britain the Soviet Union with better spin doctors. Mere numbers are simply putty in the hands of those who can always come up with an alternative reality. One explanation for this rather miserable R&D performance was that the scoreboard left out sectors such as oil and gas exploration, where spending on R&D tended to be low but Britain's presence through companies such as Shell and BP was large. Another was that it failed altogether to recognize that the place to look for innovation in the UK was not the declining manufacturing sector but the expanding service sector.

A report from NESTA (the National Endowment for Science, Technology and the Arts) admitted that, judged by the traditional yardsticks, Britain does-poorly.[12] It devotes a smaller proportion of national income to R&D, and, as noted above, that investment tends to be heavily concentrated in just one or two sectors. According to one international study cited by NESTA, only 38 per cent of British enterprises were engaged in 'innovation activities' – three percentage points below the EU average and well below Germany (61 per cent), Sweden (47 per cent) and the Netherlands and Finland (45 per cent). The picture was still worse when more radical forms of innovation were considered: only 21 per cent of UK enterprises were engaged in product innovation (firms that reported the introduction of new or significantly improved goods or services in the three-year period) compared with an EU average of 31 per cent.

Yet, according to NESTA, Britain still seemed to be doing just fine and 'has one of the strongest economies in Europe'. This, said NESTA, was a paradox. If innovation was really so important, how come the UK had been growing robustly? Its answer was simple: the data were misleading. 'The resolution

of this paradox lies in the way in which innovation has typi-
cally been measured.' Well, that might be one explanation.
Another might be that growth in Britain had been boosted by
a substantial expansion of the public sector, with Gordon
Brown using the budget surpluses built up frugally in the late
1990s to keep the economy afloat during the global downturn that followed the collapse of the dot-com boom.
Another might be that a colossal wave of property speculation allowed consumers to borrow against their main asset
and so live beyond their means for a prolonged period.

The lack of rigour in this analysis of Britain's recent macro-
economic performance hardly inspired confidence. If the
traditional measures of R&D did not really reflect the
dynamism and creativity of the UK, then an explanation was
also needed for the relentless deterioration in Britain's balance
of trade over the past 15 years. The UK has run a deficit in
manufacturing in every year since 1982, but it would be
wrong to assume – as some have – that this has been merely a
function of low-cost competition from Asia. Countries such
as Sweden and Finland, which have continued to score well
on the traditional measures of R&D and innovation that are
deemed inappropriate for the UK, have also managed to run
healthy trade surpluses. One comparison of Britain and the
United States found that between the first oil shock of 1973
and the end of the century, output from UK factories
increased by 14 per cent while American manufacturing
output rose by 114 per cent. American firms produced twice
the output with the same number of workers as in 1973;
Britain produced the same output with half the workers.

In 1973, the US produced an estimated 22 per cent more
manufactured goods per head of population than the UK.
By 2000, the difference was 91 per cent. America is a great
manufacturing nation. The same can no longer be said
about this country.[13]

NESTA's list of areas in Britain where innovation was alive and well only heightened the suspicion that it was scratching around for some good news to provide to ministers. These included creating the National Cycle Network, regulations and incentives to improve social housing, networking among NHS scientists that has resulted in new genetic tests and 'aggressive' tax planning. Now, it could be argued that a National Cycle Network is a fine idea, but so was the idea to create the National Parks in the Attlee government. Similarly, NHS scientists have been working to alleviate pain and save lives since it was founded in 1948; it's called progress. The idea that some of the smartest (and best-paid) people in Britain spend their time dreaming up ways for the super-rich to avoid paying tax rather would be fine economically, if not perhaps morally, were the proceeds of this and other novel forms of innovation sufficient to make up the deficiencies elsewhere. One glance at the trade figures suggests, however, that that is not the case, even with the most liberal possible definition of innovation.

Still, the fantasy lives on that even if Britain eventually outsources all its manufacturing to cheaper countries abroad it will still be able to do the tough and lucrative bits – the design for new products – at home. In the days of Cool Britannia back in the late 1990s, Mr Blair called the UK 'the design workshop of the world', while three years later the Department for Culture Media and Sport (DCMS) noted that 'Britain is a top exporter of design world-wide and many design consultancies earn a significant portion of income from work outside Britain'.[14]

Not, however, as much as they did. Overseas earnings from design fell from £1.4 billion in 2001–2 to £699 million in 2004–5, while the number of people employed in the design workshop of the world fell from 82,000 in 2000–1 to 71,000 four years later.[15] This comes as little surprise to manufacturers. Writing in the *Journal of the Royal Society for Arts*, Ivor

Tiefenbrun, who founded Linn Products, a Glasgow-based company making sound systems, said:

> What I call design is so closely coupled to manufacturing and so competitive that it cannot survive if the links are too tendentious. The reason Britain has fewer in-house designers than competitor countries who have retained more of their manufacturing base is because our manufacturers are so debilitated that they cannot afford, or do not choose to invest in, sufficient in-house capacity.[16]

Mr Tiefenbrun made the point that nobody in Britain has actually managed to build a major manufacturing company from scratch since the Second World War, adding that it was 'not possible to sustain world-class education or research without world-class manufacturing. Manufacturing funds, originates, supports or facilitates around three-quarters of all research.'

There is no shortage of explanations for the failure of the UK over the past six decades to emulate the South Koreans, the Japanese, the Germans or the Americans in building a major manufacturer from scratch. Some put the blame on cultural factors: the distaste the British Establishment has always had for anything that smacks of 'trade'. Others say the explanation has been the liberal arts bias of the education system, which has pushed the elite graduates away from industry and into the media, the law and the City. Another faction has argued that the only time the UK was a serious manufacturing power was in the nineteenth century, and that happened to be the only time that the nation's political centre of gravity was in the North rather than in London. For the rest of the time, the demands of big finance for high interest rates and a strong pound have hobbled manufacturing.

Whatever the impact of long-term cultural factors, the high level of the pound during Mr Blair's period in office was a constant handicap for exporters in the manufacturing sector. It helps to explain the loss of a million jobs, most of them in areas of traditional Labour support, and the fact that manufacturing output in the UK – unlike that in other developed nations – stagnated. For almost the entire period that Tony Blair was in Downing Street, sterling traded higher on the foreign exchanges than it did on Black Wednesday in 1992, when its self-evident over-valuation made it a sitting duck for George Soros and other currency speculators (see p. 38).

Investment bank Goldman Sachs produces regular estimates of what the fair value of a currency should be. These show that the pound started to rise sharply in the autumn before Labour came to power in 1997, and that after a decade of being clearly overvalued, sterling was some 12 per cent above its fair value. As with the overvaluations of the pound at the start of the 1980s and the 1990s, the exchange rate proved a silent killer for British industry, intensifying the competitive pressures from globalization and eroding profitability. In 2006, the service sector – which is far more domestically concentrated and thus less vulnerable to the exchange rate – was enjoying a return on capital of 20 per cent; in manufacturing the comparable figure was 6 per cent, the lowest since the recession of the 1990s. Instead of investing in innovation, the priority for manufacturing has been to survive by cutting costs.

The reason sterling has been a silent killer is that the rest of the country has been too busy partying to notice. Consumers have actually benefited from the strong pound, since the higher exchange rate has lowered the cost of imported goods. Not only have households found their money has gone further, but the disinflationary pressure from a high pound has allowed the Bank of England to keep interest rates lower than they otherwise would have done, further stimulating consumer spending and those large chunks of the service sector that are immune from foreign competition.

Sterling's overvaluation, in other words, made the economy less balanced. There was a relatively short-lived period of four years after Black Wednesday when the pound was undervalued, according to the Goldman Sachs measure, and during this time manufacturing output rose, the trade deficit narrowed and industry's payrolls increased, if not by much. Since 1996, however, it has been a different story. The Bank of England has acknowledged that the strong pound hurt manufacturing:

> The UK's export market share has declined steadily for a number of years, both in aggregate and in many industries within the manufacturing sector. A major determinant of demand for an industry's exports is the price of those exports relative to the prices of international competitors.[17]

According to the Bank, UK firms have little scope to pass on the costs of a higher pound to their overseas customers through higher prices, and just as with R&D, there are only two or three sectors of manufacturing that have bucked the trend to increase their market share. To a greater extent than their US or eurozone competitors, UK firms have had to take it on the chin.

Pharmaceuticals was, of course, one of the sectors singled out by the Bank for doing well, and by any yardstick it is a world-class industry, accounting for 3 per cent of global sales but 10 per cent of global R&D on new drugs. It is stretching optimism to the limit, however, to assert that the success of GlaxoSmithKline has provided proof positive of Mr Wilson's 'white heat' prediction all those years ago.

Optimism, though, is what Bullshit Britain is all about. Some of it, to be fair, is justified. Britain has real and enduring strength in business services: in accountancy, banking and insurance the UK runs a healthy trade surplus. The City is one of the world's three financial hubs, and perhaps the most vibrant of the three. Some of the claims made for the new knowledge economy are, however, nothing more than hype, and nowhere is this more true than in the case of the creative industries.

The Culture Vultures: cashing in (or not) on creativity

The idea that Britain could be the Athens to the rest of the world's Rome, compensating for its dearth of economic and political clout through intellectual and cultural superiority, is not new. Indeed, it was evident once the UK's political establishment finally admitted to itself, around the middle of the last century, that the torch of global supremacy had been passed on to the United States. As one commentator noted, British civil servants sang a little ditty to keep up their spirits when the economist Maynard Keynes was sent to Washington to help the ambassador Lord Halifax negotiate a loan to keep the Attlee government afloat at the end of the war: 'In Washington, Lord Halifax once whispered to Lord Keynes: It's true they have the money bags, but we have all the brains.'[18] The fantasy has been an enduring one. In 1996 David Puttnam wrote that Britain was no longer the 'island of coal surrounded by fish' that Nye Bevan had talked of, a self-evident truism given that over the previous decade all but a handful of the coal mines had been shut down and that since Britain had joined the Common Market in 1973 its waters had been relentlessly sucked dry. More questionable, however, was the second part of Lord Puttnam's analysis – that Britain was now 'an island of creativity surrounded by a sea of understanding'.[19]

New Labour was only too happy to go along with this notion. Tony Blair made much of the fact that he was a member of the rock'n'roll generation, inviting members of the Britpop aristocracy for champagne receptions and letting it be known that he liked to play a few guitar licks on his Fender Stratocaster. As New Labour's thin veneer of liberalism peeled away to disclose a more authoritarian approach just below the surface, rock stars quickly backed off. They soon worked out that the fact that Mr Blair could play the guitar did not mean he was right on; it simply meant he was a neo-liberal who happened to know the chords to *Stairway to Heaven*.

Even so, the creative industries still feature heavily in government propaganda. Shortly after the last election, DCMS minister James Purnell noted that the UK was 'arguably the world's most creative nation'.[20] NESTA's report on how Britain could develop world-class creative industries said: 'The UK film industry has been described as "the most important film in the world after the US".'[21] You have to go to the footnotes to find out who was responsible for this assessment. It was, in fact, the UK Film Council, hardly an unbiased judge, one might think.

A large number of people work in the creative industries, broadly defined, although not nearly as many as the hype would suggest. There are three times as many people working in domestic service as there are in advertising, television, video games, film, the music business and design combined; the creative industries represent around one in 20 of the people working in Britain today. Between them they account for around 4 per cent of all UK exports of goods and services, but as the NESTA report made clear, it is hard to make serious money.

The UK's creative industries are facing increasing international competition. In particular, creative businesses and policymakers need to appreciate the scale of the competitive challenges now facing the sectors in the UK. From film production to design, new international centres for creative businesses are developing rapidly. These are challenging established businesses, including those based in the UK. UK television exports have fallen for the second year running (despite an overall increase since 1998). In design, overseas earnings have halved since 2001, while the value of exports in music, the visual and performing arts in 2003 was down 20 per cent from 2000.[22]

The report then goes on to note that employment in advertising had fallen by 20,000 in three years, after reaching a high in 2001. Film production spending was nearly a third lower in 2005 than in the previous year (including international productions filming in the UK). The number of people working in games development had fallen by 6 per cent since 2000, despite the continued growth in the market.

Despite repeated attempts to use Hugh Grant romantic comedies to revive the British film industry, there is not the remotest sign of Hollywood's stranglehold on the UK market being weakened. In 2004, American-financed films accounted for almost three-quarters of UK box office receipts, while the number of UK films in 2005 released stood at 37, well down on the peak of 84 in the late 1990s. 'The UK's creative and technical talent in film has not created a strong domestic industrial sector that produces sustainable commercial growth,' concluded NESTA. 'This is because the UK industry is vulnerable in structural terms. It is organized primarily around individual film projects rather than sustainable production and distribution companies, as in the US.'

That is, perhaps, one way of looking at it. Another way is to draw the conclusion that Hollywood operates like a proper industry; it makes films it thinks punters will want to watch. The UK industry, as James Heartfield noted in 2000, is dominated by dilettantes who make films they think punters ought to want to watch:

> Amazingly, 68 per cent of UK-based films remain unreleased a year after being made. Until 1989, the percentage unreleased had not gone into double figures. The two-thirds of UK films that are not released are a reminder that we call a film 'industry' is no such thing. For the most part, it is a hobby for inspired geniuses who have no real expectation that their films will be distributed. The United States has a film industry – a 'mass civilization' film industry in which a wealthy elite makes films for the working classes. In Britain we have a 'minority culture' film industry. Down-at-heel bohemians make films about the working classes. Unsurprisingly mass audiences find these patronising diatribes uniquely unappealing.[23]

The idea that the same may be true of British television has gradually been percolating in the national consciousness over the past few years. The proliferation of channels as a result of satellite and cable was touted as an extension of consumer choice; what was not mentioned was that the increase in the quantity of programmes would come at the expense of quality. Spreading the money available for programmes ever more thinly has resulted in a collapse of standards. True, there is still the occasional lavish costume drama, to deflect criticism of dumbing down, but they look increasingly like forlorn relics from a bygone age. This is the age of *Big Brother*, shows where middle-class and working-class couples exchange partners and a seemingly indistinguishable clutch of programmes giving advice on how to add value to houses.

Jimmy McGovern, who created one of the better TV series of the past two decades, *Cracker*, went on the attack at the 2006 Edinburgh Festival against 'latte-drinking, pesto-eating middle-class' TV executives for their patronizing and offensive treatment of Britain's working classes. 'I am delighted to see the state ITV [Independent Television] are in,' Mr McGovern said.

> It is simply because they have utter contempt for their audience. These executives don't sit around and say, 'what kind of intelligent, informative, thought-provoking programmes would we like to watch?' They think, 'what will the ignorant plebs that watch our channel want to see?' They have total contempt for their audience, which is largely working class.[24]

When TV executives are not pushing at the boundaries of trash TV, they are importing programmes from abroad to fill the gaps in the schedules. Although the UK television industry employed more than 111,000 people in 2004 and spent more than £2.6 billion on original programmes, it was still not enough to meet demand. In 2005, Britain had a deficit of £332 million in TV (although it did run a surplus of £163 million in film).[25]

Finally, there is music, a sector that has been a real breadwinner for the UK ever since the Beatles arrived in New York in February 1964. Here, too, the recent signs have not been encouraging. A month after they appeared on the Ed Sullivan Show, the Beatles filled the top five places in the US charts; in 2002, for the first time in the subsequent 38 years, a year went by without one British artist making it into the US top 100. The same trend applied to albums. Somewhat surprisingly, perhaps, the peak year for British dominance was not the heyday of the Beatles and the Rolling Stones in the mid-1960s, nor even the early 1970s when Led Zeppelin and The Who were in their pomp, but 1986, a time when the early UK lead in music videos resulted in a 32 per cent market share. By the early part of the current decade that had fallen to 0.2 per cent, with no particularly strong evidence of imminent recovery. Of the top 10 UK albums in the United States in

2005, two were by the Rolling Stones, two were by Rod Stewart, one was by the Bee Gees and one was by Def Leppard. Coldplay, Gorillaz, Joss Stone and Keane made up the rest.[26]

With a touch of understatement, NESTA admits the Brits have a problem. Total music sales are down, as are exports and employees in the music business, while import penetration from the United States is up.

> The UK industry has been struggling in the US market. The market traditionally accounts for more than a third of global sales revenues and has been one of the cornerstones of the UK music industry's success. However, from the mid-1990s onwards the UK has failed to produce a major international act of comparable stature as rap, soul and R'n'B became leading music forms among young American consumers.[27]

So, to sum up, the film industry is in trouble, the television industry is in trouble and the music industry is in trouble. The creative industries, for all the attention lavished upon them by New Labour, were actually in a much healthier state when Harold Wilson and James Callaghan were in Downing Street. That, after all, was the era of David Bowie, Basil Fawlty and Martin Amis. One way of looking at the British economy of today is to say that there are clusters of excellence around science, finance and the arts. Another way of looking at the economy is to say that the pharmaceutical industry will eventually migrate to the United States, where the money is; that big finance would come a cropper in the event of a bursting of the debt-driven speculative bubble; and that Bullshit Britain reaches its apotheosis in the lionization of the cultural industries.

It is conceivable, just, that Bullshit Britain really is the future, but that those of us wedded to traditional measures of success are not sufficiently hip to cotton on to the fact. But consider: China and India are churning out more graduates than the UK; science departments in British universities are being closed down; the British band that attracted the most attention in the United States last year was not the Arctic Monkeys but The Who. It would be comforting to think that Sir Paul McCartney had passed on responsibility for fixing the hole in the balance of payments to his fashion-designer daughter, Stella. The reality, though, is that the iconic figure in modern Britain is neither Sir Paul nor his daughter, but his second wife Lady Heather Mills McCartney. She managed to woo one of Britain's richest men into marriage and claimed a share of his £800 million fortune when the blissful partnership strangely went sour after four years. And she understood the essence of the bullshit economy: with luck and attitude, you can make a tiny amount of talent go a very long way.

5

Going Once, Going Twice: the Fantasy of Ever-Falling Prices and Ever-Higher Living Standards

[T]he UK experienced a *non-in*flationary *c*onsistently-expansionary – or *'nice'*– decade.

Mervyn King, Governor of the Bank of England, speaking at an East Midland Development Agency/ Bank of England dinner, Leicester, 14 October 2003

Globalization is cutting the prices of basic goods from electronics to clothes, putting what were luxury goods into the hands of ordinary households.

Gordon Brown, Chancellor of the Exchequer, speaking at the Mansion House, London, 21 June 2006

And residents from raw estates, brought down
The dead straight miles by stealing flat-faced trolleys,
Push through plate-glass swing doors to their desires –
Cheap suits, red kitchen-ware, sharp shoes, iced lollies,
Electric mixers, toasters, washers, driers –

Philip Larkin, *Here*[1]

Counting down to Christmas 2006, British shoppers may have been forgiven for believing they had never had it so good – at least in terms of the cost of seasonal gifts. Across a range of products traditionally given as presents during this season, their pound seemed to be going further than ever. In the 12 months to November 2006, the price of electrical appliances, as measured by the Retail Prices Index (RPI), had fallen 3.4 per cent; the cost of audio-visual equipment by 9.6 per cent; the price of compact discs and tapes by a more modest 0.1 per cent; and that of toys, photographic products and sports goods by 4 per cent. Those who fancied a cup of Christmas cheer would find wine and spirits prices over the 12 months had fallen 0.5 per cent, as had the price of off-sales of beer. These price falls take no account of inflation. They are actual cuts in the ticket price of the goods concerned. Once RPI inflation of 3.9 per cent in the 12 months to November was taken into account, the real-term declines were even steeper.

The only fly in the ointment in terms of despatching these generous gifts to their lucky recipients was a 13.1 per cent rise in the cost of postage over the 12 months to November 2006. But then, with petrol and oil prices down 4.6 per cent over the same period, it might have been more cost-effective to deliver the presents in person. Alternatively, given that the abundance of lower-priced goods in the shops must have made it so easy to believe in Father Christmas, perhaps present delivery ought to have been entrusted to him.

The appearance of steady or falling prices has been one of the more remarkable features of the last few years, particularly remarkable given the warm welcome these apparent price falls have been given by politicians and the public. Few people, if any, seem even to have considered the possibility that the price of their own labour, whether in producing goods or services, may also be about to tumble. In the inflationary 1970s it was said that one man's pay rise was another man's price rise. One would have expected the reverse also to be true – that one man's price fall was another man's salary cut – but, apparently, not a bit of it.

We, it seems, are to reap the benefits of lower prices while continuing to enjoy rising incomes. Our own contributions to the national and global economy will be ever more highly valued. The losers from falling prices are safely 'out there', whether toiling in Chinese factories or struggling on remote hill farms in rural Britain. Not that we look down with smugness on the losers. On the contrary – the notion that many things that used to be expensive (whether telephone services or newspapers) are quite rightly now cheap or even free is a form of economic idealism, echoing the principles of the hippy commune of the 1960s.

Should you detect a strong whiff of fantasy about all this, you would not be far wrong. Our contention is, first, that the supposed price slide is not all that it is cracked up to be and, second, that to the extent that it *is* taking place, the aspects most threatening to those living standards are likely to prove more enduring than the aspects more beneficial to British people. Real and imagined price falls have been a 'free lunch' for New Labour, generating an effortless feel-good factor. But all good things come to an end, this one included.

Everything must go: the rise and rise of the giveaway economy

By 2007, the list of goods or services that could be obtained for either next to nothing or simply nothing seemed to be growing by the week. There was 'voice over internet protocol' (VOIP), a near-costless telephone service offered by (among others) a firm called Skype (silly names seeming to be something of a feature of this line of business). For those subscribers prepared to make telephone calls while sitting at their computer wearing a sort of air-traffic-control headset, the prospect beckoned of limitless conversation across any distances. In the newspaper business, London's already-existing free morning title, *Metro*, had been joined by two afternoon publications, *London Lite* and *thelondonpaper*. (As with the rebranding of Lloyds the chemist chain as Lloyds pharmacy, those behind this last title clearly believed there was some residual fashionability in having a name that sounded like a website.)

In 2005, the business paper *City AM* was launched, also free. In May 2006, the *Manchester Evening News* began to distribute a free edition in the city centre. Meanwhile, up in the air, the cost of flying with the new breed of 'budget' or no-frills airlines was dwindling to vanishing point. In November 2005, cheap-travel pioneer Michael O'Leary raised the prospect of free flights in a near future in which the cost of running his Ryanair company would be met by the profits from in-flight gambling and other services. 'Entertainment is where the real money will be made in future,' Mr O'Leary declared. He added that, were a rival airline to start paying passengers to travel, 'we will pay them more'.[2]

Nobody was (quite yet) suggesting paying consumers to buy food, the real cost of which to shoppers remained subdued throughout the 2000s, and would have been even cheaper had the huge new supermarket chains passed on the full savings that they were squeezing out of Britain's ailing farmers. That much of British farming seemed to be on life support for much of the decade was of only intermittent interest to those living away from agricultural areas, not least Tony Blair.

During the catastrophic outbreak of foot and mouth disease in 2001, the unequal struggle between the farmers and the retailers seemed to move the Prime Minister. Speaking on 1 March, he told one farmer: 'There is no doubt that we all want cheaper food in our shops. But on the other hand the supermarkets, not to put too fine a point on it, have pretty much got an arm-lock on you people at the moment. We have got to sit down and discuss that.'[3]

Felicity Lawrence wrote in the *Guardian* of the results of the discussion:

> The big retailers have got themselves off the hook again. A year ago, at the height of the foot and mouth crisis, Tony Blair promised a policy commission to investigate the 'armlock' the big supermarkets held over farmers. This week he called farmers, food industry leaders and environmentalists to Downing Street to talk action. But there was no mention of the retailers' stranglehold, which is, if anything, stronger than ever.[4]

She added: 'The big five chains control nearly 80 per cent of grocery sales in this country. There is a greater concentration of retailing power in the UK than in any other country in the world.'

But if cheap food was portrayed, too often for the comfort of the big supermarkets, as a boon to the many with terrible costs for the few, no such opprobrium attached to the heartland of the new cost-free, no-price-tag economy – the internet. On the contrary, here was the closest the early twenty-first century was likely to get to the madcap idealism of the 1960s. In May 2006, the *Sunday Times* profiled Craig Newmark, whose on-line advertising service Craigslist had mushroomed from a computer bulletin board in San Francisco in the mid-1980s to a 35-country business empire two decades later, one, moreover, that was giving the so-called mainstream media serious cause for concern. In true bohemian fashion, the company, according to the article, 'carries no corporate adverts on its site . . . [charges] no fee for registration, and . . . makes all its money by charging employers in three cities a fee for listing jobs: $75 in San Francisco, $25 in New York and Los Angeles.'[5]

Its attitude rang alarm bells among the economically orthodox. The article quoted one of the paper's own columnists, economic expert and consultant Irwin Stelzer:

> Capitalism is about maximising profits. There is a real problem here for companies trying to compete with a company that is not interested in the capitalist system. When your primary purpose is making money, how do you compete with free?

One answer, from Rupert Murdoch, publisher of the *Sunday Times,* was to buy a piece of the revolution. In July 2005, he paid $580 million for the on-line networking and blogging site MySpace, a huge virtual venue for young people, in a move reminiscent of 'square' 1960s record executives desperately trying to sign 'psychedelic' and 'hippy' musicians.

But if the 'cyber-world' may have shown some idealistic features, the super-cheap manufactured goods on offer in recent years may have played a rather less elevated social role, according to Dhaval Joshi, strategist with banking group Société Générale in London: 'Wage growth has been concentrated at the top end of society, so the way of keeping affluence going has been cheap consumer goods. The trade-off is a deteriorating current account.'[6] Indeed, the state of Britain's balance of payments offers one suggestion of why the triumph of low inflation may not be all it appears. When Labour came to power, the balance of payments was pretty much flat. By 2005, it was in deficit to the tune of £31.8 billion. If the inflation rate is one way of measuring excess demand in the economy, then a balance of payments deficit is another. Without the ability to import to the extent that we have been doing in recent years, the inflation rate would have shot up.

Of course, behaviour would doubtless have adjusted had that been the case, and rather fewer flat-panel television sets and the like would have been sold. Rather more important is the fact that, even were there to be no balance of payments deficit at all, the notion of low or falling prices all round – give or take the odd grumble about Council Tax, fuel prices and the cost to commuters of railway tickets – is highly misleading. With some partial exceptions (clothing and footwear being one), those goods whose prices have fallen or stagnated in actual nominal terms, even before inflation (i.e. a £5 price ticket falling to £4 or staying pretty well unchanged) are the same sort of goods whose prices were falling even 20 or 30 years ago, but whose price falls were masked by the 'smoke' of very high levels of general inflation. Consumer electronics, foreign holidays, private cars and telephone services are four obvious examples.

As we saw above, in the 12 months to November 2006, there were price falls for audiovisual equipment, toys, photographic products, sports goods and electrical appliances. But so what? Those are the sorts of goods and services that have been getting cheaper for decades. In 1970, a stereo music system was a luxury item; in 1980 it was not. In 1970, a camera was still sought after by young children; in 1980, it was well on the way to becoming a commodity product. After all, the mass availability of cars, foreign holidays and telephone services practically defined the expansion of affluence in the second half of the twentieth century. DVD players, largely unheard-of in the mid-1990s, have gone from costly must-have item to routine household kit in a short period. But the same thing happened in the high-inflation years, notably to the digital watch: from a luxury product in Christmas 1979 to a generous gift in Christmas 1980 to being given away free in petrol stations by Christmas 1983.

As we shall see later, the overall inflation picture is very much more mixed than may be supposed. It is our belief that today's agreeably shrinking price tickets are not quite what they seem. And because of this, the assumption of permanently subdued prices is an illusion; it is yet another fantasy.

But first, a short history lesson is required, charting our course from high inflation to apparent price stability.

'Money, it's a crime': inflation in the 1970s

For the strawberry growers of the West Midlands, it was an excellent opportunity for free publicity. Their products, on display at the Royal Agricultural Show in Stoneleigh, Warwickshire, were being sampled by two distinguished visitors, Prime Minister Harold Wilson and his wife Mary. The date was Monday 30 June, in the gloriously hot summer of 1975.

But for Mr Wilson, it was to prove an unwise choice of refreshment in terms of public relations. Many miles from Warwickshire, sterling was in deep trouble on foreign exchange markets. That day it had dropped five cents against the dollar; as the *Guardian* reported the following morning: 'The international financial community was stunned yesterday by the biggest slide in the value of the pound against major world currencies to take place on one day within living memory.'[7] As Lord Wilson recalled in his memoirs: 'Next day, the press had photographs of me in an abdicatory posture, eating strawberries while Rome was burning.'[8]

The cause of sterling's precipitous slide was not hard to find. All major economies had suffered severe inflationary problems since the autumn of 1973, when a fourfold increase in the price of oil had been accompanied by rocketing costs for other commodities, including metals, agricultural produce and minerals. But by the summer of 1975, it was clear that Britain was suffering more than most from vertiginously rising prices. Special political factors inhibited the

Labour government from taking the sort of action that, in other leading industrial nations, had at least capped the rise in living costs. A bitterly fought election in the crisis winter of 1973–4 had been triggered by the Conservative government's attempts to maintain statutory wage controls. Labour had won that election on a specific pledge not to introduce such controls.

Other weapons in the armoury were similarly denied Mr Wilson and his Chancellor, Denis Healey, by the political realities of Labour's tiny parliamentary majority. Deep cuts in public expenditure were off the agenda in 1974–5, as was the simple expedient of letting joblessness rise until those still in work moderated their wage claims. Finally, aggressive use of interest rates to get inflation back under control – the so-called 'monetarist' solution – would have caused uproar.

Inflation, as measured by the all-items Retail Prices Index, was running at 8.9 per cent in the year to August 1973. In the year to August 1974, it was running at 16.9 per cent. And in the year to August 1975, it stood at 26.9 per cent. Foreign-exchange dealers dumping sterling were not alone in responding to the fever of rising prices. Plastic containers of the type more usually used for storing anti-freeze were presented in pubs for filling for home consumption by drinkers keen to escape the next rise in beer prices. The National Union of Railwaymen (now part of the Rail, Maritime and Transport Union) rejected a pay offer of 27 per cent, demanding instead rises of up to 35 per cent. The previous November, Conservative Party leadership challenger Margaret Thatcher disclosed that her larder was stocked with tinned food as a precaution against inflation, and she rode out with ease the subsequent suggestions of 'hoarding'.

Thirty-one years later, in the 12 months to November 2006, the all-items Retail Prices Index rose by 3.9 per cent, up a little from 3.7 per cent in the year to October. It is fair to say that Mr Wilson would have swapped any amount of strawberries for an inflation rate of 3.9 per cent. Today, we are told, we have inflation pretty well licked. Different explanations are given for this apparently happy state of affairs: increased global trade (bringing low-cost imports to our shops); intense price competition driven by the see-through nature of modern price lists thanks to the internet; savvier, more 'streetwise' consumers; the smashing up of old monopolies, whether state or private, with the consequent rise in competition; the ability of independent central banks to use interest rates to control inflation, and a more stable world monetary scene in which the abolition of exchange controls by the major developed nations has allowed currency markets to deliver near-instant 'verdicts' on what they may believe to be inflationary behaviour by governments or central banks, thus making such behaviour less likely.

Thirty-one years ago, Robert Moss, the editor of *Foreign Report*, could write thus: 'The recent trends that are pulling us towards strato-inflation are related both to an inflation of expectations in the post-1945 consumer society, and to a loss of broader concepts of patriotism and citizenship.'[9] Something, it would seem, has gone terribly right in the years since Mr Moss put pen to paper. The notion has gained ground that high inflation is a sort of economic version of scarlet fever, a once-feared illness for which we now have the cure. But we believe the inflation of yesteryear – just like the disinflation of today – resulted from special factors that are far from permanent. Without a firm understanding of the inflationary era, it will be difficult if not impossible to grasp the essential facts about the current, allegedly disinflationary era.

As the inflationary surge approached its peak, President Gerald Ford addressed the US Congress on the rise in the cost of living, insisting: 'We must whip inflation right now.'

Mr Ford added:

> Our present inflation to a considerable degree comes from many years of enacting expensive programs without raising enough revenues to pay for them. The truth is that 19 out of the 29 years I had the honor and privilege to serve in this Chamber [Mr Ford had been a Representative from Michigan], the Federal Government ended up with Federal deficits. That is not a very good batting average.[10]

In the years since, the notion that inflation is generated by excessive government deficits and unbridled credit creation ('printing money') has come to be associated with a conservative, right-wing or 'monetarist' position. But at the time when, in Britain at least, it was widely assumed that inflation was largely or entirely caused by pay claims and that the overriding need was to 'discipline' the trade unions, Mr Ford's candour was refreshing. The Great Inflation had indeed been triggered in large part by the US government's refusal to raise taxes to pay for its war in Vietnam and by that fact that, under the pre-1971 fixed exchange rate system, this inflation could be, and was, exported to other countries.

By the end of the 1960s, the system – known as Bretton Woods after the New Hampshire town in which it had been drawn up in 1944 – was breaking down under the weight of the extra dollars conjured into existence. In April 1968, convertibility of dollars into gold (hitherto the right of any non-US person, company or government) was restricted to governments only. In August 1971, convertibility was suspended entirely. Shortly afterwards, any fixed relationship between the dollar and other Western currencies broke down completely.

For most of the post-war period, small quantities of inflation had been accepted in the majority of Western economies as the price for lubricating the economic wheels and maintaining near-full employment. But the rates had been modest. Between January 1955 and January 1968, the absolute peak was 7.3 per cent in the 12 months to March 1956 (the same rate held for the 12 months to April 1956). However, this was freakishly high. More common were 12-monthly rates of between 3.5 and 5.5 per cent. Indeed, there were occasional falls in the 12-monthly rate in the late 1950s and very early 1960s, the largest being one of 0.8 per cent in the 12 months to June 1959.

But as Bretton Woods collapsed, there was a vast upswing in inflation across all economies in response to the end of the system. Because of the huge numbers of extra dollars that had been created, those commodities priced in dollars – oil, in particular – shot up in price. Amid all the commentary about the 1973 oil-price rise being a 'political embargo' by Arab oil producers to punish the West for its support for Israel, it is often forgotten that the members of the Organization of Petroleum Exporting Countries (OPEC) were, to some extent, merely trying to recover the buying power of their product. If that product were priced in devaluing dollars, then OPEC wanted more of those dollars per barrel of oil.

The response of the Western economies to both the Bretton Woods collapse and the surge in the cost of dollar-priced commodities was initially disappointing to those who may have hoped that the end of fixed exchange rates would give the foreign-exchange markets the power to bring profligate or inflationary governments to heel by simply selling their currencies. Alas, most governments responded to the events of 1973–4 in an 'accommodatory' manner, preferring to let domestic inflation and the external value of currencies take the pressure of adjustment to the new era, rather than let the burden fall on levels of employment.

The response to dollar inflation had been a rise in commodity prices, the reaction to which was inflation in other OECD (Organization for Economic Cooperation and

Development) countries. Not surprisingly, commodity prices stayed high. In Britain, wheat alone rose in price by about 137 per cent between 1970 and 1975. Panic buying cleared UK shops and garages of tallow candles and paraffin (substitutes for domestic lighting and heating in the power cuts of the winters of 1970–1, 1971–2 and 1973–4, the first two caused purely by strikes, the last by a strike plus the effects of the OPEC-induced oil crisis). But in the jittery atmosphere of 1973–4, there were 'runs' on the unlikeliest items, including sugar and lavatory paper.

Along with oil, the source of much heating and lighting, food was, unsurprisingly, a source of high anxiety as prices took off. In Britain, the incoming Labour government of February 1974 put in place a package of food subsidies to stabilize what, in those homelier times, was referred to as 'the weekly shopping basket' (which was, inevitably, the property of 'the housewife'). In the United States, President Ford preferred a more hands-on solution. Speaking one week to the night after his above-mentioned address to Congress, he addressed the Future Farmers of America in the municipal auditorium in Kansas City. His answer to rising food prices was to 'grow your own'. He told the meeting: 'Ten dollars' worth of seeds on a 25-foot by 30-foot plot will grow $290 worth of vegetables'.[11]

Less than a year later, Britain was voting on whether to remain a member of the European Economic Community (now the European Union). That the vote was two to one in favour of 'staying in' is common knowledge. What has been forgotten, in an era in which even the most passionate British pro-Europeans condemn the 'nonsense' of the EU's farm-support scheme, the Common Agricultural Policy (CAP), and demand its abolition, is that European self-sufficiency in food was one of the main reasons touted for a 'Yes' vote in 1975. The government's leaflet, distributed to every home in the country to argue for remaining a member, mentioned 'secure supplies of food at fair prices', and announced:

> [Many] food prices in the rest of the world have shot up, and our food prices are now no higher because Britain is in the [Common] Market than if we were outside . . . [and] *we shall be more sure of our supplies when food is scarce in the world.* (Emphasis added.)

One final piece of the seventies inflationary jigsaw, before we return to the present, was financial deregulation in the UK. As Robin Ramsay recounted, Tory Chancellor Tony Barber was 'bounced' at a dinner in January 1971 into accepting a radical package of financial liberalization by Bank of England Governor Lord (Leslie) O'Brien.[12] But the timing was unpropitious, to say the least. Deregulating credit creation in the UK at a time of roaring inflation and 'the printing of money' around the world might almost have been designed to have the effect that it did – a runaway boom in commercial and residential property, a parallel boom in consumer spending and an economy horribly vulnerable to the explosion in commodity prices (especially oil) in the wake of events in late 1973.

Getting all this under control was enormously painful. Attempts by the Conservative government of Edward Heath (1970–4) to persuade trade unions and business to accept lower wages and prices/profits in the national interest ended ultimately in failure, with the industrial disruption of the winter of 1973–4. The Labour government had more success, at least initially, in getting its union allies to agree reductions in living standards for their members to rein in the cost of living. On an index taking 1971 real household income as 100, the figure dropped from 114.5 in 1973 to 113.5 the following year. It bounced back to 114.7 in 1975 before falling to 114.3 in 1976 and 112 in 1977.

Unsurprisingly, it became a commonplace to bemoan stagnant or falling living standards.

> From 1975, the average standard of living, for all workers, professional, managerial, technical, clerical and manual, began to fall – and unemployment began to rise.[13]

For the middle class, a new phenomenon threatened – downward mobility. The world of those who had never quite 'got it together' professionally and found themselves driving minicabs or managing laundrettes was brilliantly captured by Guy Bellamy in his 1977 novel, *The Secret Lemonade Drinker*.[14]

Exacerbating the pressure on living standards was the use of wage controls to try to bring inflation to heel. As we saw above, this meant real-terms reductions in earnings. But the policy was stoking resentment, particularly among those who had been relatively low-paid even before the policy had bitten. In the early weeks of 1979, the lid blew off. Whereas the Heath government's battles had been largely with industrial unions, requiring those with an interest in current affairs to get to grips with the TGWU, the NUM, UCATT, USDAW and ASLEF,[15] the so-called Winter of Discontent had been led by public-sector organizations, and the air was thick with talk of NUPE, NALGO and CoHSE.[16] On the face of it, the pay awards that followed that bitter winter gave UK inflation another upward shove, to 21.9 per cent in May 1980, to within sight of the mid-1975 figure. But the momentum behind high inflation was waning. The special factors that had brought it into existence in the late 1960s and early 1970s had faded. The next inflationary peak, 10.9 per cent in September and October 1990, was well below the May 1980 figure, and 1975 had seen the high-water-mark. In retrospect, perhaps a celebratory strawberry or two would have been in order after all.

The price is slight: disinflation, myths and reality

In short, the Great Inflation was the result of a violent disruption of monetary relationships and values. Once it took hold, many people in high places assumed it would be permanent. Mr Wilson himself, then in opposition, told an international symposium in New York in May 1971 that a voluntary prices and incomes policy is 'the pattern of the future for democratic societies'.[17] There seemed no end to inflation.

New Labour was far from convinced the dragon had been slain back in 1997. That was why it set up the Monetary Policy Committee as an independent body to fix interest rates at however high a level might be needed to bear down on inflation. This far-seeing act, claim ministers, coupled with the government's sagacity in embracing globalization, has ushered in today's era of relative price stability.

Just as there once seemed no end to inflation, today there has seemed to be no end to disinflation. We do not claim that there is an exact mirror-image between the 1970s and our own time. The Great Inflation was a freak storm; our own more subdued cost-of-living picture is closer to the long-run norm. Inflation tends to be low except during times of war. The price level was lower at the outbreak of the First World War in 1914 than it was at the time of the battle of Waterloo. Capitalism is all about competitive markets, and they tend to keep inflation in check.

Despite this, the disinflationary decade from the mid-1990s to the mid-2000s was itself the result of a disruption of monetary values and relations, a set of circumstances as unlikely to prove permanent as the inflation of yesteryear. In brief, these have included:

- The artificial under-valuation of China's currency, the yuan, and the subsequent over-valuation of the US dollar and its junior sidekick, sterling. This has kept down the price of Chinese manufactures, if only because, in the words of Dhaval Joshi, the strategist from the bank Société Générale: 'The exchange rate is the mechanism whereby Chinese people are not being paid enough for their work.'[18]

■ The accumulation of dollar-denominated assets by Far Eastern 'tiger' economies as a precaution against a repeat of the so-called 'meltdown' in the late 1990s, when they lacked the foreign-reserve firepower to help themselves out of trouble.

■ Advances in stock control and production as a result of new technology, meaning cheaper goods emerging from a more efficient chain.

■ Freer trade worldwide in foodstuffs and, perhaps more importantly, the ability, via amalgamations, of a small number of very large supermarkets to squeeze farmers. One has only to recall a few of the long-lost names of British retailing (Keymarkets, Bishops, International Stores) to realize the extent of the consolidation.

■ The fall-out from a glut of oil, gold and other commodities in the late 1990s and consequent price falls at that time, which may have made a generation of investors very wary of commodities.

■ The favourable reaction over time to the notion of an independent central bank setting interest rates. One does not need to be an unqualified fan of the new arrangements to find, in retrospect, something sweetly childlike about the notion that chancellors in the past sought to try to cut base rates during the party conference season in the autumn.

None of these factors can be expected to exercise a permanent downward pressure on inflation. Indeed, at the time of writing, disinflation is starting to unwind. In the late autumn of 2006, the *Economist* food index hit a nine-year high, 'led by higher grain and soya prices'. It added: 'End-season world grains stocks will be the lowest for 29 years.'[19] Meanwhile, the gold price was up more than 20 per cent on the year. True, oil prices were down on 12 months earlier, by nearly 5 per cent, but then that came after a spectacular run-up to well over $60 a barrel.

The glory days of the late 1990s and early 2000s, when it was openly wondered why Britain bothered having a farming industry, when Chancellor Gordon Brown could cheerfully sell off huge quantities of Britain's gold reserves and when oil was at or just below $10 a barrel, seemed a long way away. Furthermore, as we saw above, the prices of consumer electronics and other products may be in decline. But that in no way translates into general, routine price declines. Disinflation for some items needs to be matched by inflation for others if the disruption of deflation is to be avoided. We are happy to report that large numbers of businesses have buckled down to their patriotic duty: publicans, for example, who, in the 12 months to November 2006, pushed up beer prices by 3.6 per cent; wine-bar owners and others, who hiked the price of on-sale wine by 3.3 per cent; owners of takeaways and snack bars (up 3.2 per cent); those involved in the repair and maintenance of domestic property (up 4.5 per cent); furniture suppliers (up 2.5 per cent); car maintenance firms (up 6 per cent); providers of domestic services (up 5.5 per cent); and providers of what government statisticians refer to as 'entertainment and other recreation' (up 5.1 per cent).[20]

None of this is especially surprising. It is of a piece with the pattern of price movements during recent decades, movements that may have been hidden by the flurry of general inflation but which were present nonetheless. Manufactured goods get cheaper; services, whether a restaurant meal, a concert by a top performer or even a 'daily' to clean your house, become relatively more expensive. Not only are productivity improvements very much more marked in manufacturing processes, but worldwide competition in manufactured goods is reasonably intense. Service businesses, by contrast, are very much more sheltered. Few people are going to fly to India for a haircut, and gardeners, cooks and bartenders in one town are hard to exchange for those in another town, let alone in another country. If service personnel have competitors they tend to be either machines (an entryphone replacing a porter, for example) or their own customers (at a pinch, people can cook their own meals, mow their own lawns and so forth).

Beyond this, an intriguing 'take' on ultra-cheap manufactured goods by David Hillier, the chief UK economist with Barclays Capital, suggests once again that disinflation may not be all it is cracked up to be. In May 2004, he identified what could be described as 'stealth inflation'. 'Western companies, who cannot possibly compete on labour costs with Asian producers, have had to resort to reducing the quality of the materials used,' he wrote. Recalling a visit to a shirt shop, he added: 'It's true the shirts cost less than I paid for them five years ago, but they were three times as thin.' Nor is this quiet reduction in quality confined to clothing and footwear.

> If you have a barbecue this weekend, have a look at the plastic garden furniture you are sitting on and the paper plates and paper napkins you use. I am willing to bet that they will all be thinner than they used to be. Try lighting the fire with matches and the strike surface will be so thin you won't be able to get a light. If you do manage to get a flame, you'll find the firelighters are much smaller. Bag up the rubbish afterwards and the refuse sacks are almost wafer-thin.[21]

Mr Hillier's experience would strike a chord with many people. Few cannot have experienced at one time or another the bathroom towel rail apparently constructed out of silver paper and thus barely able to support a table napkin, the dishwasher guaranteed to wash only those dishes that were cleaned before being loaded, the vacuum cleaner apparently reluctant to suck up much in the way of dust, the CD player that takes early retirement soon after its guarantee expires and the kettle that follows suit. Furthermore, in what may be thought of as a pincer movement to this 'stealth inflation', is the fact that private enterprise devotes a great deal of time and energy to increasing the price-value of goods and services. In an article on the revival of the vinyl record, journalist Peter Wilby noted:

> Capitalism abhors anything that is free. If you are getting something for nothing, capitalism will eventually find a way of persuading you to pay for it. Exercise used to be free; people went for brisk walks or scrubbed their front steps. Now they are persuaded that they must go to the gym. The story is similar with water.[22]

But even with the possible pincer effects of deteriorating quality and clever marketing-led price rises, the results of the 'giveaway economy' are not exactly spectacular. According to the 2006 Annual Survey of Hours and Earnings (ASHE) mean annual pay for all employees was £24,301, a 3.9 per cent increase on the previous year.[23] And the Retail Prices Index in the 12 months to September 2006 was, as we have seen, running at 3.6 per cent.

Looking to the future, such disinflation as continues to exist is likely to prove increasingly uncomfortable for ordinary British families. As we saw above, the six special factors that have subdued prices up until now, and which are likely to lose their force, have largely produced disinflationary effects beneficial for Britain: cheaper electronic goods, clothes, foodstuffs and the rest. More enduring disinflation will be driven by irreversible technical and legislative changes, and here is where the effects start to hurt Middle Britain, in particular the salaries and status of the middle class.

In some areas, this has started already. Free banking, combined with the centralization of customer services in remote call centres, has greatly diminished the role of the once all-powerful bank manager. Now another pillar of the British high street, the solicitor, looks set to go the same way: the *Daily Telegraph* reported that the Conservative Party was warning that hundreds of local law firms faced closure as a result of proposed legal changes allowing supermarkets to set up booths offering conveyancing and other services.[24] Prices might fall, but so would earnings. Much the same goes for accountancy services (likely to be increasingly 'off-shored' to India and other developing countries) and aspects of technical design and other specialist professional activity (ditto). In every case, lower prices will mean smaller incomes.

But how could it be otherwise? Given that most people's incomes are linked directly to earnings from employment, how can shrinking prices be squared with a rise in the general standard of living? They cannot – in the real world. But in the dreamy fantasy world we have inhabited, making the impossible appear commonplace is no problem at all.

6

The Tottering Empire State: Crisis in the Public Sector

And I learned this morning that in ten years the number of health service administrators has gone up by 40,000 and the number of hospital beds has gone down by 60,000 . . . Furthermore the annual cost of the health service has gone up by one and a half billion pounds. In real terms! But Sir Humphrey seemed pleased when I gave him these figures. 'Ah,' he said smugly, 'if only British industry could match this growth record.'

Jonathan Lynn and Antony Jay,
The Complete Yes Minister[1]

Caesar's double bed is warm
As an unimportant clerk
Writes I DO NOT LIKE MY WORK
On a pink official form.

W.H. Auden; *The Fall of Rome*

Through voluntary associations, churches and faith groups and then on into public service we, the British people, have consistently regarded a strong civic society as fundamental to our sense of ourselves – that moral space, a public realm in which duty constrains the pursuit of self-interest.

Gordon Brown, giving the
Hugo Young memorial lecture, 13 December 2005

It says much for Labour's handling of the public sector that at the start of 2007, a Conservative Party led by an Old Etonian was running a campaign on its website to 'stop NHS cuts'. Anybody, least of all a Tory, proposing such a political gambit back in the days when the theme tune to Tony Blair's premiership was *Things Can Only Get Better*, would have been the subject of ridicule. The voters had believed Mr Blair's hyperbole on the eve of the 1997 election that there were '24 hours to save the NHS', yet by 2006 the public felt short-changed. Despite the biggest cash injection in the 58-year history of the NHS, the news from the health service was as relentlessly negative as it had been for John Major in the dog days of his administration a decade earlier. The stories were not of cuts in waiting times or of increased life expectancy, though both were a reality. The public took these as much for granted as they had low inflation and falling unemployment under Mr Major, and thought they were the least that could be expected, given the extra resources being stumped up by the taxpayer. Instead, the media coverage was dominated by plans to close Accident and Emergency departments; by concerns that the spread of the superbug MRSA was the result of skimping on cleanliness in order to save money; by stories of hospitals so financially hamstrung by the Private Finance Initiative that they were forced to cut front-line services.

The Conservatives took delight in twisting the knife. Spending on the NHS was never actually cut in the Thatcher–Major years (it rose by just over 3 per cent a year in real terms) but the increases had come in fits and starts, and had not been enough to keep pace with the tendency of inflation to rise faster in the NHS than in the rest of the economy. In the first half of the first decade of the twenty-first century, spending on the NHS rose by 7 per cent in real terms year after year. And still it did not appear to be enough; it was certainly not enough to prevent the Conservatives getting a bit of their own back. Under a banner showing Gordon Brown wielding a giant pair of scissors, the Tory website proclaimed: 'David Cameron's Conservatives are backing a new, national campaign to underline our support for the staff of our NHS and the patients they serve.'[2] Those surfing the site were invited to sign a petition calling on the Chancellor to 'Stop Brown's NHS Cuts'.

Labour's response, initially, was to scoff. This, the government said, was a shameless and bogus attempt by the Conservatives to feign concern for the NHS. Following three thumping defeats, Britain's main opposition party was desperate to appear humane, reasonable – and electable. Yet the attempt to rehabilitate the Tories as a party that could be trusted to look after the public services was modelled closely on Labour's own campaign a decade earlier to convince voters that it could manage the economy, and it appeared to be equally successful. Opinion polls showed that the Conservatives – excoriated for their under-investment in the health service between 1979 and 1997 – were more trusted to look after the nation's health than the party that had created the NHS in the first place and which had displayed its enduring natural love by doubling spending to £100 billion under Tony Blair's premiership.

The Prime Minister, in his valedictory address to Labour's annual conference in 2006, mounted a robust defence of his handling of health and education. 'Over the past ten years Britain has invested more in our public services than any comparable nation in the world,' Mr Blair said, adding in one of his trademark verb-less sentences: 'From near the bottom in Europe to the average in a decade.' The extra spending was the Prime Minister's answer to those who saw his reform programme – billed as greater choice to patients and parents – as privatization by any other name.

Three hundred thousand more workers, treble the money, 25 per cent more pay in real terms and the largest-ever hospital programme; that is an NHS being re-built not privatised. Refurbishing or rebuilding every state secondary school in the country. 92,000 more classroom assistants, 36,000 more teachers, pay also up 17 per cent in real terms. This isn't privatising state education; it's producing the best schools results ever.[3]

Yes, comrade citizens of Great Britain and Northern Ireland, there had been another year of socialist advance by the shock troops of the revolution at the chalk face and in health factories across the land. Had the Prime Minister's speech not been cheered to the echo by the party faithful, you could have heard the wind whispering through the corn growing lustily on the steppes and the distant strumming of a balalaika. Only counter-revolutionary defeatism could explain the failure of the masses to appreciate just how good life was under Labour. Well, perhaps. The voters greeted the litany of achievements with the same sort of world-weary cynicism characteristic of the Soviet populace under Brezhnev; they assumed the figures were meaningless and that the real beneficiaries of the extra spending were the bureaucrats. They were right on both counts.

The best years of their lives: fiddling our way to the top of the form

Durham University is a centre of excellence for education and its academics have looked closely at exam results. It investigated one set of tests – the Key Stage 2 tests for 11-year-olds – to see if there was evidence of grade inflation between 1995 and 2000. The first piece of bad news for the government was that the Durham researchers found evidence of the tests becoming easier to pass.

It is possible using all the information to estimate the true rises and it would seem that over the years the percentage of children achieving level 4 (the benchmark) or above in English should have risen from 48 per cent to 58 per cent, not the figure of 75 per cent actually recorded. In mathematics, the percentage of children achieving a level 4 or above should have risen from 44 per cent to 62 per cent not the officially reported figure of 72 per cent.[4]

The second bit of bad news for Labour was that the biggest increases in the pass rates that were actually achieved happened in the years before Tony Blair arrived in Downing Street; the extra billions poured into education from the turn of the millennium onwards had had only marginal impact.

In 2003, Professor Carol Fitz-Gibbon of Durham University gave evidence to the House of Commons Select Committee on Education and Skills. Professor Fitz-Gibbon, somewhat to the discomfort of the Labour members of the committee, made it clear that she did not think the relentless increases in pass marks in examinations were due to pupils becoming smarter: 'We see that for the same ability the grades are higher and higher, year on year, so we have grade inflation.' Barry Shearman, the chair of the committee, asked Professor Fitz-Gibbon to expand her argument, something she was only too willing to do.

> Yes, for example, at A level . . . the grades have gone up and up. If you look at those who got an A* in A level mathematics, if it was not grade inflation, then when they got to universities, the universities should be pleased that standards have risen. In fact, the universities are dismayed. The University of York has been testing for 20 years, and now they have had to give up the test because nobody can do any of it. So there is a maths test when you get to York to do a mathematically-orientated subject, and I have heard that they cannot use it any more.[5]

For a government that had been insistent that better grades were due to the hard work of teachers and pupils, this was obviously hard to swallow, so Mr Shearman persisted: 'You are saying that whereas the Government's tests suggest there is an improvement across the board, year-by-year, you are saying there has been a decline in performance year by year.' Professor Fitz-Gibbon replied: 'Yes, except in primary school numeracy.'

Throughout its time in office, Labour was in category-one denial about the dumbing down of the exam system. In 2006, Jim Knight, the schools minister, welcomed the increase in the number of GCSE students securing five good passes in the A* to C range. 'I would like to congratulate school staff, pupils and parents on these excellent results which show improvements across the board', Mr Knight said.

> The last few weeks have seen a range of pessimists criticise our schools and teachers, describing even quickly improving schools as failing. In actual fact, the results today show that fewer schools are failing their pupils with a record proportion of children leaving with five good passes including English and maths and more and more children hitting the highest grades.[6]

Actually, you could cut the statistics another way. The government's decision to stop making a foreign language compulsory in the national curriculum after the age of 14 meant that the number of 16-year-olds getting four passes in subjects that included maths, English, science and a foreign language had fallen by four points in four years to below 25 per cent. Moreover, the arrival of a new, more 'relevant' science curriculum in the autumn of 2006 had already been dismissed as 'dumbing down' by members of the science establishment.

Mr Knight typified the approach highlighted by Alison Wolf in her book *Does Education Matter?* The government had an unshakeable belief that more education led to higher growth and therefore set quantitative targets – the number of 11-year-olds passing numeracy and literacy tests, GCSE passes, the number of young people entering university – which it ensured were met.

> This approach is precisely analogous to the way in which Soviet planners ran their economy, and it has precisely the same drawbacks. Numerical targets have to be concerned with things that can be counted easily (like tractors or examination grades), not with more complex attributes which require judgement and are open to debate (such as whether the tractors work at all well, or the quality of different curricula).[7]

In the Soviet Union of the 1930s, those who raised doubts about the ability of the tractors to plough the land could expect a knock on the door from the KGB in the middle of the night. Under New Labour, those who said degrees in media studies were not worth the student debt attached to them were dismissed as elitists. But as Professor Wolf pointed out, it was not difficult to see why standards were suffering; it was getting harder and harder to attract the same calibre of graduates into teaching as in the 1950s, and the increased demand for teachers at all levels made it even more tempting to bear down on salaries. Similarly, the doubling of the student population at university has been accompanied by a steady fall in spending per student, to less than half the level seen in 1976. The new graduates, in many respects, were no better qualified than those leaving school with A levels a generation earlier, but believed they were entitled to a steady job at a good salary. The government duly obliged by creating more white-collar jobs in the public sector.

Dr Cameron's casebook: cutting up rough on health

Politically, though, education was a less acute problem for Labour than health. David Cameron's need to play down his 'toff' background meant that for tactical reasons he pulled his punches on the education system, not only promising to match Labour's spending but – if possible – to send his own children to state schools. Cameron felt less encumbered when it came to the NHS, particularly since voters, after almost a decade of Labour spin, were becoming harder to convince, although for somewhat differing reasons. Those who had always suspected that the extra investment would be wasted unless it was accompanied by fundamental reform appeared to be vindicated by the members of the government, up to and including the Prime Minister, who shared the same view. Gordon Brown's spending increases were the last hurrah for the old command-and-control model; the answer, free-market critics argued, was to introduce more choice into the system, providing power for consumers (patients) to pick and choose where to have their treatment and to force hospitals to compete with each for business (patients). Hospitals that proved popular would expand; those that failed to prosper in a payment-by-results environment would close.

Those who had always suspected that Labour had a hidden privatization agenda were not mollified by the Prime Minister's honeyed words. Labour's new credo, they said, was that the private sector ran things more effectively and efficiently than the public sector, and if ministers believed that this was true for Britain's air traffic control system and the country's nuclear power stations – as indeed they did – then presumably the same logic applied to the health service. Mr Blair's vision was of the NHS remaining true to its founding values but being remodelled along private-sector lines. This meant, first, responding to the dictates of the consumer age by giving the patient 'choice'. It also meant that independent hospital trusts would be 'freed' from state control and free to borrow on the private capital markets.

This was a choice piece of Fantasy Island thinking, with profound and potentially fatal consequences for the NHS. Despite the language of consumerism there was not the remotest indication that patients in 2007 were scouring the 'Good Hospital Guide' with the avidity of gourmets in search of a three-star blow-out. Rather, the patients of 2007 wanted exactly what the patients of 1948 had wanted: good treatment, free of charge in a clean, well-kept hospital close to their home. Government-commissioned academic research showing precisely that fact – that people were not shopping around for the best hospital – proved an inconvenient truth for ministers and mysteriously disappeared from the NHS website.

Under Mr Blair's plan, the money would follow the patient, which would be good news for those hospital trusts in demand. What it meant for the less popular trusts was less clear. In the private sector, a company suffering from weak demand can either cut costs to balance its books or it can borrow money to invest in new products and services. In addition, of course, there is an insolvency mechanism to protect creditors in the event that the private company goes bust. There is huge doubt as to which assets would be available to creditors in the event that a hospital trust went to the wall, because there is a provision for the Health Secretary to earmark certain services as essential for mandatory NHS activities. At the time of writing, there is no rigorous framework for trust insolvency, although one has been pledged by Whitehall. Unsurprisingly, perhaps, the government has preferred not to draw the public's attention to the idea that official receivers could be drawing up a list of the assets at the local infirmary; the public would have the right to wonder which planet ministers were on. The notion that a hospital would be allowed to go bust is itself a piece of utter fantasy. At least, let's hope that is the case and that Mr Blair's failure to make a mention in his conference speech of the hospital trusts forced to cut jobs and beds in response to financial deficits, or the plans to hand the running of NHS hospitals over lock, stock and barrel to private health care companies, was merely an oversight rather than evidence of a prime minister who needs to get out a bit more.

Polls still suggested that the public liked, even cherished, the NHS. There was no desire to move away from a tax-based system that provided care free at the point of use, let alone to import the free-market model favoured by the wild-eyed ideologues of the right. But according to one survey, only one in seven members of the public thought the extra investment was going to cut waiting lists and lengthen lives rather than go to higher salaries for the NHS's burgeoning bureaucracy.[8] According to the Conservatives, in 2006 there were more administrators in the NHS (264,012) than there were beds (175,646).

This was a statistic that resonated with the public. Labour's claim to be trusted with the public services rested on the claim that it was the party of the caring nurse and the life-saving doctor. By 2006, though, this was a myth. Labour was now the party of the target-setting bureaucrat, the cost-cutting management consultant and the anti-obesity coordinator. Like the Socialist Party in France, New Labour had lost touch with its traditional urban, blue-collar, working-class supporters, the group that stuck solidly by the Attlee government and gave Labour its biggest-ever share of the vote in the lost election of 1951. Mr Blair, helped by two recessions in manufacturing and the housing meltdown of the early 1990s, had pieced together his own coalition of blue and white collars, but by Labour's third term this had splintered. What was left of the working class after the loss of a million jobs in manufacturing was abstaining, toying with the idea of voting for the British National Party or, at best, reluctantly backing Labour. Iraq had been the final straw for the middle-class intelligentsia, while the commuter-belt bourgeoisie was grumbling about taxes and the trains. All that remained for Labour was its new core vote – the swollen army of white-collar, public-sector bureaucrats.

It was little wonder that the body representing management consultants strongly advised its members to vote Labour in the 2005 election, since there was no point in killing a goose laying such lucrative golden eggs. Nor was it unsurprising that, having asked the former NatWest Bank chief executive Derek (now Sir Derek) Wanless to prepare a report in 2001 arguing the case for extra state spending on the NHS, Gordon Brown politely declined the offer of a follow-up study to see whether the money had been well-spent. Mr Brown knew very well what the finding would be: the doubling of spending had not been matched by a doubling of productivity, or anything like it. Stories abounded of GPs raking in £100,000 a year – and in some cases up to £250,000 a year – for doing the same job they had been doing before, simply because they were able to hit specified government targets and tick the right boxes. Undaunted, Sir Derek launched an independent inquiry into how well the extra money had been spent, having accepted an invitation to do so for the King's Fund, an independent health think tank.[9]

There were some in the government willing to accept the view of Andrew Dillon, the chief executive of the National Institute for Health and Clinical Excellence (NICE), the body that decides which treatments and drugs should be available on the NHS. 'To me, the extra NHS money feels like rain after a long drought, taking a long time to sink in before you see it on the surface.'[10] Others, however, were more impatient for results. In the same newspaper on the same day, the former Health Secretary, Alan Milburn, was proposing 'a new wave of health reforms based on giving patients NHS credits to choose some of their own health care'. The scheme, according to Mr Milburn, would 'empower patients, cut costs and radically redistribute power in society'.[11]

The public had every reason for bemusement at Mr Milburn's Big Idea. What, they could reasonably ask, was the difference between NHS credits and plans previously floated by the Conservatives to hand out education vouchers so that children in poor areas had the chance to buy their way out of failing schools? The answer, of course, was that there was no difference whatsoever. In Labour's fantasy world, there was to be a perfect marriage between the state and the market. The state would provide the cash – and lots of it – together with targets to be met by the public sector; the private sector would do its bit by providing management expertise and a dose of healthy competition. The 'perfect marriage' is now in serious trouble; the partners have never really got on but are trying to keep up appearances for the sake of the children.

Permanently passing go: playing Monopoly with New Labour

The government did not seem to realize – or if it did realize, it did not seem to care – that the public was being fleeced by the private sector. Labour had opposed the privatization of the big utilities under the Conservatives, arguing that water, gas and electricity, railways and Britain's airports were natural monopolies that were never likely to be subject to market forces. With one exception, Labour accepted the status quo inherited from four terms of Conservative rule, in which the frontiers of the state were decisively rolled back, and left the utilities in private hands, relying on regulation to ensure that the public was not short-changed. Looked at from the perspective of the market, there was nothing wrong with this arrangement. An Australian bank, Macquarrie, was involved in a bid for BAA, then returned to snap up Thames Water, Britain's biggest supplier and one with an abysmal record for leakages. As the *Guardian* put it, Thames Water had 'so much Victorian pipework on its books it would be more appropriately run by the National Trust'.[12] Yet Macquarrie was no white knight riding to the rescue of the consumer, for whom the reality was inflation-busting bills and drought orders; it was there because it could rely on weak regulation and a natural monopoly to provide a steady income stream.

The one exception was the rail network, and in that case the effective renationalization of the track, stations and signalling was forced upon Labour rather than the result of a deliberate policy choice. Railway privatization had been the last attempted by the Conservatives; Mrs Thatcher, even with her landslide majorities, had believed it too difficult, and so it proved. One private company, Railtrack, owned the infrastructure; separate operating companies won franchises for running the trains. As with every other privatization, the first thing that happened under this 'radical' shake-up was that the people at the top handed themselves enormous pay increases to reflect their new private-sector status. The second thing that happened (at Railtrack, at least) was that the people who knew how the railways worked – the engineers – were replaced by people who couldn't tell a sleeper from a siding but knew their way round a balance sheet. The third thing that happened was that the money men looked for efficiency savings to boost profits for shareholders. In the rest of the private sector, the consequences of these 'efficiency savings' rarely show up. On the railways, skimping on maintenance led to a train crash at Hatfield in which four people died.

When the railways were state-owned, it was customary for teams of four to six men to inspect the tracks, and on busy lines such as the East Coast Main Line, which runs through

Hatfield, the four lines of track would have been inspected once a week. A team of up to six men allowed each track to be closely inspected, with a lookout at front and back to warn of approaching trains. Under the privatized railways, cutting costs by 3 per cent a year was necessary to attain the same level of profit and, as a result, the gangs were pared back to just two men who, because of the real risk of being hit by an express travelling at 115 mph could not walk the narrow gaps between the lines and instead tried to inspect the rails from the trackside paths. As one rail expert put it: 'The accident at Hatfield was not caused by a broken rail. It was caused by total mismanagement by Railtrack and its contractors.'[13]

The government was forced to introduce an urgent programme of repairs and maintenance that required strict speed limits on lines. Far from being able to cut costs, Railtrack was faced with a serious financial crisis, but when it asked for more money from the Treasury to fund its rising repair bill, the plea was turned down and the company was forced into administration. Ironically, the Transport Secretary responsible for turning Railtrack into Network Rail, a not-for-profit body effectively answerable only to the government, was Stephen Byers, a politician close to Mr Blair who often floated ideas too radical to be seen coming out of Downing Street. It was symbolic of Labour's confused approach to the public services, however, that the train operating companies remained in private hands. Extra money, a year of speed restrictions and the return from retirement of railwaymen who knew how to make the network work meant the state of the track improved; the mood of commuters obliged to pay inflation-plus increases in fares for the privilege of standing on crowded trains did not.

In one sense, though, the return of Railtrack to the state sector was easy for Labour. The company was effectively bust, so there was no exorbitant compensation bill for share-holders, and such was the repugnance at the skimping on safety that ministers knew they were going with the grain of public opinion. But it was not the start of a trend, as some on the left dearly hoped, because pulling in the opposite direction were far more powerful forces: New Labour's obeisance to the legacy of Thatcherism, its desire to be on good terms with the City and the instinctive wariness of the Treasury to extra public spending. What the Blair government wanted was a mechanism for achieving the traditional goals of the public sector (universal access, equal opportunity and an ethos of care) with the tools of the private sector (the profit motive, competition and failure). It was this – New Labour's desperate search for its own philosopher's stone – that made the Private Finance Initiative so attractive.

Fatal addiction: Labour and the PFI

The strange thing about the Private Finance Initiative (PFI) was that it had been about to die from neglect until New Labour came to power. The PFI emerged in the early 1990s when the Tories were hard up. In order to win the 1992 election, John Major's government had played fast and loose with public finances: cutting taxes and allowing public spending to rise even though the budget deficit was already rising rapidly as a result of a recession. With the election won, the Conservatives were forced into a period of prolonged belt-tightening; they raised taxes and cut back on public spending, including spending on the nation's infrastructure. Voters were assured, however, that the cuts in capital spending were not real cuts because the PFI would mean schools and hospitals would still be built; all that would happen is that the cost would be taken off the government's books.

This was always a scam, and was treated as such by Kenneth Clarke when he was Chancellor from 1993 to 1997. Mr Clarke quickly saw through the weakness of this modern variant of living on the never-never, namely that it would lumber the Treasury with long-term costs. As one observer put it:

> Two years after Lamont's launch of PFI, in a speech to the CBI Clarke reinforced the two conditions for PFI schemes: the private sector must really take the risks involved and the taxpayer must receive value for money. This was too onerous for the nervous banks and construction companies that needed to be persuaded of the prospects of making some serious money. Although a couple of billions pounds' worth of deals had been signed by 1996, there wasn't sufficient interest in the scheme for it to gain any significant momentum under the Tories.[14]

Little did the banks, construction companies, management consultants and lawyers know in May 1997 that things, for them, could certainly only get better. When New Labour arrived in office, Gordon Brown was faced with the problem of how to reconcile the apparently irreconcilable. On the one hand, he had vowed to keep to the eye-wateringly tough spending limits bequeathed by Mr Clarke, even though it had been clear from the moment the plans had been announced that the outgoing Conservative Chancellor made no secret of the fact that he would not have stuck to them. Mr Brown, though, was determined that the City – so often the agent of destruction for Labour governments – should be left in no doubt as to his obeisance to financial orthodoxy. The early Gordon Brown was much like the late Phillip Snowden – the Chancellor who had forced through spending cuts in a vain attempt to keep the pound on the gold standard in the early 1930s – and about as popular with his colleagues running Whitehall spending departments.

On the other hand, Labour had to offer something to voters who had been promised by Messrs Blair and Brown that something would be done to remedy 18 years of Tory under-investment in the public sector. After his '24 hours to save the NHS' spiel, it was not remotely feasible that the leader of the first Labour government in almost two decades could delay action to remedy Tory cuts. Mr Brown's way of squaring the circle – and, as an added bonus, of further sucking up to the City – was to beef up the PFI. Geoffrey Robinson, Mr Brown's Paymaster General and a millionaire businessman himself, was given the task of drawing up new guidelines for PFI projects, designed to make them more attractive to the private sector.

Ahead of the election, senior Labour figures had warned, accurately as it turned out, of the drawbacks of PFI. Alistair Darling, the Shadow Chief Secretary to the Treasury, high-lighted the dangers of a live-now, pay-later scheme in the *Financial Times* early in 1997. PFI looked seductive to cash-strapped governments because they could build new schools, hospitals, prisons and roads without incurring any up-front capital costs. But like a family taking out a mortgage on a house, the cost of the project had to be paid back over several decades, and just like the repayments on a home loan, this revenue stream was far in excess of the original capital cost. As Mr Darling pointed out: 'Apparent savings now could be countered by the formidable commitment on revenue expenditure in years to come.'[15] Harriet Harman, a year earlier, had noted that the PFI was a 'Trojan horse' for privatization, adding that 'when the private sector is designing, building, financing, operating and running the hospital, and employing the doctors and nurses, that is privatization and that is what the Conservative Government are all about.'[16]

By the time Labour arrived in government, these objections were no longer voiced. Far from being a ruinously expensive way of providing public infrastructure, Mr Brown convinced himself that PFI was a way of forcing the private sector to shoulder the risks involved in a crash programme to rejuvenate the public realm. Far from being privatization by any other name, this was New Labour principles in action: harnessing the dynamism of the private sector to replace gloomy Victorian wards and leaky temporary classrooms with gleaming new schools and hospitals fit for the Britain of the twenty-first century.

Mr Brown's short-term fix had disastrous long-term consequences for the NHS, which was the focus for the first wave of PFI projects. Within a year of Labour's third election victory, and despite the biggest sustained injection of cash in the history of the NHS, trusts were piling up financial deficits that forced bed closures and the cancellation of operations. Outsourcing of catering meant that in many cases patients found the food inedible; skimping on cleaning by private contractors resulted in the spread of infections and so-called 'superbugs'. In a faint echo of Florence Nightingale in the Crimea in the 1850s, patients in the hospitals fit for the Britain of the twenty-first century were sometimes not dying of cancer or heart failure but because the wards were dirty.

Mr Robinson made two big changes to make PFI look more attractive to the private sector. First, they could boost their profits if the costly financing built into their bids became cheaper – not a difficult thing to do when interest rates were falling worldwide and money was available on easy terms. Secondly, the public sector would take more of the risk, the private sector less. In truth, the public sector had always had to shoulder the risk for PFI projects since it was inconceivable that a general hospital in Leeds, Manchester or Newcastle could go bankrupt and simply stop admitting patients. But Mr Robinson and his private-sector advisers identified an array of new risks that had made it less likely that the private sector would want to get involved in a PFI project. Once they agreed to take on these risks, they could push up the cost of the project.

> The PFI deal, under this taskforce of bankers and consultants, soon got a whole lot better for the industry, and private-sector scepticism quickly turned to salivation as the financiers, builders and consultants eyed the margins on offer from PFI, which in some cases give margins of over 50 per cent.[17]

Not to put too fine a point on it, the government was effectively involved in a fiddle to ensure that PFI projects always looked more financially attractive. As a sovereign body that cannot go bust, the state can always borrow more cheaply than a private company, but the figures were then doctored to ensure that the PFI project emerged as the cheaper option. NHS trusts that wanted a new hospital quickly got the message that the PFI was the only game in town. 'If the answer comes out wrong,' said the assistant head of the National Audit Office, 'you don't get your project. So the answer doesn't come out wrong very often.'[18]

And as a result, the answer came out right for the private sector, so much so that even Conservatives of the more robust, right-wing stamp blanched at the profits being made. The new Norfolk and Norwich hospital was a case in point, with the original bid put in for the capital cost of the new building bearing no resemblance to the final figure (£200 million). The higher capital cost resulted in higher charges for the trust that was renting the hospital from the PFI consortium, which further swelled its profits through a refinancing deal at a lower interest rate, netting an extra £115 million. Edward Heath is far from being revered by the modern Conservative Party, but Edward Leigh, the Tory chair of the Commons Public Accounts Committee, could find no better description for the consortium than that invoked by Sir Edward to describe the activities of Tiny Rowland's Lonhro: 'the unacceptable face of capitalism'.[19]

As far as Labour was concerned, it was money well spent. Alan Milburn said PFI had made possible 'the largest hospital-building programme in the history of the NHS'.[20] That was true, but as Allyson Pollock, a staunch critic of the PFI, noted, what Milburn did not add was that PFI also ushered in the biggest hospital closure programme since Nye Bevan set up the NHS in 1948: 'The PFI was paid for by major cuts in clinical budgets and the largest service closure programme in the NHS's history.'[21] The evidence suggests she was right. The first 14 PFI hospitals saw 30 per cent bed reductions. A report on the Cumberland Royal Infirmary in Carlisle, the first completed PFI hospital, noted:

> The hospital has been plagued by reports of blocked sewerage pipes which spewed out waste into sinks, flooding in the maternity unit, overheating in the atrium and of a patient injured after falling in the hospital's revolving door.[22]

In some ways the most alarming part of this report was not the flooding of the maternity unit, since all projects, however procured, can have teething troubles, but the mention of the atrium and the revolving door. Why does a hospital need an atrium, a feature more commonly associated with the sort of modern flashy hotels favoured by high-rolling executives? And would not swing doors of the traditional sort be more suitable for the sick or the physically impaired?

In some ways, Labour's crash programme of hospital building – it was putting up more new hospitals than the rest of Europe put together – was a mirror image of the home-owners who failed to realize that paying back a mortgage can require financial sacrifices. And, as many trusts found, when income fails to meet expectations, life can become difficult.

It slowly became clear, however, that the large, inflexible PFI deals the government had been suckered into didn't work in the reformed health service of Labour's third term. Hospitals would compete for the 'business' of treating patients and be paid largely according to how successful they were in attracting the sick, while their expenditure on huge PFI deals was fixed for a generation regardless of how much use they had for the facilities. Towards the end of 2005 increasing numbers of trusts lumbered with multi-million pound annual PFI commitments were running up unsustainable deficits.[23]

One of these was the West Herts Hospital Trust, which ran hospitals in Watford, Hemel Hempstead and St Albans. The trust found itself in a familiar bind: it ran up a financial deficit and, as a result, had to cut back on services to balance its books. That resulted in a poor rating in the annual national assessment, leading to further pressure to make the service more efficient. David Law, the chief executive of the trust, said: 'We had particular problems with A&E (accident and emergency) last winter and reduced bed numbers to balance our finances but we couldn't sustain performance.'[24] Allyson Pollock's argument is that there was not a lot wrong with the NHS that better funding could not have put right. Britain's health statistics compared well with other developed nations when the Conservatives took over in 1979, even though it had 'suffered 30 years of serious underfunding and a good deal of administrative reshuffling. Its hospitals were often dilapidated and some still dated from the Victorian era.'[25]

In both health and education, the Conservatives had made profound errors. In health, Mrs Thatcher had decided that the answer was not more money – she had, after all, an ideological dislike of the public sector – but better (private-sector-style) management and a strong dose of market forces. In education, since the late 1980s and early 1990s, the Department for Education and Skills and its predecessors has been responsible both for regulating the standard of examinations and for increasing the number of pupils passing them. For the public sector as a whole, the Conservatives introduced the idea of the Private Finance Initiative. Labour's historic error has been not just to stick with these flawed Conservative policies but to take them further. By 2006, the NHS was awash with consultants from PriceWaterhouseCoopers sent in to sort out the mess left by the consultants from Ernst & Young (and vice versa), and Labour's education statistics had become as discredited as the unemployment figures under the Tories.

To take one final example, the prison service has become the apotheosis of the PFI dream since everything – buildings, maintenance and the running of penal institutions – could be outsourced to the private sector. Money was duly saved, but only in the narrowest definition of the term. Cutting the pay of prison officers meant quality suffered, with the Young Offenders Institution at Ashfield branded the 'worst' prison in the country by the Chief Inspector of Prisons. The impact on re-offending rates has yet to be quantified, but it is a fair bet that the outcome will not be an example of the government's much-vaunted 'joined-up' thinking.

Labour is now in some difficulty on the public services. Increases in taxes were needed to fund the expansion of the public sector, yet the public remains unconvinced that the investment has really paid dividends. There is already a lack of trust on the part of voters that can only grow as the rate of spending slows in response to the unfavourable state of the government's finances. There are remedies, some of them cheap and painless, such as having one body responsible for setting targets and giving another body the duty of monitoring them. Other cures, however, will be harder to swallow. A short-term priority is to cut the cost of management and eliminate egregious examples of waste. A scheme to provide every patient with their own electronic medical record has spiralled in cost from £6 billion to a staggering £20 billion and is two and a half years late. The NHS has a bountiful – nay, excessive – supply of in-house managers yet still managed to chomp its way through a £1 billion bill for external management consultants in 2005. As the number of hospital trusts facing financial difficulties grows, there will be pressure for better management, but better does not mean more, it means less: fewer targets, fewer pointless demands on medical staff that stop them doing their jobs effectively. Already there is the threat of a rise in unemployment among the young doctors recruited as part of Labour's growth strategy because not enough older doctors are retiring from the profession. As far as we know, there is no plan for a mass cull of NHS management, but there should be. Finally, it is clear that the PFI was a bad idea whose time has come. Labour should do the sensible thing and scrap this flawed concept; if it does not, it will regret failing to heed the words of the Tory Chancellor who first thought up the idea. 'It was never intended to be a way of simply finding alternative finance,' said Norman Lamont, 'and I think it is dangerous because the reality is that private finance is more expensive.'[26]

Perhaps the opinion polls showing that Labour was less trusted on the NHS than the Tories were not so bizarre after all.

And overall, Labour's allegedly masterful policy of 'resources and reform' in the public sector has been almost a mirror image at any one time of what might have worked. It started with a spending freeze when what was needed, according to senior Conservative MP David Willetts, was more money.[27] But it had to do something, so it reorganized. Then it threw money at the public sector, and now it is dissatisfied with the poor returns the extra money has delivered, so it is reorganizing again to make the public sector look more like the public sector that existed when the Tories left office. It is hard not to conclude that this is a government that is fixated with the idea of doing something, no matter what. To be fair, previous Conservative governments have been no different. But Labour has also managed to get the worst of all possible worlds: a public sector where much of the extra money is being creamed off by the private sector but without the supposed efficiency that the private sector is supposed to bring in terms of higher productivity. Indeed, the attempt to have its cake and eat it in the public sector illustrates in microcosm the theme of this book.

Hi-Ho, Hi-Ho: the Wonderful New World of Work

Britain has 75 per cent of adults in work, a higher rate than America and the euro area, and 170,000 more people in work than a year ago.

> Gordon Brown, Budget speech, 22 March 2006

The smartest and most forward-looking organisations will see that by putting work-life balance at the heart of their cultures and their strategic plans they will not only be satisfying employees and creating more equitable workplaces, but increasing their productivity and responding competitively to significant changes, such as our growing 24/7 lifestyle.

> Alexandra Jones, *About Time for Change*[1]

Sgt. Carter: I used to work for you and now I work for Mr Castle. The hours are regular and the wife's happy.

> *Regan*[2]

Greg Norman won the British Open Golf Championship, Martina Navratilova and Boris Becker triumphed at Wimbledon and pop singer Boy George was convicted for the possession of heroin. In the middle of a humid and heavy British summer, July 1986 had its moments. But perhaps the most important of these became clear only much later.

Unemployment in that month hit 3.09 million. The following month it edged down to 3.08 million. The upward trend since the late 1960s had been broken. Fifteen years later, the total would fall below one million, for the first time since 1975. Unemployment, as with its evil twin, inflation, seemed well and truly licked.

Then, unemployment was a grave crisis. Today, by contrast, jobs seem to appear in abundance, as if supplied by some benevolent utility, rather as gas or water is available on tap. Ministers boast that we have more jobs than we know what to do with, that we need migrant labour to fill them all, along with schemes to encourage older people, women and others back into the workplace. Furthermore, we are told, our labour market is sufficiently robust not only to find work for all who want it, but also to bear an ever-increasing burden of entitlements and workplace rights, from 'prayer areas' for religiously inclined employees to assorted measures to enable people to fit work round their family commitments. Finally, we are told, this labour market is sufficiently flexible to compete on the global stage with the low-cost, low-regulation workforces of the emerging economies.

Should your head be spinning from the contradictions of the ever-more-regulated 'flexible' labour market, which supposedly both feeds demand for more workers (precisely because it is so flexible and employer-friendly) and satisfies that demand (precisely because it is so regulated and worker-friendly), then that is hardly surprising. The British jobs 'miracle' is, in reality, a British jobs mirage, another fantasy. All the signs are that we have built up a labour force in excess of our long-term needs, that not only the size but the structure of the labour market is going to fit badly with the economy of the near future and that the consequences of these developments could be dire once the economic tide turns.

Bust to boom: the incredible shrinking dole queue

July 1986 had marked the post-war peak in joblessness in the UK. From 1986 onwards, unemployment was on a downward path, interrupted only by a sharp, upward movement in the early 1990s. Chronic unemployment, the curse of most of the 1980s, was beginning to fade. Those who left school or university during the worst of that period are now advancing into their forties. So it is unsurprising, and even, perhaps, welcome that an entire generation of younger employees has no memory of the two decades up to the early 1990s in which joblessness was seen as one of the gravest issues – sometimes the gravest issue – facing the nation. This lack of awareness is compounded by the fact that, in contrast to the more severe downturn of the early 1930s, the dole-queue years have left behind little by way of cultural mythology, despite distinguished pieces of fiction specifically addressing the blight of unemployment such as *Boys from the Black Stuff* and *Looks and Smiles*. Punk rock had arrived too early to capture the full impact of joblessness on young workers, although there were signs of the looming trouble in songs such as *Career Opportunities* by The Clash. Individual hit songs *(Don't Give Up* by Kate Bush and Peter Gabriel is one example) faced the issue head-on, but they were the exception.

Only the 1984–5 miners' strike appears to have any resonance today, and even this is muted by the fact that great sympathy for the defeated colliers seemed rarely to be matched by any sense that they ought to have won and their coal mines kept open. Public attitudes appear muddled. Estimates by Professor Stephen Fothergill of Sheffield Hallam University suggest that just over half the men who lost their jobs after the miners' strike are now back in work, but work of a rather different nature, by and large.[3] At

Cortonwood, where the strike started in 1984, there is a Morrisons supermarket where the communal showers used to be, and a B&Q superstore covers the old mineshaft.

Regardless of the faint imprint that it was to leave on popular culture, mass unemployment in the 1970s and 1980s was never far from the headlines or from the minds of public figures. 'We worried about it all the time,' former Labour Cabinet minister Peter Shore told the authors in a private conversation some years ago. In public, Labour's Conservative successors were assumed by the cynical to be putting up a token show of concern about joblessness to hide private insouciance. But this bluff may well have been a double-bluff, with the insouciance masking mounting panic as the total climbed through two to three million – and beyond. Existing job-creation schemes (dressed up as 'training') already confronted the unemployed with a thicket of acronyms – YOPS (for the young), TOPS (for adults) and STEP (hand-outs for firms to hire temporary workers). Under the Conservatives, yet more millions were poured into programmes that would get people off the unemployment register, the best-known (and probably costliest) being the Youth Training Scheme. By the early 1980s, any employer requiring a minibus full of work conscripts needed merely to lift the telephone and put in a request with the Area Manpower Board. That the recruits may have been of variable quality, to put it mildly, was another matter, as was the variable quality of the statistics, adulterated by no fewer than 30 changes under the Conservatives. The first had the effect of increasing the number officially unemployed, the next 29 made the figures look better.

Meanwhile, soothsayers warned that mass unemployment was here to stay – that the full employment of the 1950s and 1960s had been the exception and that a witches' brew of new technology and Britain's dismal economic performance would mean lengthy dole queues into the foreseeable future. It later emerged that there were two other problems in the early 1980s: the increase in the workforce as the children of the baby boom generation started to look for work and the hardline anti-inflationary policies of the Conservatives.

In 1979, Clive Jenkins, a senior trade union leader with the gift of the gab and a compelling television presence (neither exactly common attributes among 'the brothers' at that time), spelt out the so-called go/no-go options for Britain. In a book entitled *The Collapse of Work*, Mr Jenkins and a union colleague, Barrie Sherman, prophesied:

> Remain as we are, reject the new technologies and we face unemployment of up to 5.5 million by the end of the century. Embrace the new technologies, accept the challenges and we end up with unemployment of about five million.[4]

That Mr Jenkins was General Secretary of the Association of Technical, Managerial and Scientific Staffs – whose white-collar members had been assumed to be likely to benefit hugely from the march of science and technology – added to the chill that such predictions sent down the spine of what would become known as Middle Britain.

Even those who challenged the Jenkins and Sherman predictions with regard to the impact of the silicon processor – notably Rodney Dale and Ian Williamson in *The Myth of the Micro* – feared that the decaying state of the British economy could achieve high levels of job destruction without any help from new technology.

> In the 1980s we face a period of absolute industrial decline where our manufacturing industry is shrinking in real terms. High unemployment in future will come from this absolute decline; not from the silicon chip or industrial robots.[5]

As it happened, growth in the economy led to a rapid and hefty fall in unemployment in the second half of the 1980s, and an even bigger drop in the jobless count after 1992. Monetarists such as Milton Friedman, writing in the 1970s, had predicted that any attempts by governments to create jobs by boosting demand were doomed to failure, and stoking inflation would eventually mean even higher unemployment. But what happened for a lengthy period in the 1980s, and for an even longer period in the 1990s and beyond, was that unemployment fell without any increase in inflation. Eventually price pressures did emerge, but policy makers could get a lot of bang for their buck.

Even so, assumptions of continuing high levels of joblessness persisted well into the 1990s. Mr Jenkins' fellow Welshman, Ian Angell, professor at the London School of Economics, highlighted the increasingly global nature of business and finance, and the increasing power that this gave to the rich, to predict that very large numbers of people would find themselves economically inactive. In *The New Barbarian Manifesto* he identified three main groups of workers: the 'symbol-analytic' problem-solving elite of knowledge workers and, at the other extreme, the routine production workers whose jobs could quite easily be 'outsourced' to poorer countries. In the middle, he saw 'in-person service workers' – a precarious archipelago stretching from hairdressing through accountancy, law, medicine, shop-assistant work and teaching.[6]

'A company cannot survive without its knowledge workers,' wrote Professor Angell, 'but its routine production services and office work can either be replaced by robots or exported elsewhere on the globe where wages are lower.' The middle group may find life a little easier, he wrote, but automation was making inroads:

> The banking sector is at the leading edge of job losses here, although losses will soon become increasingly apparent in other parts of the financial sector. The retail industry and

the non-specialist mass teaching of schoolchildren and second-division undergraduates are also candidates for computerisation.[7]

Not for nothing was he nicknamed the LSE's 'professor of alarm and despondency'.

Twenty years after the high-water-mark of post-war unemployment, and the blood-curdling predictions of yesteryear seem to have been turned on their head. Ministers routinely refer to a shortage of skilled workers, insist that older people will have to remain in work for longer and warn of a slackening in the pace of economic growth if more employees are not found, either from the ranks of the economically inactive at home or from abroad. Unemployment seems to have anchored itself at just above 900,000, and the Treasury policy of 'mandatory work-focused interviews' for the long-term unemployed (a Labour version of the Conservative's 'Restart' scheme in the 1980s) could reduce this figure further.

No one talks fearfully about the 'silicon chip' anymore. Nobody believes robots are taking over the workplace. The clapped-out old banger that was the job-destroying British economy of 1980 is now held up as a pacesetting sports car, a model for others to follow. Clive Jenkins died in September 1999. Professor Angell has recently turned his attention to penning a more uplifting book, the story of how 1960s nightclub singer Nick Charles beat his own alcoholism and went on to help others to do the same.[8]

Nor is this success story confined simply to finding work for the people left out in the cold 20 years ago. Work has been found, too, for two million more employees than were in the labour force in 1986. The so-called 'Polish plumbers' – the skilled workers from Eastern Europe arriving in Britain in their hundreds of thousands – are not here to admire the scenery. They know the work is available. But even this aspect of the apparent British job-spinning miracle is not the end of the story. Not only are there more jobs than ever. Not only have these jobs been created without any cuts in take-home pay (with the exception of the migrant-heavy business sectors of hotels and restaurants, and agriculture, hunting and forestry). But 'work' itself is being made an ever-more pleasant and amenable experience.

This is taking two forms, official and unofficial. Officially, ever more laws are passed to ensure that employers fit in with their employees, rather than, as was traditional, the other way round. For example, there is a batch of employment law measures that came into effect on 1 October 2006. So-called 'gangmasters' employing (largely migrant) labour would be required to have a licence. New fire-safety regulations for business also came into force, as did regulations requiring firms to give notice to the Department of Trade and Industry at least 30 days before issuing collective notices of redundancy. Various new rights were bestowed on women in the workplace who had been pregnant for fewer than three months. The national minimum wage was increased to £5.35 an hour (for those aged 22 and over), to £4.45 for 18–21-year-olds and to £3.30 for 16- and 17-year-olds. Ironically, in light of this age-banding, the major new piece of regulation was a set of sweeping provisions relating to age discrimination. The history and thinking behind this is examined in greater detail later (p. 160). For now, it is sufficient to say that the new rules covered recruitment, promotion, retirement and a good deal else besides.

Nor is there any sign of a let-up in efforts to bestow ever more rights on employees. In July 2006, it emerged that, as a contribution to a Whitehall review of discrimination law, the Trades Union Congress (TUC) was urging ministers to allow those representing low-paid workers (usually women) in equal-pay cases to cite a 'hypothetical comparator' – effectively, an invented male employee on a higher salary. The thinking behind this was that some firms had 'got round' the equal-pay laws by employing only women, whom they then paid low wages. Had they employed male workers as well, whom they would presumably have paid more than the women, they would have been open to action under employment laws. In order to correct this position, the TUC suggested that women in such cases ought to be able to act as if such a male employee existed and then produce him as evidence. Having gone from the right to equal pay for doing the same work as a man to equal pay for work ruled to be of equal value to that done by a man, it was now suggested that women ought to have the right to be paid the same as someone who did not exist.

This proposal, by breaking the link between equal-pay cases and the actual position in any particular workplace, would effectively give those ruling in such cases the right to award higher pay to employees on no ground other than that, had the workplace been arranged differently, they might have been entitled to it. In principle, perhaps ours would be a better society if disinterested panels of experts could make such pay awards. But how would such a system be compatible with the ruthlessly competitive global economy in which ministers assure us we are now operating?

These official, legal attempts to transform the individual job from a contractual hire-and-fire affair (a no-strings-on-either-side 'adult' relationship that lasts only as long as both parties 'get something out of it') into a parson's freehold (or a complex form of matrimony) are just part of the story. Equally important is a new expectation about the nature of work, an expectation described thus by Father Timothy Radcliffe, a Dominican friar and former master of the order: 'There are some young people for whom the meaning of work is changing. They are coming to see work as a form of leisure. While their parents went to work, they go to play.'[9] Father Radcliffe adds: 'Admittedly it may still be a small percentage of people who see work in these terms, mostly people who are young and often Western, but it may be a sign of the future for most of humanity.'

This phenomenon was most noticeable during the so-called dot-com boom of the late 1990s, when tales abounded of internet businesses run by young people barely out of university, meeting in their unstructured boardrooms or holding 'break-out' sessions in 'chill-out' areas. Visitors were urged to 'grab a beanbag', take a beer or help themselves to the buffet, to cast off business attire and take part in some 'blue skies thinking'. One did not need to be a psychologist to spot in this emphasis on eating free food, rebelling against the dress code and lying around on squishy furniture while claiming to be engaged in thinking big thoughts nothing very new or high-tech at all – rather, the time-honoured behaviour of the public-school layabout. But it was a mistake to assume that the crash in the value of dot-com shares in the early 2000s marked the end of the trend to make the workplace a sort of home extension with the odd desk thrown in. The excessive, dressed-down version with complementary designer nibbles and optional working hours may be less prevalent than before, but a more modest variant seems to be spreading far from its original high-tech base through adver-tising and media, the professions and even the civil service.

Father Radcliffe quotes Jeremy Rifkin, who believes younger people in business belong to 'a world that is more theatrical than ideological and orientated more to a play ethos than to a work ethos'. Mr Rifkin added: 'The economy is being transformed from a giant factory to a grand theatre.'[10] Or, as Father Radcliffe puts it: 'If Ford was the typical industry of the old solid capitalism, then Hollywood is typical of the new. All business is show business.'[11]

When you think about it, this is a remarkable turnaround. Throughout the twentieth century, show business (cinema, popular music, popular sport, comedy) was the dream escape-route from work. Now, work and show business are starting to merge – at least for those in the more amenable parts of the labour force. And this is merely the cherry on the cake in terms of the apparent transformation in the world of work since 1986 – many more jobs, tumbling unemployment, steady or improving wages for most people, an increasing number of rights for employees and obligations on employers, and an increasing expectation that work itself, both in terms of the physical workplace and the general ethos of that workplace, will be not merely pleasant and rewarding but positively enjoyable. Conservative leader David Cameron has urged more employers to provide showers in order that staff would be able to freshen up after cycling to work. It was the cycling that Mr Cameron was trying to promote, as an aspect of his environmental policy. But his remarks underlined the huge change in attitudes – 30 years earlier, the only way to be sure of getting a shower at work was to get a job down a coal mine.

Of course, for many people, those at or near the bottom of the pile, their experience of the workplace has rather less in common with Hollywood, or even with the sort of premises in which Mr Cameron has been accustomed to ply his trade, than with the conditions encountered by journalist Polly Toynbee when she went undercover to investigate the plight of the working poor. The resulting book took the reader into a world of which most of us are barely aware, one of dreadful pay and almost zero status.[12]

Even those more fortunate, those not trying to keep body and soul together on or near the minimum wage, may have noticed something of a gap between the rights and entitlements which (according to newspapers and broadcasters) ministers, or sometimes judges, have bestowed on them, and the reality of life in the office, shop or factory in which they work. In theory, quasi-judicial 'disciplinary' or 'grievance' procedures are supposed to ensure fairness between one employee and another and between employees and employers. But it is a reasonable bet that, in a conflict between a lowly clerk and a firm's star salesman, the former would come off worse, given the commercial realities. Not for nothing, perhaps, is one of the best-drawn characters in the BBC television comedy series *The Office* the 'legendary' (i.e. boorish but apparently unsackable) sales rep Chris Finch (played by Ralph Ineson).

Furthermore, even when the employee-protection system is working as planned, it seems too often to involve curtailing the activities of real-life employees in order to safeguard the rights or avoid hurting the feelings of imaginary ones. The case of British Airways check-in employee Nadia Eweida, who fell foul of company rules in 2006 for insisting on wearing a Christian cross on the outside of her uniform, may well have aroused the public support that it did for no better reason than that it involved one small person standing up to the bureaucratized 'corporate policy' machine, with its 'human resources' executives forever using words such as 'inappropriate'.

All that said, the notion that both formally and informally, legislatively and socially, the workplace is becoming ever more pleasant and ever more convenient for the employee is a major feature of our time. You can read all about it in magazines such as *Management Today* and publications from organizations such as the Work Foundation. You can hear all about it on Radio 4 programmes such as *You and Yours* and *Moneybox*, on which assembled experts will (no doubt correctly) assure those hard done by on the employment front that their employer has 'acted illegally'. The message is unmistakable: workers are hired hands no longer; rather, they are special people entitled to be treated at all times and in all ways with respect. And this is a dynamic process. Should something not be a 'right' now, then it will be next April, or from October, or when new regulations are laid before Parliament, or when the European Commission publishes its next directive.

Most people in work are employees, rather than employers or self-employed, the present authors included. Thus we, along with most workers, are hardly likely to object to these developments, at least not on grounds of self-interest. But in the interests of intellectual honesty, it seems at least worth asking how this is supposed to square with the ruthlessly competitive global economy in which the government assures us the UK is having to operate, and with the flexible and deregulated labour market that it claims as a great British advantage vis-à-vis our competitors in continental Europe. Is the great strength of our workforce its flexibility? Or is the great strength of our society the ever more generous protections being bestowed on our workforce?

Question either the Treasury or the Department of Trade and Industry and you will be told pretty much both things at the same time – one indication that fantasy has supplanted reality. Another indication is the suggestion in official quarters that even to ask the question is in rather bad taste. Here is the introduction to the 'employment matters' section of the DTI's website, with emphasis supplied by us:

> *Guided by the principles of flexibility and partnership,* our aim is to improve the quality of working life for individuals, and create the conditions for business success. We support better regulation and are working to promote best practice and effective employment relations.[13]

Given that 'partnership' is code for 'employment protection', the DTI's approach to the labour market is guided by both a synonym and its antonym, by flexibility hand in hand with inflexibility.

It is the same story round at the Treasury, many of whose assorted Budgets and Pre-Budget Reports (PBR) contain references to similarly strange bedfellows: 'enterprise' with 'fairness' in the 2005 PBR, 'stability, enterprise and fairness' in the 2002 PBR and 'an enterprising, fairer Britain' in the 2002 Budget.

Of course, it could be that ministers simply believe that none of this hair-splitting really matters, that the apparently miraculous job-creation machine of modern Britain is sufficiently robust to deliver enterprise and regulation at one and the same time; in other words, that it is the wondrous labour market that makes it possible to promote fairness and entrepreneurship simultaneously, not that the mixture of fairness and entrepreneurship has brought about the wondrous labour market. This would certainly make a little more sense than the inelegant official attempts simultaneously to dance round the two opposing maypoles of social justice and enterprise. But as we shall now argue, the 'miracle' job market is much more fragile than may have been hoped; thus its ability to bear these burdens is very much smaller than has been suggested.

Now you don't see them ...

Let us start with the obvious. The real level of unemployment is higher than that indicated by either of the government's two main measures – the claimant count and the Labour Force Survey (LFS). Put simply, the claimant count measures unemployment purely on the basis of the number of people drawing unemployment-related benefits. It is the traditional measure of joblessness and is the one used by the media when, for example, comparing unemployment now with 20 years ago. We ourselves used it in this way at the start of this chapter. The LFS measure is broader and records those wishing to work, regardless of eligibility for benefits.

One way in which both measures would seem to be underestimating the level of unemployment relates to sickness and disability. Since 1979, Britain has become a healthier and fitter country, but according to the official data there are now around 2.5 million adults of working age too ill or disabled to hold down a job – four times as many as there were when Margaret Thatcher became Prime Minister. This increase reflects a pool of hidden unemployment, concentrated in Britain's old industrial heartlands – regions that used to make ships, dig coal and forge steel. Interviewed on Radio 4's *You and Yours* programme about unemployment in Barrow, Professor Fothergill put it this way:

> The fundamental problem is that in some areas of the country there is massive imbalance between the potential workforce and actually the number of jobs that are out there and Barrow is a classic example of this. And what has actually happened as a result of that huge loss of jobs is competition – the people with health problems and disabilities have been one of the major groups that have been marginalized and you see this pattern all across the country in the old industrial areas, which is where the incapacity benefit problem is concentrated; this is not a problem of prosperous Southern England.[14]

On 5 March 1985 Britain's coalminers returned to work after the longest and most bitter industrial dispute in modern times. This was swiftly followed by massive pit closures. Total employment in the coal industry has fallen from 220,000 at the time of the strike to only 7,000, and the number of pits from 170 to just 8.[15] Twenty years on, new research by Professor Fothergill's team documented the extent to which the economy of the English and Welsh coalfields has recovered from these devastating job losses.[16] Some 60 per cent of the coal job losses since the early 1980s have now been replaced by new jobs for men in the same areas. Also, the pace of new job creation has quickened in recent years, partly as a result of the sustained growth in the national economy and partly because the regeneration initiatives put in place a few years ago (such as the English Partnerships programme of coalfield site redevelopment) are now coming to fruition.

But on the other hand, 90,000 coal jobs have still not been replaced, and some former mining areas, such as South Wales, are still lagging badly. And the research showed that claimant-count unemployment data give a misleading impression of the state of the local labour market. In the former coalfields there are five times as many adults of working age out of work and claiming incapacity benefits as there are claiming unemployment benefits. Although, as the report's authors acknowledged, the former coalfields do have higher underlying levels of ill health, the big rise in incapacity benefit numbers points to extensive hidden unemployment. While the vast majority of incapacity claims are entirely legitimate, comparisons with prosperous parts of the country indicate that many claimants with health problems would have been in work in a genuinely fully employed economy.

Reclassifying some of the unemployed as unfit for work is one way in which the official joblessness numbers can be reduced. Another is by 'parking' large numbers of what had been one of the age groups most vulnerable to unemployment in the early 1980s – the young – in higher education. In the late 1960s, just 10 per cent of those leaving 'upper secondary education' went into higher education. By the very early 1980s, it had reached 20 per cent. Now it is above 40 per cent, and ministers have said it should go higher still. Let us assume every single one of these new recruits is engaged in the right degree for them, from which they (and perhaps society as well) will benefit enormously. Even so, the fact remains that tens of thousands of people each year are being put outside the full-time employment market, and thus cannot be unemployed. To the extent that the taxpayer is financing their education, this could be seen as a simple re-labelling of the envelope containing the cheque. To the extent that student loans and subventions from parents have paid for the student, it could be suggested that private individuals have been persuaded to use their own money to keep themselves or their child away from the world of work. These sorts of higher education participation rates would have made the frightening youth-unemployment figures of the early 1980s rather less scary.

If college or university is another way of 'parking' people somewhere out of the reach of unemployment, then public-sector employment has, in recent years, effectively become another, despite tough talk from ministers about cutting a swathe through staff numbers in the name of efficiency. In the second quarter of 1997, the public payroll totalled 5,174,000. By the second quarter of 2006, that had risen to 5,841,000. But within that near-13 per cent increase of more than 600,000 people, there were winners and losers.

Losing out were public-sector construction workers, down over the period from 124,000 to 64,000, and HM Forces, down from 220,000 to 204,000. Contrary to the impression given in some sections of the media of a recruitment bonanza in this field, the category known as 'other health and social work' saw a decline, from 435,000 to 386,000. Winners over the same nine-year period included the police (up from 230,000 to 277,000), 'other public sector' (up from 706,000 to 724,000) and public administration (up from 1,139,000 to 1,247,000). But the two biggest gainers were education (from 1,130,000 to 1,393,000) and the National Health Service (from 1,190,000 to 1,546,000).[17]

With 9.5 per cent more administrators, 2.5 per cent more people working in 'other public sector' (a category including two organizations whose payrolls might, if anything, have been expected to decline – Royal Mail and British Nuclear Fuels) and a total of an additional 619,000 people working in health and education, it is clear the state sector has proved a plentiful employer during recent years. The quality of the outcomes generated by all this activity was studied in chapter 6. Suffice to say that all this additional employment has had a powerful depressive effect on unemployment figures.

What links those signed off for reasons of sickness and disability, those enjoying higher educational activities previously restricted to a much smaller slice of their age group and those employed in a burgeoning public sector is that they represent, to a greater or lesser extent, individuals kept well away from the prospect of unemployment through (again, to a greater or lesser extent) the operations of the public purse. But paradoxically, having caused one substantial-sized workforce to disappear, the New Labour magicians have, with another puff of smoke, brought a second workforce into being, one to which we now turn our attention.

. . . Now you do!

The 1970s, infamously, saw a phenomenon previously believed to be a textbook impossibility – inflation and unemployment rising at the same time. Britain in the mid-2000s, however, managed to go one better, with employment and unemployment rising at the same time. This may sound nonsensical, but in fact merely reflects the fact that, while the number of jobs had grown, it had done so at a lesser rate than the growth in the workforce.

Whence came these extra workers – and why?

The first question is easier to answer. Three key groups have contributed to the creation of this parallel workforce: women, older people and immigrants. For women with families, in particular, the government has supplied a range of incentives to return to part-time or full-time work, with contributions towards child-care expenses being possibly the most significant. Perhaps unsurprisingly, the total number of women of working age recorded as not wanting a job fell from 3,606,000 in the period May–July 2004 to 3,495,000 in May–July 2006. During the same period, the number of working-age men not wanting work also fell, albeit rather less, from 2,273,000 to 2,253,000. Again during the same period the number of women recorded as wanting a job but not looking for one during the previous four weeks, because they were looking after their family and/or their home, dropped from 2,137,000 to 2,102,000. There was a small rise in the number of men recorded in this way, from 190,000 in May–July 2004 to 196,000 in May–July 2006.[18]

Initially, the government's efforts to increase female participation in the labour force had been promoted under two banners: one was that of requiring women on benefit (effectively, single mothers) to try to earn some of their keep, while the other concentrated on providing assistance in returning to work for those women who wanted it. More recently, in the December 2005 Pre-Budget Report, there was the suggestion that the government wanted to see the end of the full-time working-class mother regardless of individuals' preferences. It was not put in quite that way, but rather as 'outreach support' for 'the non-working partners of people in low-income families' to try to overcome 'barriers to employment'. Given that these 'partners' were not on benefit, one wondered what business it was of the Treasury whether they worked or not. The Treasury insisted its interest lay not in social engineering but in maintaining a stable ratio of workers to pensioners into the twenty-first century, as the average age of the population increased.

One way to do this is for the pensioners themselves to become workers, something that is already happening in a modest way and may well grow further in the years ahead, not least because of fears that pension provision is inadequate. In the three months May–July 2004, the number of

people in work who were over retirement age (65 for men
and 60 for women) was 998,000. By May–July 2006, it had
risen to 1,159,000. During the same period there was an
increase too, in the numbers of those in work in the years
running up to retirement (50–64 for men and 50–59 for
women) from 6,282,000 to 6,475,000.[19]

But perhaps the biggest single contributor to labour
market growth has been immigration. In August 2006, the
Office for National Statistics (ONS) reported that the British
population increased by 375,000 in the year to mid-2005,
the largest annual rise since 1962. Natural population
growth accounted for one-third of the increase, with 'net
migration and other changes' making up the other two-
thirds. ONS added: 'Net international migration into the UK
from abroad is the main factor in population growth.'[20]
Figures showed net migration rose from 146,200 in 2001–2
to 248,300 in 2004–5.

The justification behind this mass importation of alternative workers varies depending upon the audience. Thus the
then-Home Secretary Charles Clarke, in a private meeting of
Labour activists in February 2005, was reported as insisting
that large-scale immigration was somehow a good thing in its
own right: 'We want more migration, more people coming to
study and to work. We want more people coming to look for
refuge.'[21] A more common line of reasoning is that the
economy is suffering from huge 'skills gaps' and that immigrants are needed to fill them. In June 2006, Tony Blair's official spokesman stated: 'We recognize the positive
contributions immigration makes to the country and the
economy . . . If we don't have migration, we don't have the
growth from the economy that we all benefit from.'[22]

This argument brushes over a number of issues. First, it
suggests that little can be done about the two-million-plus
people listed as 'economically inactive' in the most recent
figures and who say they want a job (this figure is in addition

to the unemployment data). Secondly, it threatens to set up an immigration 'ratchet effect', as the newcomers themselves boost demand for goods and services, thus exposing new 'skills gaps' that can be filled only by immigration . . . and so on. Thirdly, it ignores entirely the question of why a first-world country needs to import skilled people from less developed nations, rather as discussion of the balance of payments deficit veers away from asking why British consumers are borrowing money from countries such as China, whose people are poorer than we are. We would suggest that while the payments deficit is a measure of our refusal to live within our means, the mass importation of skilled personnel is a measure of our refusal to acquire proper skills, preferring, in too many cases, the infamous 'Mickey Mouse subjects' attacked by the then-Higher Education Minister Margaret Hodge in 2003.[23]

Above all, it ignores what must be one of the main motives behind allowing in so many migrant workers: that they help to keep wages down and thus please New Labour's business allies while leaving their friends in the trade union movement unable to do much by way of protest, hamstrung as they are by fear of accusations of xenophobia or racial prejudice. It is not as if business has made much secret of its enthusiasm for migrant labour – Sir Digby Jones, former head of the Confederation of British Industry, spelled it out in the *Sunday Telegraph*: 'We have a tight labour market in the UK and yet wage inflation has not been a problem. Immigrants are doing the work for less.'[24]

Yes, quite.

Indeed, all the parallel labour forces of women, older people and immigrants have probably helped depress wage increases generally. To employers, the government has seemed almost to misquote Groucho Marx: 'Here is our workforce. If you don't like it, we have others.' But the danger is that the next economic downturn will leave us with a labour force far in excess of the economy's real needs. It happened before, in the 1950s, when alleged labour shortages were used to justify large-scale immigration. Only later did it become obvious that much of the 'shortage' had been caused by large-scale over-manning and restrictive practices. The transport industry was a particular offender, with diesel trains boasting 'two men in a cab', with rural buses carrying not only a driver and conductor but sometimes an inspector as well, and with docks in which every piece of cargo had to be loaded and unloaded separately, using barrows little-changed since the time of Dickens.

As now, large numbers of people had been 'parked' away from both the open labour market and the danger of unemployment. But when that state of affairs started to unravel, unemployment shot up, as we saw earlier, and social tranquillity was damaged. Elsewhere, we detail the pressures and weaknesses that we believe will bring down our current economic house of cards. For now, it is enough to note that the lessons of recent history suggest that a country that hallucinates into existence a robust and buoyant labour market is storing up terrible trouble.

Three score years . . . and counting

One meeting point for two of the key developments we mention above – the search for new workforces and the generation of new rights for employees – has been the legal change, noted earlier, which outlawed discrimination in the workplace based on age.[25] This change is noteworthy for a number of reasons, not the least being that what started out as a modest-looking proposal is now threatening to make illegal large tracts of previously unexceptional employment practices.

Given the post-war cult of youth, it is not surprising that the notion that discrimination against older people is a bad thing took some time to catch on. When it did so, it was often tied to other types of discrimination; writing in the *Guardian*, Celia Dodd warned (male) company bosses that 'the impending shortage of staff in the 1990s' would mean that the notion of the secretary as 'an attractive young woman' would give way to the hiring of older women in that role.[26] But as the 1980s gave way to the 1990s, attempts to stir up outrage at the iniquities of 'ageism' were hampered by suspicion in some quarters that it was precisely those very same beneficiaries of the cult of youth in the 1950s and 1960s who were now at the top of institutions such as the BBC, and were keen to make illegal any attempts to oust them.

But, in the way of these things, a voluntary agreement on 'non-ageist' job advertising, supported by some recruitment agencies and publications, was followed by a pledge by New Labour (in opposition in 1995) to outlaw age discrimination, and so it finally came to pass. In contrast to the controversy sparked by the sex discrimination legislation of the 1970s, controversy that is far from extinct even now, there was a muted response to the 'ageism' laws. Media commentary was largely confined to warnings that employers needed to 'be ready' for 1 October. Perhaps given that age, unlike womanhood, is something that happens to us all, there was little to get excited about. More importantly, we think, were the different ways ministers sold the new rules to different groups, a sure reason for suspicion. Furthermore, the fact that ministers appeared to believe all these different reasons at the same time was, we argue, a further piece of evidence of fantasy in high places.

■ To those of an economically authoritarian bent, the rules were all about keeping older people's noses to the grindstone in order to make good deficits in pension schemes. Far from being a warm blanket, cosseting people with new legal rights, this was a blast of realistic cold air.

▪ To the liberal-left constituency, the rules were another brave step forward in the march to eliminate discrimination in all its forms

▪ To those heading towards retirement age, the rules were all about their right to choose when to hang up their hats and leave the workforce, rather than have the choice made for them by corporate bureaucracies.

▪ And to employers, the rules were an opportunity to take advantage of this pool of talented and experienced older workers. As with the anti-smoking activists who long argued that if landlords were banned from allowing people to smoke in pubs, they would end up making more money than they do now because non-smokers would flock to their premises, so ministers and bureaucrats have a tendency to believe they know more about employment than do employers.

Belatedly, as the coming into force of the new rules was imminent, journalists, lawyers and other commentators realized quite how widely drawn they were, that they applied just as much to young people as older ones (making it potentially legally hazardous to advertise for 'experienced' staff), that long-service bonuses were now circumscribed and that, according to the CBI, even sending birthday cards could get an employer into hot water.

Under one hat, the age-discrimination regulations encapsulate perfectly the two major trends we have identified in this chapter: the bestowing of ever more legal benefits on employees and the encouragement of ever more recruits to the labour force. Either or both would be compatible with an economy whose interaction with the outside world was at least partially managed by the state, perhaps along the lines of the French or Scandinavian economic models of years gone by. Neither is compatible with New Labour's vociferous commitment to global free trade. And the only way in which these two developments could be sustained would be if the British economy were to be, for some hard-to-fathom reason, such a remarkable job-creation machine as to be able to bear almost any burden: new employment legislation, rising immigration, rising staff expectations and fierce international competition.

As we have seen, that notion, just as with all the others connected with the employment market, is simply a fantasy.

8

All Along the Watchtower: the Fantasy of Britain as a Military Superpower

Ship me somewheres east of Suez, where the best is like the
 worst,
Where there aren't no Ten Commandments an' a man can
 raise a thirst.

Rudyard Kipling, *Mandalay*

I was really quite a nice guy before I came out here . . . What's
happened to me? . . . Belfast, that's what.

A.F.N. Clarke, *Contact*[1]

This is a moment to seize. The Kaleidoscope has been shaken.
The pieces are in flux. Soon they will settle again. Before they
do, let us re-order this world around us.

Tony Blair, addressing the Labour Party conference
in Brighton, 2 October 2001

Christmas Eve was drawing to a close across Britain as 11 p.m.
struck and pubs started to empty. The good-natured raucous-
ness of the city centres contrasted with the more discrete
inebriation of those drinking behind closed doors in family
homes – beer for some, champagne for others – prior, in
some cases, to tottering off to attend Midnight Mass at a
local church.

But in Basra, second city of Iraq, Christmas Day 2006 had
already dawned. It was 2 a.m. local time, better known, no

doubt, as 'oh two hundred hours' to the troops of the British army's 19 Light Brigade and their colleagues in the Royal Engineers and Royal Military Police. Their mission that night was to attack the Jamiat police station, free a number of prisoners who had been tortured and were now said to be facing execution and then destroy the two-storey concrete building. The military police were to arrest any of the allegedly 'rogue' police officers found on the premises. In the event, all had fled, but otherwise the mission was accomplished. Seven Iraqi gunmen were killed in an initial firefight, and 127 captives, some of them suffering serious torture-related injuries, were released. There were no British casualties and none reported among the Iraqi troops who had accompanied them.

On one level, there is little of note about the attack on Jamiat police station. Few can be surprised that fully trained British soldiers proved more than a match for Iraqi gunmen, nor that members of an army ranked as one of the very best in the world carried out their mission as planned with the minimum of fuss. Yet take a step back, and its extraordinary features multiply.

To start with the most obvious, the operation aroused remarkably little interest at home, and would have aroused even less had it not hit British newsdesks on traditionally quiet Christmas Day. Even the Boxing Day edition of the *Daily Telegraph* (a newspaper with a keen interest in military affairs), while leading on the story, gave it scarcely more prominence than the death of the soul singer James Brown. True, the BBC explored the issues surrounding the Jamiat operation and examined its implications for relations between the army and the people of Basra. But within 24 hours there was another story coming out of Iraq – the confirmation on Boxing Day of the death sentence for former president Saddam Hussein.

Equally strange was the silence of the politicians. Thirty, twenty or even ten years ago, imagine the scene as James

Callaghan, Margaret Thatcher or John Major learns over a secure telephone line from the Ministry of Defence of a daring and successful mission to snatch helpless wretches from certain death, a mission led by British troops, none of whom was lost in the action, and which ended with the climactic, Hollywood-like detonation that flattened a notorious citadel of pain and terror. No prime minister worth his or her salt would have passed up the opportunity to broadcast a few statesmanlike words, standing perhaps in front of the Christmas tree at Chequers, offering congratulations to our armed forces and asking the nation to rejoice in the success of this bold operation, which had been in the finest traditions of British derring-do. As with the Sierra Leone rescue mentioned in chapter 1, a successful Jamiat-type mission in the 1970s, 1980s or even 1990s could have swung the next election.

Partly, as with Sierra Leone, the public has simply become acclimatized to a constant background hum of military activity. The British people vaguely expect their service personnel to be 'doing things', some boring, some, as with Jamiat, more exciting. For Tony Blair to beam himself into the nation's living rooms on Christmas Day to tell people what they already knew might well have simply irritated the voters.

Furthermore, and perhaps more importantly, any attempt to cash in on the success of the Jamiat mission might have drawn attention to more remarkable features of the whole affair. One such feature arises from the fact that Basra had been occupied by the British for three and a half years by the time of the assault on Jamiat. Had the UK military authorities only just discovered that the Basra police's 'serious crimes unit', based in Jamiat, may have boasted a title vaguely reminiscent of a Scotland Yard specialist squad, but was in fact a nest of violent organized criminals? Apparently not; it had been obvious for some time. According to analysis by journalist Graeme Baker, the raid followed intelligence that the captives were due to be executed. Furthermore, it showed a clear will to rid Basra of rogue police and their associated sectarian mobs. It is a tactic that is being employed as British forces prepare to 'draw down' from the city eventually to hand it over to the Iraqis.[2]

The British authorities' line of reasoning (for want of a better word) seems to run like this: allowing Jamiat-type outfits to flourish was fine when we thought we would be here indefinitely, but now we know we are clearing out at some point we had better do something about them. This may be terribly unfair. With Iraq, it is hard to know. But, fairly or unfairly, there was little rejoicing at home over the successful Jamiat raid, despite the insistence of a British army spokesman that 'ultimately it is going to make Basra a better place'.[3] Nor did there seem much sense of satisfaction at the news that Saddam was to be executed. Opinion polls showed the public was increasingly sick of Iraq. More than that, it was clear that Iraq was the main force behind the slow-motion disintegration of Tony Blair's authority during 2005–7.

Some asked how it had come to this, how Tony Blair's extraordinary winning streak – in military matters as much as in domestic military matters – had gone cold. But for those with longer memories, the question was how a Labour government had so completely reversed the party's post-Attlee stance of extreme aversion to armed action of any sort. That a British prime minister could have waded into the quagmire of Iraq was bad enough; that a Labour prime minister could have done so beggared belief.

Illustrating the 180-degree swing-round is a minor incident from the late 1960s, during the premiership of Tony Blair's predecessor as a Labour election winner, Harold Wilson. British officers were on loan to the government of Oman in the Persian Gulf, fighting communist guerrillas attempting to overthrow the country's ruler, Sultan Sayyid Said bin Taimur. On one occasion, when a member of the Sultan's forces was injured, it seemed a source of help was close at hand. The British aircraft carrier *HMS Hermes* was, by happy chance, not far out to sea, with helicopters and a fully equipped sick bay. One of the Sultan's on-loan British officers, the soldier/playwright Peter Thwaites, recalled later that radio contact was made with the ship, which responded that, for reasons of policy, no help would be given.[4] Lieutenant-Colonel Thwaites, the injured man and the other British officers on loan to the Sultan were 'off the books', as far as Whitehall was concerned, and consequently they were on their own. The government's July 1968 defence white paper set a timetable for the ending of all British commitments 'east of Suez', with the sole exception of Hong Kong. Mr Thwaites described the incident as the low point in the Wilson government's policy of scuttle. But as it turned out, the incident was to prove the high-water-mark of British non-intervention and military quiescence.

Fast forward to the Blair years. It is the early autumn of 2001 and 23,000 UK service personnel are taking part in Britain's biggest overseas training manoeuvre since the end of the Cold War. Called Exercise Saif Sareea II, using the Arabic translation for 'swift sword', this enormous exercise is taking place in Oman. Nor is there anything secret about it; not that secrecy was really an option, given that it includes a naval task force of 17 ships led by the aircraft carrier *HMS Illustrious*, a Royal Marine Commando brigade and a British army armoured brigade. Indeed, far from it being kept under wraps, the then-Defence Secretary Geoff Hoon boasted that it would show 'Britain's ability to deploy rapidly, a considerable force with real punch over strategic distances'.[5] One by-product of the Saif Sareea manoeuvres was that when, in the immediate aftermath of the 11 September attacks on New York and Washington it became clear that Afghanistan, home of the radical Islamic Taliban movement, was to be the immediate target of

America and her allies, a large slice of Britain's military fire-power was halfway there already.

Clearly, something significant had changed in Britain's overseas military stance between the Labour government of 1966–70 and that of 2001–5. The apologetic furtiveness of the sixties had given way to the Union Jack-waving show of force 33 years later. The scale of this change is underlined by the fact that Saif Sareea had been unusual at the time only in that it was an exercise rather than the real thing. During the four years of the first Blair government (1997– 2001), the real thing, rather than manoeuvres (however impressive), had dominated military activity. In 1998, British forces took part in a series of air and long-range artillery assaults on Iraq, Afghanistan and the Sudan, in partnership with US forces. This last target had seemed particularly dubious; allegedly aimed at a plant for the creation of chemical weapons, it seemed the assault had instead destroyed a factory producing aspirin and veterinary medicines.

In March 1999, Britain joined the United States and other NATO countries in using massive military force to drive Serbia out of one of its own provinces, Kosovo, on the grounds that the Serbs were persecuting Kosovans of Albanian origin. And lest anyone imagine that the UK was incapable of doing much beyond providing assistance to American forces, in May 2000 the British public learned that their country had just invaded and effectively taken over the small West African state of Sierra Leone; the helicopter carrier *HMS Ocean* and the *HMS Illustrious* accompanied 1,500 service personnel in the operation, aimed in part at restoring order to a country torn by civil war. Given this new belligerence, it would have been odd had British forces not been despatched to Afghanistan in the wake of the 11 September attacks.

The UK had, famously, sat out the Vietnam War in the 1960s. It had responded to the unilateral declaration of independence by Rhodesia (now Zimbabwe) in 1965 by arranging international sanctions, rather than with military force. Despite helping Malaysia in the early part of the decade to face off threats in Borneo from Indonesia's President Sukarno, the British 'intervention' that seemed to sum up the country's attitude to far-flung military adventures in the 1960s was the response, in 1969, to a mini-rebellion in Anguilla, then as now a British colony in the West Indies. A tiny force of British troops was despatched, along with officers from the Metropolitan Police, and the 'revolt' was ended without incident.

Today, it is hard to imagine Britain 'sitting out' any major military operation in which it had been invited to join. Mr Blair has embroiled Britain in four significant conflicts – Kosovo, Sierra Leone, Afghanistan and Iraq. What explained this remarkable turnround? Perhaps more to the point, how was it all being paid for? Labour's sweeping defence cuts and reluctance to commit troops to action in the 1960s had been as much about finance as about ideology. One field of government operations able to compete with Labour's cherished social services in terms of rapidly escalating costs was defence. A million pounds spent on weapons is a million pounds that could not be spent on hospital equipment or new schools.

Denis Healey, Defence Secretary throughout Labour's term in power from 1964 to 1970, wrote later:

> In the fifties and sixties the cost of naval frigates doubled, the cost of much army equipment quadrupled, and the cost of military aircraft increased tenfold. Costs are rising even faster nowadays . . . current trends could mean that within a century the number of modern weapons which a country like Britain could afford would have fallen to single figures.[6]

So what was Mr Blair using for money?

The short answer is that he wasn't using anything. In 2002–3, total public spending for the Ministry of Defence was £35.4 billion. The following year, it was £35.6 billion, and the estimated out-turn for 2004–5 was £36 billion. The planned total for 2005–6 was £36.3 billion, for the year after £37.5 billion and for 2007–8 £39 billion.[7] In other words, the defence budget was to creep up by just over 10 per cent in cash terms during a seven-year period. Taking the 2 per cent inflation target as a crude measure, and the rate of price increases ought to total 14 per cent over the same period. Of course, John Major's Conservatives had scaled back defence spending in the early 1990s. But then, they had scaled back the commitments too, as the Cold War drew to a close. Mr Blair, by contrast, appears to want a muscular military stance at minimal cost. On Fantasy Island, it would seem, you can fight ever longer and bloodier wars without replenishing the war chest.

Contrast this with the planned path of 'total central government spending on education in England', from £20.6 billion in 2002–3 to £31.9 billion in 2007–8, a rise of 54.8 per cent.[8] It would seem that funding Mr Blair's mission to 're-order this world around us' is of rather less importance than keeping sweet Labour's vast payroll vote in school staff rooms, university faculties and the burgeoning education bureaucracy. Or perhaps Mr Blair had grasped the fact that his own party would go along with military grandstanding provided, first, that the cost did not eat into social expenditure and, secondly, that it could be presented as high-minded intervention for worthy, liberal motives rather than a piece of old-fashioned imperialist gunboat diplomacy. For those tempted to resist, there were always two crushing election defeats – 1983 and 1987 – to remind them of what the voters thought of the merest whiff of neutralism or, worse, pacifism. The first of those election campaigns had been a shambles, the second a masterpiece of modern political marketing. The outcomes were much the same, and a common factor had been the party's policy of nuclear disarmament. Furthermore, Labour's unilateralists had been winded by the unravelling of the Soviet Bloc; those who had appeared glamorous and forward-looking in the early 1980s could now be portrayed as losers.

Then there was a minor-key 'Falklands Factor' at work. In the immediate aftermath of the 1982 battle to reclaim the Falkland Islands, even some of those who had supported the despatch of the military task force had assumed that the whole affair had been very much the last of its kind. Twenty-five years later, and the South Atlantic campaign stands up rather well in the early drafts of history. It can be seen as having been the first of a new type of conflict rather than the last of an old line. In Kuwait, Kosovo and Bosnia, Western firepower has been assembled to see off alleged interlopers. Rather, what looks, with hindsight, somewhat eccentric and out of date now is the view held by many on the left in 1982 (along with a fair number of liberal-ish Tories) that negotiating with Argentina's fascist dictators was the 'civilized' course of action.

Of course, Falklands-sceptics and outright opponents of the campaign are not alone in appearing on the wrong side of recent military developments. Those who demanded a 'gloves off' approach to dealing with the IRA and other armed groups in Northern Ireland have scarcely been vindicated. But they had never featured largely within Labour's ranks. Rather more numerous, particularly among the party's activists, had been supporters of the position of the 'Troops Out' movement, those who argued that Britain had no business being in Northern Ireland and was only making things worse. Had their advice been taken in the 1970s or 1980s, there would, presumably, have been no peace process at all, and certainly not one in which the UK was a participant. Thus even the sole military de-escalation of the Blair years was far from being an unalloyed vindication of those whose constant preference was for a low- or no-profile stance from the country's armed forces.

Mr Blair seemed to understand this. More, he understood that the attitude of the British public to armed conflict was far from the sort of reflex scepticism common in some European countries, in parts of American society and on Labour's own backbenches. Born in May 1953, Tony Blair would have been three at the time of the Suez crisis, that great eye-opening moment for the post-war Establishment. By having been far too young to have participated in the governing class's collective loss of nerve in 1956, Mr Blair had the great advantage of instinctively sharing an attitude to the use of force with the majority of British people, who seemed rather less affected by Suez and its aftermath and thus tended to take a robust approach to supporting 'our boys'. It was an approach that Mr Blair, in words if not in deeds, was to display in full measure. But as we shall now see, it was in sharp contrast to 30 years of Labour defence policy.

Beating retreat: Singapore, Suez, the Sixties

It is one of the ironies of history that the fatal blow delivered to British imperialism as an idea came neither from domestic liberals nor from an uprising by oppressed colonial peoples but by the armed forces of the Empire of Japan. Colin Cross put it this way:

> While the Japanese militarist dream that swift aggressive action by a well-trained, well-equipped army could form a permanent Co-Prosperity Sphere in the Far East was even more ephemeral than the British imperial dream, it did have enough success to weaken permanently the magical

'prestige' on which the British had relied so much. In particular, the fall of Singapore was a supreme catastrophe.[9]

The Suez crisis of 1956, as has been noted, brought the
curtain down on the notion that Britain alone – or, in this
case, allied with France – could wage a major long-distance
war. Anglo-French collusion in an Israeli attack on Egypt
that would give the two European countries a pretext to
intervene to 'separate' the combatants and 'secure' the Suez
Canal (an Anglo-French asset nationalized by Egypt) not
only failed in its objective, but also, because of the large
amount of official deception involved, dishonoured the
concept of such long-range military missions. And, as was to
be seen only too vividly in the 10 years after Suez, the
rationale behind Britain's external military stance stood or
fell as a piece. Removing one brick would threaten the
whole structure.

There was no shortage of falling masonry during the
1960s.

With the failure of the Suez operation, an immediate question mark appeared over the two pillars of Britain's 'east of
Suez' commitments, the main Middle East base in Aden and
the sister-base in Singapore. What were they for, if the sort of
conflict for which they were ideally suited was now out of
the question? Furthermore, without these commitments, it
was hard to justify full-sized aircraft carriers or the swing-
wing nuclear bomber, the TSR2. Without any aircraft carriers, the navy's Fleet Air Arm looked vulnerable to abolition.
Once the cutbacks started, where would they end?

Compounding this was the decision, conscious or uncon-
scious, in the post-Suez period to liquidate Britain's remaining territorial empire. Even after the independence of India
and Pakistan in the 1940s, it had been assumed that Britain
would remain in Africa for an indefinite period of time,
albeit exercising stewardship of a post-war, welfare-state

type. Harold Macmillan's 'wind of change' speech to the South African Parliament in February 1960, whatever its original purpose, has since been seen as signalling the so-called 'scramble out of Africa'. The final act in this drama came with the abandonment of Aden in the mid-1960s and then the remaining two legs of the East of Suez position. These were, first, the so-called Trucial States (now the United Arab Emirates), a group of British client-statelets in the Persian Gulf and, secondly, the base in Singapore.

It is worth remembering that all this was taking place under a Labour government and came to be seen as part of an almost cosmic shift in priorities, from battleships and foreign bases to domestic assets such as new towns, new universities and the promotion of new technology. Then-Defence Secretary Lord Healey recalled:

> I was under pressure from the Treasury to cut spending, and from the Foreign and Commonwealth Office not to cut commitments . . . At the same time there was a growing clamour among Labour MPs for us to abandon our East of Suez role immediately.[10]

Lord Healey added that two usually antipathetic wings of the party were united on the issue: 'In this chorus, the voices of the Common Marketeers provided a counterpoint to those of the anti-colonialist Left.' Joining the Common Market (now European Union) was exciting and progressive; so was decrying imperialism and militarism. There was nothing exciting or progressive in supporting costly and apparently pointless military commitments around the world.

Tony Blair turned all this on its head. During most of his time in office, it has been the coming men and women who have been most gung-ho about the use of arms. Sceptics have been decried as 'old Labour', as living in the past and of failing to support our servicemen and women in their dangerous tasks. Gordon Brown has repeatedly demonstrated his modernity by lavishing praise on the armed forces and even making an apparently off-the-cuff and uncosted commitment to replace Britain's submarine-launched ballistic missile system, Trident. Indeed, only since well after the March 2003 invasion of Iraq has the identification of military hawkishness with impeccable New Labour credentials been seriously dented. Even with the Iraqi entanglement and its associated appalling problems, there seems little sign of the party returning to the military quietism of the late 1960s, when Philip Larkin's mournful elegy for the East of Suez posture announced:

> Next year we are to bring the soldiers home
> For lack of money, and it is all right.

Larkin concluded:

> Our children will not know it's a different country.
> All we can hope to leave them now is money.[11]

It was to be a different country, all right, albeit not in a way that Larkin would have recognized. In the middle of 2006, Britain was engaged in two major theatres of war. In one of them (Afghanistan), Tony Blair had decided to stand and fight in a country where even the Victorians had decided it would be prudent to call it a draw and clear out. It was hard to recall that, in 1964, Labour had actually won an election on the implicit pledge to cancel the Polaris nuclear missile system and to abandon the attempt to remain an independent nuclear power. But Tony Blair, the arch-belligerent, did not appear out of the blue and persuade an otherwise pacific nation to support military adventures. Much of the spadework had been done already, by senior defence chiefs, by politicians and others who had never accepted that the East of Suez decision was irreversible, and by the press of events that could not have been foreseen.

Fighting back: the silent military renaissance

By the late 1960s, much of the glamour of the military life appeared to have drained away. Britain's chief external commitment was to NATO, through the British army of the Rhine (BAOR) in Germany, whose role gave little scope for derring-do. In a training film shown to army cadets in the 1970s, an attack by the Soviet Union and its Warsaw Pact allies would be followed by 10 days or so in which Britain and other NATO forces would be able temporarily to contain the assault and hope that matters could be resolved on a political level. If not, then the only counter to over-whelming Soviet Bloc conventional superiority would be nuclear weapons. For BAOR personnel, it seemed, the two futures on offer were (a) boredom or (b) annihilation. Unsurprisingly, this was not an easy 'sell' to potential service personnel, thus the development at this time of recruitment advertising stressing the opportunities for water skiing, scuba diving and other exciting leisure-type pursuits, not to mention foreign travel of what seemed to be a fairly non-bellicose kind. Joining the army, according to one such advertisement, involved seeing the world and meeting inter-esting new people. A Royal Navy lapel badge for school-children invited them to 'Fly, sail, dive'.

But for the forces, some 'action', albeit of a low-intensity type, was just round the corner.

In the world of fiction, the gathering gloom of the late 1960s impelled one writer to imagine a savage civil war between the north and south of England. Arthur Wise, author of *The Day the Queen Flew to Scotland for the Grouse Shooting*, was very nearly spot on.[12] Economic failure and past resentments *did* explode at the end of the 1960s. Wise's only mistake was to pick the wrong 'north'. The 80 men of the Prince of Wales' Own Regiment who entered Waterloo Place in Londonderry just after 4 p.m. on 14 August 1969 were to prove the advance guard of an enormous commitment of British troops to the affairs of Northern Ireland. What Home Secretary James Callaghan had described as 'a limited operation' was to last for decades.

If Northern Ireland was a very public example of British troops in a live conflict far removed from rock climbing or water skiing, then a very private example was under way in none other than Peter Thwaites' old stamping ground, Oman. The Conservative government that took power in June 1970 had opposed the retreat from East of Suez. In opposition, party leader Edward Heath had suggested a low-key return to the Far East as part of a five-power Commonwealth agreement to deter external threats (the powers being Britain, Australia, New Zealand, Singapore and Malaysia). This agreement was duly signed when Mr Heath took office. He had hoped to reverse the decision to withdraw from the Gulf but, as his then-Political Secretary Douglas Hurd wrote: 'Mr Heath's government withdrew from the Gulf after all.'[13]

Well, yes and no. In September 1970, the practice of lending the Omanis certain British officers was replaced by direct military involvement by British units. This more or less secret war by Britain culminated, after five years, in the defeat of the communist guerrillas by British and Omani forces.

But despite both Northern Ireland and Oman, Britain's grandeur, military and otherwise, appeared in further steep decline during the 1970s, culminating in the sterling crisis of September 1976, in the wake of which Britain was portrayed as going 'cap in hand' to the International Monetary Fund (see p. 53). Not that British soldiers were inactive. Earlier in the year, dozens of British mercenaries arrived in Angola to fight with the FNLA, one of the participants in a three-cornered civil war. Before long, it became clear that the biggest threat to the 'mercs' was their own mentally unstable commander, a former corporal in the Parachute Regiment called Costas Georgiou, who styled himself 'Colonel Callan'.

Yet beneath the surface, 1976 was to mark something of a turning point for British military policy. Two events were, in retrospect, rather more significant indicators of the future than the problems of the pound or the behaviour of 'Callan' and his confederates.

The first, early in the year, involved the announcement that, in the wake of a horrifying series of inter-communal killings, the government was despatching to Northern Ireland members of an organization of which few people, at that time, had ever heard: the Special Air Service Regiment. Just four years later, the SAS would appear on television screens around the world freeing hostages being held at the Iranian Embassy in London, later prompting cynical suggestions that the SAS was the world's most publicity-conscious 'secret' outfit.

The second development involved Britain's nuclear missile system, Polaris. By the early 1970s, it was clear that Polaris was already out of date, in that its warheads were not manoeuvrable after launch in the manner of the successor system, Poseidon. Tory ministers decided in 1973 to upgrade Polaris, a project code-named Chevaline. The incoming Labour government of February 1974 could have cancelled Chevaline, but did not, preferring to proceed quietly without upsetting anti-nuclear backbench MPs. As Lawrence Freedman wrote later:

> In early 1976, intense suspicion was aroused among Labour backbenchers when it was announced that it had been

decided to produce tritium in Britain. This is an isotope of hydrogen used in the fabrication of thermonuclear warheads and has, up to now, been imported from the United States.[14]

The official explanation, wrote Professor Freedman, was that this would save money, boost Britain's own nuclear industry and even open export opportunities. But his own view was that it indicated 'a continuing interest in sustaining a capability for nuclear weapons production'.

Chevaline became available for service in the early 1980s, by which time the Conservatives, under Margaret Thatcher, had announced that Polaris/Chevaline was to be replaced by the enormously expensive US-made Trident system. This, coupled with the decision to allow American 'theatre' nuclear weapons, principally cruise missiles, to be based in the UK, caused a political firestorm that needs no retelling here. But as navy cuts were unveiled, even some of a hawkish disposition were asking whether or not Britain was giving itself the ability to unleash Armageddon but depriving itself of the conventional forces needed to handle more modest conflicts – a terrorist hijacking of a North Sea oil rig was one example.

In the event, it was not an oil rig, nor in the North Sea. But the 1982 Falklands campaign effectively cauterized the scars of Suez and showed the armed forces playing a role far removed from their supposed main function, that of preparing for 'high-intensity warfare' in Europe. Furthermore, the campaign made acceptable, even praiseworthy, the sort of military-political risk-taking at which Tony Blair has excelled. From the distance of 25 years, it is hard to recall just what a gamble the despatch of the South Atlantic Task Force was, not in terms of its likely operational success (although that was certainly a huge risk) but in terms of political acceptability at home. Nobody really knew how the public would react, nor whether substantial public support for the task force could be counted upon.

An idea of what some in high places may have feared can be gleaned by turning again to the writings of Douglas Hurd, who became a long-serving cabinet minister. *Truth Game* is a political thriller published in 1972, and anybody who does not wish to know the ending should skip this paragraph. The Tories are in power; a Falklands-type incident occurs in the Indian Ocean; the Prime Minister wants to sell out the islanders; so do most of the cabinet and the Labour opposition. But the Foreign Secretary insists troops are sent; the public votes the government out; and the troops are withdrawn. We can assume, perhaps, that this is what the author believed at the time would be the likeliest outcome of such a military expedition.[15]

But even after the South Atlantic success, Margaret Thatcher trod carefully. The 'Armilla Patrol', established before the conflict, in 1980, had restored a permanent Royal Navy presence in the Persian Gulf, and Mrs Thatcher was determined that Saddam Hussein would be pitched out of Kuwait, which he had invaded in 1990. For most of her premiership, however, the Cold War remained the main event.

For her successor, John Major, military success came early, in January 1991, just two months into his premiership, when British forces joined US and other troops in the expulsion of Iraq from Kuwait. Rather like an Italian football captain determined to take no risks once the team is ahead, Mr Major seemed to feel that one military victory against no defeats was an entirely respectable score that should not be jeopardized. One of nature's civilians, Mr Major kept a tight grip on military commitments.

On 2 May 1997, Tony Blair thus inherited a military machine that was well-thought-of internationally and a source of some pride domestically to a population that had lost whatever hang-ups it might have developed in the 1950s and 1960s about engagement in long-range conflicts. But it was far from clear what Mr Blair intended to do with this machine – if he intended to do anything much at all.

Escalation, escalation, escalation: Tony Blair goes to war(s)

In March 1990, a dinner was held for British journalists in a private room at the Bristol Kempinski Hotel, Berlin. Among those present was an official whose card declared him to represent the British Military Government, the body charged with administering the UK sector of what was still an occupied city divided among four powers: the Soviet Union, the United States, France and Britain. His calling card, he explained, was out of date.[16] The new title of the organization for which he worked was 'British Mission', a more civilian-sounding name felt to be more appropriate in light of the extraordinary events of the previous November, when the Berlin Wall had been breached and the two Germanies put on the road to unification. That Britain had a continuing role to play in the once and future German capital did not seem open to question. One must hope that not too much was invested in the production of new 'British Mission' calling cards. Come the end of 1994, and the British had left Berlin.

To the tough-minded proto-New Labourites of the early 1990s, this 'calling card' episode would have been typical of a failure to grasp that the world had completely changed, and that Britain's place in it had changed as well. On the face of it, the collapse of the 'socialist' bloc had been bad news for the British left, as it became abundantly clear that given the choice, the peoples of Eastern Europe would reject communism. But it was also a great relief; the bitter arguments about defence and security could now be consigned to the past. Let the British right look old-fashioned as it rejected

European integration. The left could concede that standing up to the Soviet Union might, after all, have been the right course, while 'moving on' (to use a favourite piece of Blairite terminology). If the Cold War had allowed Britain to sit out or even deliberately slow down the process of European unification by stressing its special relationship with the United States, then the new era would afford no hiding place for British 'xenophobes' (a catch-all phrase in the liberal press for those who opposed European federalism). If, furthermore, the Cold War had allowed Britain to run a sort of post-imperial mini-empire, from West Berlin via the sovereign bases on Cyprus through the barracks of Belfast to the Falklands and the Gulf, then this entity, too, would eventually have to be dismantled.

Funnily enough, an opportunity arose to do just that immediately after Labour's May 1997 election victory. The end of British rule in Hong Kong in June of that year marked the loss of the UK's last substantial colony in both economic and population terms. Tony Blair could have used the occasion to deliver a second 'wind of change' speech that would anchor British foreign policy firmly in Europe, scale down defence commitments and 'modernize' the UK's diplomatic and military profile once and for all.

Indeed, there were those who seemed under the impression that this was indeed Blairite policy, including his own Foreign Secretary, the late Robin Cook. An interview with the *Observer* produced a report that began as follows:

> Foreign Secretary Robin Cook, the leading left-winger in the Cabinet, yesterday promised to open a radical new era of British foreign policy – in which Britain will take its rightful place as one of Europe's Big Three within the European Union in order to launch a new international framework ranging from better global economic co-operation to the promotion of human rights.'[17]

Noting the 'imperial splendour' of his new department, the paper quoted Mr Cook further:

> The foreign policy of the Foreign Office is not a rather pompous, grey and mildly tedious job of pouring oil on troubled waters. Foreign relations are central to our political project. We want to take Britain out of a position of isolationism, out of inward-looking chauvinism and into being a leading member of an international community. Personally, I think we are entering a period when international politics is coming of age.

This must have been music to the ears of one of the two interviewers, the paper's then-editor Will Hutton. For years, the author of the best-selling diagnosis of Britain's post-Thatcher ills, *The State We're In*,[18] Mr Hutton had spotted how little traction the old Tory defence card retained now the Cold War was over, and how the disappearance of the Soviet threat gave Britain a chance to rationalize its defences. Now, it seemed, a Labour government with a huge majority agreed with him. True, its leader had not actually said very much about defence. But he hardly looked the martial type. Furthermore, he had described Britain as a 'young country', announced that he would never allow Britain to be isolated in Europe and proved to be an enthusiast for the Northern Ireland peace process. Guitar-playing Tony Blair, with his religious convictions and feminist wife, hardly looked the type to engage in gunboat diplomacy. If anything, he looked quite capable of 'modernizing' the armed forces in a radical way, by cutting budgets.

What happened? A number of things.

First, even had Mr Blair wanted to slim down the forces, he would have ducked it, just as he ducked calling a referendum on joining the euro and ducked introducing a proportional-representation voting system. Not only would a far-reaching slim-down of the armed services have been highly controversial, it could have riled parts of Middle Britain and revived memories of Labour's neutralist leanings in the 1980s. Secondly, by the end of his first term, Mr Blair may well have decided, after his unsuccessful forays into public-service reform, that the armed forces were one part of the public sector that actually worked, not least in helping to grapple with the Millennium floods that hit Britain in the autumn of 2000. Thirdly, as the Falklands and Kuwait had shown, foreign wars are popular, provided they are reasonably limited and with a low level of casualties. Fourthly, Mr Blair seems to have had few doubts about the desirability of his 'humanitarian' military interventions abroad, despite the fact that neither of his two major wars (Afghanistan and Iraq) falls into this category. Finally, Britain and its allies seemed, in the early years of the Blair premiership, to have a knack for winning in conflicts. Afghanistan appeared at first to confirm this winning run as, in the very early days, did the invasion of Iraq in March 2003. Iraq was to mark the end of this hot streak, although that was far from clear at the time. In the immediate countdown to the invasion, there were suggestions that Mr Blair's post-victory popularity would be so towering that he would be able to get his way on any issue – joining the euro being an obvious example. As triumph was inevitable, the only question was how Mr Blair would spend the political capital thus accumulated.

There were omens a-plenty that Iraq would be a very different proposition from Britain's other military operations. There were no ready-made friendly forces, as in Afghanistan. The grounds for war kept shifting (from weapons of mass destruction to the desirability of ousting Saddam). There was the pretence in late 2002 and early 2003 that Saddam could remain in power if he cooperated with weapons inspectors, part of the bigger pretence that no final decision to invade had yet been taken. But like an out-of-

towner in a slick casino, Mr Blair had convinced himself that
he was a top-class gambler. In Kosovo, Sierra Leone and
Afghanistan, he had upped the stakes every time and won
handsomely. True, the pile of blue plaques was now alarm-
ingly high. Only the timid, however, would allow themselves
to be fazed. Was he not a true leader, someone who took
'tough choices'?

Until Iraq, Mr Blair had seized the chance to look good
while doing good, and without it costing undue amounts of
money. The trappings of a military superpower could be had
on the cheap, it seemed. Furthermore, the whole process was
undergirded by the fact that not one of these conflicts
involved threats to the United Kingdom, its people or its
immediate interests. The one conflict with which New
Labour has had to deal that involves real threats to the lives
of British people, the destruction of British property and a
menace to British public security has been in Northern
Ireland, and this is the one conflict where Mr Blair has been
risk-averse, conciliatory and low-key. The terrible irony of
the Blair circle's strenuous efforts in 2002 and early 2003 to
claim that Iraq posed a threat to the country is that, on the
evidence, had it actually done so, Mr Blair's approach would
probably have mirrored the 'jaw-jaw' attitude of continental
leaders such as French President Jacques Chirac. A sure way
of telling that an opponent is no real danger to the UK is that
Mr Blair has waged war on him.

And had Mr Blair stuck firmly with his original war-
making style – using overwhelming force against weak and
unpopular opponents – all might have been well. But Fantasy
Island is full of siren noises, and Mr Blair's military strategy
started to unravel when he persuaded himself to fight some
real wars instead of largely pretend ones. Thus, while our
forces are engaged in two savage theatres of conflict, we are
treated to the extraordinary spectacle of regimental mergers
and financial uncertainty for the defence establishment.

In December 2006, the recently retired head of the British army, General Sir Mike Jackson, used the Dimbleby Lecture to highlight the financial strain under which the forces were now operating. 'The defence budget at some £32 billion is just over two per cent of our gross national product, having been at the end of the Cold War double or more that figure,' he said. 'It's some five-and-a-half per cent only of the £550 billion, which is today's Government spending.'[19]

Sir Mike went on, in words that were to be blazoned across the news media:

> The armed forces' contract with the nation which they serve and from which they very largely recruit is to take risks, if need be, the risk of life. But this must be a two-way contract, it has to be reciprocal. Military operations cost in blood and treasure, because risk-free soldiering, which some seem to think is possible, is simply a contradiction in terms. It is our soldiers who pay the cost in blood; the nation must therefore pay the cost in treasure.

On 27 December 2006 – two days after the Jamiat assault with which we opened this chapter – the head of British forces in southern Iraq, Major General Richard Shirreff, said:

> The nation needs to understand that the quality work done by these courageous men and women out here only happens and can only continue if . . . our soldiers are properly supported back home in terms of the support for training, infrastructure, barracks, accommodation.[20]

Had Mr Blair wanted Britain to become a sort of latter-day Prussia, ready to fight anywhere, then he ought to have put this notion to the electorate, complete with an estimate of the likely bill. It would have put him in direct descent from Clement Attlee, whose willingness to maintain an enormous military establishment was almost as striking as the setting up on his watch of the welfare state and independence for India and Pakistan.

Peter Hennessey lists the fighting strength of the army in 1947, the blackest year for the Attlee government, with fuel shortages, the sterling convertibility crisis and the resignation of Hugh Dalton. In addition to the 30 infantry battalions and 17 armoured regiments stationed at home, the army's overseas bases produced this impressive tally: Egypt (three infantry battalions, two armoured regiments); Libya (three infantry battalions, two armoured regiments); Cyprus (one infantry brigade); Somaliland (two infantry battalions); Sudan (one infantry battalion); the Far East (13 infantry battalions); Jamaica (one infantry battalion); and West Germany (18 infantry battalions and 8 armoured regiments).[21]

This list demonstrates the gulf between Mr Attlee and Mr Blair. The former spent as much as 6 per cent of GDP on defence and, as Sir Mike noted above, the total was between 4 and 5 per cent at the end of the 1980s, dropping to about 2.5 per cent now. The 1945–51 Labour administrations may have been misguided in trying to maintain a superpower role for Britain, but at least they made no bones about the cost. New Labour seems to believe a superpower role can be had for the price of a well-trained and dedicated but essentially modest defence force.

Thus by October 2006, Mr Blair was making this pledge on forces radio to the troops in Afghanistan: 'If commanders on the ground want more equipment – armoured vehicles for example, more helicopters – that will be provided. Whatever package they want, we will do.'[22] This was despite it being widely believed that no money was available to pay for it. Six weeks later he told British forces in that country: 'Here, in this extraordinary desert, is where the future of world security in the early twenty-first century is going to be played out.'[23] However extraordinary the desert in question, its ability to astonish must pale beside that of Mr Blair, who, with his forces fighting apparently unwinnable wars on two fronts, had decided his hard-pressed, under-manned and under-funded forces were to bear the burden of twenty-first-century security.

It was the culmination of a remarkable nine-year fantasy, one whose casualties were only too real. One of these was Sergeant Steven Roberts, a tank commander accidentally killed by a comrade at a vehicle checkpoint in Basra in March 2003. This was the finding of Oxfordshire assistant deputy coroner Andrew Walker:

> To send soldiers into a combat zone without the appropriate basic equipment is, in my view, unforgivable and inexcusable, and represents a breach of trust that the soldiers have in those who govern them. Enhanced combat body armour was a basic piece of protective equipment. I have heard justification and excuse, and I put these to one side as I remind myself that Sgt Roberts lost his life because he did not have that basic piece of equipment.[24]

Lonely Planet: How New Labour Tries to Spin the Environment

Ten years ago, if you had asked me to put environmental obligations on business, I would have been horrified. Now I'm advocating it . . . Global warming is the greatest long-term threat to our planet's environment. Scarce energy resources mean rising prices and will threaten our country's economy.

Tony Blair, addressing Labour Party conference,
Manchester, 26 September 2006

Forget six counties overhung with smoke,
   Forget the snorting steam and piston stroke,
Forget the spreading of the hideous town;
   Think rather of the pack-horse on the down,
And dream of London, small and white, and clean,
   The clear Thames bordered by its gardens green.

William Morris, prologue *to The Earthly Paradise*

Crash on the levee, mama,
Water's gonna overflow,
Swamp's gonna rise,
No boat's gonna row.

Bob Dylan, *Down in the Flood*[1]

It was clearly a big political do. First, there was the venue. Carlton House Terrace in St James has always been the Establishment's venue of choice for a set-piece occasion.

Then there was the plethora of TV vans, the airport-style security checks and Scotland Yard's machine-gun toting anti-terrorist officers.

Finally, and most importantly of all, both Tony Blair and Gordon Brown turned up together at the Royal Society on a mild late October morning to launch the Stern Review of the economics of climate change, a government-sponsored study of global warming.[2] Barely a month earlier, the Prime Minister had been accusing the Chancellor of orchestrating a political coup attempt; the assembled journalists were aware that the two principal architects of New Labour could barely stand the sight of each other. The subliminal message was clear: doing something to cut emissions of carbon dioxide and other greenhouse gases was so vitally important that Messrs Blair and Brown were prepared – temporarily, at least – to bury the hatchet.

The Prime Minister set the tone. The 700-page tome delivered by Sir Nicholas Stern, a Treasury economist, was 'the most important report on the future produced during the government's decade in office'.[3] Not to be outdone, Mr Brown said tackling climate change was not just an environmental and economic imperative but also a moral one. The Chancellor warmed to his theme:

> So, just as in recent years Britain has led the world in securing a low interest rate, stable economy, founded on low inflation, so today I set a new ambition for Britain in future years: to lead the world in creating a stable and sustainable economy founded on low carbon – a Britain that is both pro-growth and pro-green.[4]

We leave it to others to decide whether Britain's debt-sodden, property-speculating economy is really the paragon of stability that Mr Brown believed it to be. Set against the belief that there is no contradiction – either conceptually or practically –

in marrying protection of the environment with policies to maximize growth, the Chancellor's fancy that he had discovered the philosopher's stone of low inflation permanently 'locked in' (to use one of Mr Brown's favourite phrases) was merely a harmless daydream. The fantasy that it can be business as usual on the growth front without boiling the planet is the most dangerous of them all, which is why we have left it until last in this book.

All gain, no pain: environmentalism, New Labour style

It was a fantasy widely shared in Britain in the autumn of 2006, when green was the political fashion statement of the moment. The Liberal Democrats had proposed changing the nature of the tax system to penalize firms that polluted rather than those that created jobs. David Cameron, the Conservative leader, sought to make his hitherto relentlessly untrendy party appeal to younger voters by announcing he was putting a wind turbine on the roof of his Notting Hill home and by being photographed cycling from West London to Westminster. The effect was somewhat spoiled, however, when it was revealed that his official limousine followed on behind, carrying his work suit and his official papers.

Business leaders were also getting in on the act. In the summer, a group of more than a dozen executives from some of Britain's biggest companies had written to the Prime Minister insisting on the need for bold leadership. Of particular concern to the cream of corporate Britain was that business could do little to start producing the technological cures for climate change until it was given a firm steer from the politicians. But the politicians appeared to be reluctant to do anything that they thought might upset business. New

Labour run scared from big business? Heaven knows where that idea might have come from.

And so it went on. Tesco, Britain's biggest supermarket chain, announced that it was to construct the world's greenest store, with the checkout tills powered by wind turbines and rainwater recycled to wash the company's delivery vans. This seemed to sit a little oddly with an outfit that was using scarce water supplies to ensure a year-round supply of fresh green beans from developing countries and flying red roses in from Kenya for Valentine's Day. But the small print revealed that the ground-breaking store was in Wick, a few miles down the road from John O'Groats at the northernmost tip of Scotland, and where seabirds outnumber shoppers by a considerable margin.

Not everyone was so keen to get in on the save-the-planet act. Michael O'Leary, the chief executive of the budget airline Ryanair, described the idea of green taxes on aviation as the 'usual horseshit',[5] while even Willie Walsh, the normally more emollient chief executive of British Airways, warned that failure to give approval to an expansion of Heathrow would harm London's position as the financial capital of Europe.[6] Richard Lambert, the director-general of the Confederation of British Industry, the UK's leading employers' organization, said that unilateral action by the government to tackle climate change could affect the competitiveness of the economy: 'The biggest challenge in policy terms is to arrive at a sensible balance between averting climate change and protecting jobs on the other hand.'[7]

Labour's response came as no surprise. For almost a decade and a half, Mr Blair had dominated British politics by operating a 'big tent' policy in which all but the extremists of left and right could come to a pragmatic compromise. Bill Clinton, from whom this policy was borrowed, called it 'triangulation', and the government's approach to the politics of climate change was a classic of the genre. On the one hand there were still a few climate change deniers, the remnants of the 'big oil, big auto' coalition that had long argued that rising global temperatures were nothing to do with human activities. But they were now isolated because, as the Stern Review made clear, the scientific evidence that global warming could not be explained away by the ebb and flow of nature was now 'overwhelming'. On the other hand there were the die-hard environmentalists arguing that there had to be profound changes in lifestyles if crisis was to be averted. There again, though, the Stern Review had looked closely at the economics and concluded that the world merely had to give up 1 per cent of global GDP in an insurance policy each and every year to save itself from a potential 20 per cent hit on living standards. That, surely, said the Prime Minister, was a basis on which all but the fanatics at either end of the spectrum could come together.

We shall come back to the details of the Stern Review later in this chapter. Suffice it to say at this stage that it was the perfect report for the government. Not because it was a weighty piece of academic research, even though it was. Rather, because it allowed New Labour to say it was necessary to make 'hard choices' while at the same time validating the failure to make a choice. This was the party that – as we have seen – thought it was possible to fight expensive wars while cutting the defence budget and to make Britain the knowledge economy of the world while reducing per capita spending in universities, so it came as little surprise to find it effortlessly squaring the circle on climate change.

As usual, there was plenty of rhetoric. 'Without radical international measures to reduce carbon emissions within the next 10 to 15 years, there is compelling evidence to suggest we might lose the chance to control temperature rises,' Mr Blair said.

Failure to act will make an increase of between two and five degrees inevitable. The consequences are stark, for our planet and for the people who live on it, threatening the basic elements of life – access to water, food production, health and our environment.[8]

In practice, though, Labour wanted to have its cake and eat it. Neither Mr Blair nor Mr Brown was in the slightest bit interested in taking on Mr O'Leary and the budget airline industry, but both were highly sensitive to Richard Lambert's warning that there should be no environmental measures that put at risk the 'competitiveness of the economy'. It came as no surprise, therefore, that, within a month of the Stern Review, the government welcomed Sir Rod Eddington's review of the transport system, which urged the expansion of Heathrow, and Kate Barker's report recommending a shake-up of the planning system to allow big new housing developments in the south-east to be pushed through more quickly.[9] One of these proposed developments was in low-lying land in the Thames Gateway, susceptible to flooding in the event of sea levels rising as a result of global warming. Ministers saw no inconsistency in this, even after the harrowing experience of New Orleans in August 2005, although, tellingly, the insurance industry did.

Labour's message was that there could be plenty of environmental gain without any economics pain. Indeed, there might be spin-off benefits to the economy if UK companies concentrated their efforts in sectors designed to find solutions to environmental problems, since these would tend to be highly profitable. This was a point Michael Heseltine had made at a CBI conference in 1991, when he stressed that the Swedes, the Germans and the Japanese were already eyeing up the possibilities in green technology, not just because it was needed to cut pollution but because the countries that came up with the new products and services would have first-mover advantage and thus be able to charge premium prices. Predictably, Lord Heseltine's call for government support for environmental industries went unheeded, but Messrs Blair and Brown remained confident at the time of the Stern Review launch that it was not too late. Britain's energy needs could be met cheaply and cleanly with a combination of nuclear energy, renewables and imported gas. Technological progress would be harnessed to provide greener cars and planes. A new global deal could be brokered to ensure that both developed and developing countries were committed to capping carbon emissions at a level that was compatible with the sustainability of the planet. In the meantime, it might not be a bad idea to keep the SUV in the garage and walk the children to school.

Within six weeks of the launch of the Stern Review, Britain found out what New Labour meant by leading the world in the creation of a low-carbon economy. Mr Brown, who had limbered up for his get-tough approach to the airline industry with a weekend visit to British troops in Basra (Mr Blair, incidentally, made his own carbon footprint with a simultaneous visit to Afghanistan), announced that he was committed to making passengers pay the full environmental costs of air travel. The £5 increase in air passenger duty (APD) announced by the Treasury in the Pre-Budget Report of December 2006 no doubt had them breaking out in a cold sweat at easyJet and Ryanair, for fear that demand for stag weekends in Vilnius and cultural breaks in Prague would plummet. Given that the increase in APD merely reversed the fall from £13.40 to £8.86 in the average amount collected from each air traveller between 2001 and 2005, there was little real expectation that the low-cost airlines would be going out of business. Indeed, all the talk in the media during the week of the PBR was of the boom in transatlantic flights as British consumers took advantage of the pound being valued at almost two dollars for a pre-Christmas shopping spree in New York.

Nor did Mr Brown exactly declare war on the motorist. Ever since the protests organized by road hauliers in September 2000 had briefly deprived Labour of its lead in the opinion polls, the government had been wary of alienating the motorists' vote. Mr Brown first scrapped the fuel duty escalator – whereby excise duties on petrol and diesel rose more rapidly than inflation – and then, when oil prices rose rapidly from 2003 onwards, spared motorists any increase at all for three years in a row.

In his 2006 Pre-Budget Report, Mr Brown raised excise duty on petrol by just over one penny a litre.

There was no such respite for the long-suffering rail commuter. Fares on the railways continued to rise above the rate of inflation to pay for 'improvements' to the service. By 2005, figures from the Department for Transport showed that since Labour had come to power, the real cost of motoring had fallen by 6 per cent, bus fares were up by 16 per cent and a rail ticket was 7 per cent more expensive. The fact that public transport fares were higher than in any other European countries bar Denmark and Sweden might just explain why the UK was more dependent on the car (despite having a below-average level of car ownership) than any other European country and had the worst traffic congestion. Following a 73 per cent increase in road traffic between 1980 and 2002, greenhouse gas emissions from transport accounted for more than a quarter of the UK's total. A study in 2001 showed that if the trends of car ownership and use were to continue, fuel efficiency would have to improve by 400 per cent, with the average family saloon doing an impressive 113 miles to the gallon, to achieve the 40 per cent drop in carbon emissions needed to tackle climate change.[10] In the second half of the 1990s, the UK car industry improved fuel efficiency by somewhat less than this – notching up a 3.3 per cent reduction, the least impressive in Europe.

None of this, predictably enough, was mentioned while the government was congratulating itself on its progressive approach to tackling climate change. Mr Blair noted that Britain was on course to meet its target for the 12.5 per cent cut in the 1990 level of emissions agreed under the Kyoto protocol without adding that the success was entirely due to the contraction of the economy in the early 1990s and the shift to gas-fired power stations following the devastation of the coal mining industry. Nor did he think it worth bothering his audience with the fact that emissions had gone up again in 2003 and 2004 – a period when the level of environmental taxation was cut – and that as a result were higher than at any time since Labour came to power in 1997. The government blamed higher demand for energy across all sectors of the economy as it abandoned its target for a 20 per cent cut in greenhouse gas emissions by 2010, despite having pledged to do so in three successive general election manifestos. In the circumstances, it was hard to disagree with the Green Party's Caroline Lucas, who noted that the government liked to talk 'about tackling climate change whilst pursuing the very policies – road building, airport expansion and encouraging low-cost airlines, private transport and free international trade – that exacerbate it'.[11]

Dr Lucas added that if the world were really to have a chance of achieving the 80–90 per cent cut in greenhouse gas emissions necessary to avert catastrophic climate change, there needed to be nothing short of a revolution in the way the economy was run, in the way human welfare was measured and in the way production and consumption were organized. As far as the government was concerned, it was easy enough for a Green MEP to come out with this sort of argument, since there was not the slightest chance of her ever having to put the ideas into practice. The political reality of an election every four or five years meant it would be electoral suicide to say that voters should face serious changes to their lifestyles. Political hari-kari or not, however, the fact remained that it was the government that was marooned on Fantasy Island, not Dr Lucas.

Ministers accept that since the start of the industrial age 250 years ago, there has been a significant increase in global temperatures associated with human activities. Given the weight of scientific evidence, they can hardly do anything else. What they cannot accept, possibly because it is too difficult to do so politically, is that this means that the capitalist model to which pretty much every nation in the world is now committed is bankrupt. That's a hard message to swallow, since for 250 years since the dawn of the industrial revolution, progress has been measured by how big a nation's economy is and how fast it can grow.

In the preceding 1,000 years up until 1750 growth rates had been slow, even negligible, so a peasant living in eighteenth-century England would have had an existence little different from that of a peasant living on the same piece of land in the reign of Alfred the Great. Industrialization, however, after the initial brutal stages, led to rapid improvements in living standards. People lived longer, worked shorter hours, had higher standards of nutrition and ceased to die from easily preventable diseases. A peasant from 1757 would find the Britain of 2007 a mind-boggling place, although the really big changes – electric power, the internal combustion engine, the flushing WC, the ability to make powered flight, the telephone – had all occurred by the early twentieth century.

The defects of this model, though, are twofold. At one level, growth has become the measure of success only by default. We can measure the goods turned out by factories and, with a little more difficulty, the output of restaurants, the NHS and schools. All the various remunerated outputs of those people working get lumped together and called the gross domestic product of the country. If the GDP goes up by 2.5 per cent, that's about the average of the past 100 years. If it goes up by 3 per cent, that's considered success; if it goes up by 2 per cent that's considered failure. What's more, there's no such thing as 'enough' under industrial capitalism. The idea that individuals, once their living standards reach a certain level, might not need to consume more and more in order to become happier, simply doesn't feature.

Yet there are plenty of things that GDP doesn't measure. It doesn't take account of unpaid work; it doesn't take account of rising crime, or the social costs of unemployment. Crucially, it also doesn't take account of the damage to the environment caused by growth. As Robert Kennedy once said, gross domestic product

> is indifferent to the decency of our factories and the safety of streets alike. It does not include the beauty of our poetry or the strength of our marriages, the intelligence of our public debate or the integrity of our public officials. The [GDP] measures neither our wit nor our courage, neither our wisdom nor our learning, neither our compassion nor our devotion to our country. It measures everything, in short, except that which makes life worthwhile.[12]

Over the past two decades, some radical economists have tried to construct alternative measures of well-being that take into account more than simply growth rates as represented by fluctuations in GDP. One such in the UK was the Measure of Domestic Progress (MDP), which, by taking into account unemployment, growing inequality, family breakdown, rising crime and environmental degradation, gave a strikingly different picture of post-war Britain than the steady improvement in living standards provided by the official data. Indeed, the new economics foundation (nef), the think tank that published the MDP, caused quite a stir when it announced that 1976 – the year of droughts, the IMF and Johnny Rotten – was the happiest year ever.[13]

According to the nef, per capita incomes have risen threefold since 1950, but MDP has not yet doubled. Since the stagflation of 1975, when the economy contracted and inflation hit a post-war record of 27 per cent, GDP has risen by 80 per cent, but MDP fell during the high unemployment and socially fractured 1980s and has yet to return to its mid-1970s peak. A 300 per cent increase in environmental costs since 1950, accompanied by a 600 per cent jump in social costs, helped explain why the average growth rate of MDP has been barely half that of GDP since the middle of the last century. Even so, the lodestar of economic policy, in the UK as elsewhere, is that more growth equals more well-being.

The second defect of the growth model is that developing countries, understandably, want what we have got. And if we are not prepared to accept that there are limits to growth, it is inconceivable that countries like China and India (which still have hundreds of millions of people in poverty despite being two of the fastest-growing economies in the world), let alone the even more impoverished nations of sub-Saharan Africa, will be willing to show restraint either. Carbon dioxide emissions per head have been strongly correlated with GDP per head. As a result, since 1850, North America and Europe have produced around 70 per cent of all carbon dioxide emissions due to energy production, while developing countries have accounted for less than a quarter.

The accountancy firm PriceWaterhouseCoopers believes that by 2050 a group of seven emerging economies ('E7') – China, India, Brazil, Russia, Mexico, Indonesia and Turkey – will be bigger than the current G7 – the United States, the UK, France, Italy, Germany, Japan and Canada.[14] Investment bank Goldman Sachs has separately looked at how the spectacular growth rates expected in just four of the E7 – China, India, Brazil and Russia – would affect global demand. Between now and 2050, Goldman Sachs estimates that demand for oil will double to 169 million barrels a day, with both China and India requiring more than the United States does now.[15] Where will all this oil come from? The industry remains confident that there are new sources of supply to be tapped, but some analysts say the world may be close to 'peak oil', the moment when supply starts to dwindle. Either way, prices are going to stay high and may go higher.

The oil will be needed, if Goldman Sachs is right, to power all the new cars that will be on the streets of the E7. Currently, there are around 500 cars for every 1,000 people in the United States, against 8 for every 1,000 in India, 15 for every 1,000 in China and 137 for every 1,000 in Brazil. By 2050, car penetration in the United States will have risen to 555 per 1,000; in India it will be 382, in China 363 and in Brazil 645. The arithmetic is not too difficult: China and India between them have about 2.5 billion people and at the moment around one in every 100 has a car. That means there are approximately 25 million cars in the world's two most populous countries. Now make two conservative assumptions – that the population of the two countries increases to 2.75 billion by 2050 and that there are 350 cars for every 1,000 people. That means getting on for a billion cars in China and India alone. Throw in the rest of the E7 and that adds up to a lot of greenhouse gas.

The idea, however, that the world will have to wait until 2050 to feel the impact of global warming is misplaced optimism. In the hot summer of 2005, the Association of British Insurers (ABI) noted that the 1990s had been the warmest decade since records began, with the four hottest years all occurring since 1998. In 2003, when the temperature in the UK touched 100 degrees Fahrenheit for the first time, Europe had its hottest summer ever, with the French government politically damaged by the heat-affected deaths of hundreds of elderly people. The American government, seemingly indifferent to the increased prevalence of weather-related drought in sub-Saharan Africa, had its own reality check on global warming in 2005, when Hurricane Katrina broke the inadequate flood defences protecting New Orleans and forced the evacuation of the city. A study prepared for the annual meeting of the World Economic Forum in Davos in early 2006 noted that high sea temperatures in the Gulf of Mexico may have intensified the impact of Katrina, with the degradation of marshlands and silt deposits along the coast worsening the flooding. Human-induced climate change, it added, meant the world could expect more of the same in the coming years.[16]

The ABI said it expected the world's climate to continue changing for the rest of the twenty-first century, with the floods in Carlisle and Boscastle in 2005 merely a taste of what the public could come to expect. In a worst-case scenario, a 6 percentage-point increase in average temperatures by the end of the century on unchanged policies, it envisaged the annual costs of flooding increasing almost fifteen-fold by the 2080s, leading to potential losses from river, coastal and urban flooding of more than $40 billion. Across Europe as a whole, annual costs could possibly rise by a further $120–150 billion.

> Climate change could increase the frequency and severity of extreme weather events, such as floods, storms, and very dry summers – exactly the kind of events for which insurance provides some financial protection. Many of the costs of climate change will be reflected in international financial markets, as the insurance industry looks to acquire additional capital for increasingly erratic and more costly weather.[17]

Now it could be, as some still argue, that the confluence of these events is purely coincidental. Alternatively, the explanation could be that the world's ecosystem is finding it hard to cope with the pressures being put upon it. As countries grow richer, they buy more cars, computers and television equipment, all of which increase the demand for energy. Globalization means that developed nations tend to increase their dependence on trade, buying in goods that would once have been produced locally and taking holidays in far-flung corners of the globe. Research by the nef concluded that for more than two months of the year, the world was now living on its capital, running down resources because it was unable to meet the demands being put upon it by consumers in rich, developed nations. Citing declining food self-sufficiency, decreasing energy dependence, ecologically wasteful trade and the poaching of health and education workers from poor countries to keep the public services staffed, the nef said Britain could barely get to Easter if it was expected to go it alone.

> The moment we begin living beyond our environmental means is what we call ecological debt day. At current levels of natural resource use in the UK, the average person goes into ecological debt on 16 April. As our total consumption grows, it moves ever earlier in the year. In 1961 it was 9 July, advancing to 14 May in 1981. The world as a whole is also living beyond its ecosystems' capacity to regenerate and now goes into debt on 23 October. Looking back, if the whole world had wanted to share UK lifestyles in 1961, the Earth would just have managed with its available resources – one planet would have been enough. But today, if the whole world wanted lifestyles like those enjoyed in the UK we would need 3.1 planets.[18]

If every person in the world wanted to consume like an American, incidentally, it would require five planets, not one.

On any rational basis, this is already an unsustainable state of affairs and it will become more and more unsustainable with every year that passes. Any company that behaved in this way – running its capital stock into the ground in pursuit of short-term growth – would be viewed by its shareholders as highly irresponsible. That, indeed, is one of the conclusions of the much-heralded Stern Review, which described global warming as 'the greatest and widest-ranging market failure ever seen'. Already, it said, enough greenhouse gases have been pumped out to ensure that global temperatures would rise by 2 degrees centigrade over the next 40 to 50 years, the absolute upper limit of what climate-change scientists say is possible without causing irreversible damage. The report added, however, that there is still the chance to take actions in the next 10 or 20 years that would have an impact on the climate in the second half of the twenty-first century and twenty-second century.[19]

The world, according to Sir Nicholas, could not afford to neglect the problem.

> Our actions over the coming few decades could create risks of major disruption to economic and social activity, later in this century and in the next, on a scale similar to those associated with the great wars and the economic depression of the first half of the 20th Century. And it will be difficult or impossible to reverse these changes.[20]

Scientists say global warming occurs because greenhouse gases, including carbon dioxide, trap the heat from the sun in the atmosphere. They measure greenhouse gases by parts per million (ppm) of carbon dioxide equivalent (CO_2e), with the current level of 430ppm CO_2e up from 280ppm CO_2e two and a half centuries ago. Already, there are enough greenhouse gases to ensure that the stock in the atmosphere will rise to double pre-industrial levels by 2050, assuming no future acceleration in the rate of emissions. That, however, is extremely likely, especially given the high dependency of fast-growing developing countries on fossil fuels for their energy needs. China has plans for more than 500 new coal-fired power stations to cope with an expected 50 per cent rise in energy demand: as Mr Blair noted, Britain currently accounts for 2 per cent of global greenhouse gas emissions and even if they were cut to zero the beneficial impact would be wiped out by two years of growth in China. Sir Nicholas notes that the level of 550ppm CO_2e could be reached as early as 2035, and if that did prove to be the case there would be a '77 per cent chance – and perhaps up to a 99 per cent chance, depending on the climate model used – of a global average temperature rise exceeding two degrees centigrade'.[21]

Without any action at all to address the problem, the stock of greenhouse gas emissions could more than treble by the end of the twenty-first century, giving at least a 50 per cent chance of an increase in global temperature in excess of 5 degrees centigrade during the following decades. This, as the report noted, would take humans into unknown territory, since a number of studies have estimated that the Amazon rainforest, which as a giant carbon sink absorbs greenhouse gases emitted by mankind, is drying up. One model suggests that the Amazon rainforest might suffer severe and irrevocable damage by a warming of 2 to 3 degrees centigrade.

Tweaking Armageddon: making climate change data fit with poll numbers

The Stern Review was an important contribution to the debate on climate change, but for two reasons it was not the last word on the subject. First, it was too weak in its analysis of the scale of the problem, with its proposed ceiling on emissions influenced more by what is deemed politically possible than by what is environmentally prudent. Mr Blair believes that action on climate change requires participation by the United States, but notwithstanding the increased awareness of environmental issues following Katrina, also believes that it will not be possible to broke a global deal if Washington takes fright at calls for drastic measures to curb emissions.

As a result, Sir Nicholas set an upper limit on greenhouse gases of 550ppm CO_2e, compared to around 430ppm CO_2e today. This, the report notes, would require global emissions to peak by 2025 at the latest, and then fall by between 1 and 3 per cent per year. By the middle of the century, global emissions would need to be around 25 per cent below current levels, even though the global economy is likely to be three or four times as big as it is today. But as the Stern report openly concedes, allowing emissions to reach this proposed ceiling is potentially fraught with danger.

> Delay in taking action on climate change would make it necessary to accept both more climate change and, eventually, higher mitigation costs. Weak action in the next 10–20 years would put stabilisation even at 550ppm CO2e beyond reach – and this level is already associated with significant risks.[22]

Climate change scientists say that the logic of this conclusion is that there needs to be far more urgent action than any government is prepared to accept. A paper prepared by the Institute for Public Policy Research (IPPR) showed that if policy makers wanted to be confident of keeping the increase in global temperatures to below 2 degrees centigrade, emissions of carbon dioxide would need to peak between 2010 and 2013, achieve a maximum annual rate of decline of 4–5 per cent between 2015 and 2020, and fall to around 70–80 per cent of their 1990 levels by the middle of the century. Cuts in carbon dioxide emissions would also need to be matched by decreases in other greenhouse gases.[23] The IPPR says that a safety-first approach to climate change would see concentrations of greenhouse gases peak at around 450ppm by the middle of the century, before dropping back by around a sixth by 2100.

> These conclusions go further than the Stern Review, which proposes a long-term goal to stabilize greenhouse gases at between the equivalent of 450 and 550ppm carbon dioxide. That range has a medium to high risk of exceeding a two degree centigrade rise in temperatures.[24]

The Stern Review does not quibble with this finding. It says that to stabilize at 450ppm CO_2e, global emissions would need to peak in the next 10 years and then fall at more than 5 per cent per year, reaching 70 per cent below current levels by 2050. Its point, however, is that making the necessary cuts is too difficult.

> Stabilisation at 450ppm CO2e is already almost out of reach, given that we are likely to reach this level within 10 years and that there are real difficulties of making the sharp reductions required with current and foreseeable technologies.[25]

And, although the report never quite manages to say so, with current and foreseeable levels of consumption.

This, then, is the Stern report's first fantasy – that the level of greenhouse gas concentrations in the atmosphere deemed safe can be tweaked so that policy makers find it less daunting and less unpalatable. As the IPPR paper noted, given that

> global emissions trajectories are currently heading in the opposite direction, the level of effort required to bend the global emissions curve in time is Herculean. For countries such as the UK, that could eventually mean preparing to build a zero-carbon economy by 2050.[26]

In effect, that means action now. Despite five years of haggling, the international community has failed to negotiate a modest new trade liberalization deal; securing a successor to the flawed Kyoto accord that is both comprehensive and effective will take a lot longer. A trade deal only requires a small proportion of the population to make sacrifices, while a global environmental treaty would impinge upon everybody. Moreover, the negotiations would have to overcome both the reluctance of the United States to accept any measures that might harm growth and the suspicion of developing countries that rich nations are seeking to haul the ladder up after them.

However, policy makers do have an off-the-peg mechanism for tackling climate change at a global level, known as Contraction and Convergence (C&C). This sets a level for concentrations that will take no risks with the future of the planet and brings emissions per head to a level equal for every country. Since emissions per capita are currently far higher in rich countries than in poor countries, the West would have to pay the developing world for the right to pollute, providing much-needed resources to invest in clean technology. Sadly, the UK government has shown scant interest in C&C up until now; if it is really serious about climate change, however, that will have to change. As the IPPR said:

> It is the timetable for action, above all, that our research shows we urgently need to rethink. We do not have decades in which to bend the global carbon dioxide curve: we have less than ten years. What we do now at the global level will be of critical importance.[27]

Sir Nicholas' second fantasy is his failure to accept that even if the global community does, by some miracle, come up with a beefed-up Kyoto 2, there is not the slightest prospect of individual nations abiding by it. That is not simply because policy makers always have one eye on the next election, nor that they are worried about a possible backlash from business, although both are true. It is more that serious action to tackle climate change requires policy makers to reassess their obeisance to globalization, free trade and unbridled market forces, something none of them have yet showed the slightest willingness to do.

Some environmentalists were impressed by the rigour of the Stern Review, with Greenpeace saying there were no longer any excuses for inaction. The organization could not have been more wrong; the Stern Review allows politicians the fantasy of dressing up cosmetic change as decisive action. Greenpeace, understandably, was smitten by the small economic cost of taking out a climate change insurance policy, pointing out that the 1 per cent of GDP proposed was the equivalent of what was spent annually on advertising. Others were somewhat warier. Stephen Hale, the director of the Green Alliance, criticized the report for being too timid, arguing that a temperature rise above 2 degrees centigrade would have devastating ecological costs.[28] But it was the fact that tackling climate change went against the grain of economic orthodoxy – requiring decisive government intervention and rapid increases in spending – that really concerned Hale, and rightly so. If you fall asleep in the bath and wake up to find the water level half an inch from the rim, putting your toe in the tap before nodding back off is not a long-term solution to the problem. Only turning off the tap will do.

10

Striking Out for the Shore: Escape From Fantasy Island

Thrift is part of the art of living well. Don't confuse it with meanness towards others.

Jane Furnival,
Mr Thrifty's How to Save Money on Absolutely Everything[1]

Ever get the feeling you've been cheated?

Johnny Rotten, speaking to the audience
at the final Sex Pistols concert,
San Francisco, January 1978

Bob Chesneau: We don't know for sure that everything's over.
Barbara Dean: In that case you're the only people who don't.

David Hare, *Saigon: Year of the Cat*[2]

The own goal in Zagreb could hardly have been more farcical. The England full-back, Gary Neville, rolled a back pass towards the goalkeeper, Paul Robinson, who swung a boot at the ball with the intention of banging it down the field. Unfortunately for Robinson, at that precise moment the ball hit a divot, bounced over the keeper's foot, and trundled slowly into the net. England lost 2–0 to Croatia, hardly renowned as one of Europe's elite teams.

A few weeks later the England rugby union team, the current world champion, was booed off the pitch at Twickenham following defeat by Argentina, a country that normally only inflicted damage to the nation's sporting pride at association football. In December, talk of how England would go to Australia and retain the Ashes proved predictably far-fetched after the home side inflicted a 5–0 whitewash. All in all, the autumn and winter of 2006–7 was a tough time to be a sports fan in the country that gave the rest of the world cricket, tennis, rugby, soccer and golf, and it said something for yet another year of paradise unfulfilled that the public's choice of sports personality of the year was the equestrian Zara Phillips, the daughter of Princess Anne. The dream that, after years of underachievement, there was a chance of England once again competing with the world's best – the Brazilians at soccer, the New Zealand All Blacks at rugby union, the Australians at cricket – was exposed for what it was: fantasy.

Regrettably, the same could hardly be said of the political, economic and military fantasies of Britain's policy elite that have been the subject of this book. The NHS was merely one more reorganization away from perfection; the wars in Iraq and Afghanistan would be won; Labour had made the economy recession-proof and inflation-free; the challenge from China would be met by ensuring Britain had the best-educated workforce in the world by 2020; the environmental cost of allowing developers to build over the green belt and of an expansion of airport capacity could be tackled by putting a £5 surcharge on flights and telling builders to make every new home (1 per cent of the total) carbon neutral within a decade.

Listening to Gordon Brown's 2006 Pre-Budget Report, a panegyric to his own handling of the economy since 1997, it was sometimes hard to remember that he was talking about a country awash with public and private debt, which had hollowed out its manufacturing base to the point that it was running a trade deficit in goods of around £200 million a day, a country with the second-highest living standards in the Group of Seven after the United States that was planning to axe half its rural post offices. In the health service, the chair-man of the Labour Party, Hazel Blears, joined a picket line in her Salford constituency in an attempt to save a maternity unit from a 'reorganization' designed to save £60 million across the north-west; a government plan to save £2 billion a year by farming out the responsibility for aftercare for surgical patients to GPs was described by the president of the Royal College of Surgeons as a cost-cutting measure that would put patients at risk.

Ethics and after: taking a high moral tone on the low road

In fact, as New Labour prepared to celebrate its tenth anniversary in power, there was a distinctly shabby feel about the government. Mr Blair had come into power on the back of public revulsion at the petty sleaze of the Conservative years – the freebies taken at the Paris Ritz, the brown envelopes containing the payola for MPs willing to ask questions for cash. New Labour, it was said, would clean up politics, banishing memories not just of the mid-1990s but of its own less-than-spotless history in the 1960s and 1970s, when Harold Wilson ennobled some faintly disreputable characters. Yet the fuss over Mr Wilson's resignation honours list in 1976 was nothing compared to the stench of corruption that pervaded Mr Blair's Downing Street, with the Prime Minister forced to suffer the indignity of being questioned by the police over allegations that rich businessmen had been offered peerages in return for loans to the Labour Party.

In his first interview after becoming Labour's Foreign Secretary in 1997, the late Robin Cook had said his party would be adopting an 'ethical' foreign policy; in December 2006 the Attorney General seemed effectively to have ordered the Serious Fraud Office to call off an investigation into the 1980s Al-Yamamah deal under which BAE sold billions of pounds' worth of warplanes to Saudi Arabia. Lord Goldsmith, announcing the decision, said that when deciding whether to continue examining allegations of corruption by BAE and its senior executives, it had been 'necessary to balance the need to maintain the rule of law against the wider public interest'.[3]

As an illustration of everything that was rotten about New Labour, the Attorney General's statement took some beating. At one level, it was the attempt to dress up a squalid act of appeasement as a deliberate act of policy. At another, it reflected the intellectual vacuity at the heart of government; the cabinet's senior law officer failed to see that the rule of law can't be balanced against the public interest, since the rule of law *is* the public interest. It is the rule of law that defends the freedom of the citizen against the exercise of arbitrary power by the state; it is adherence to the rule of law that delineates a democratic from a totalitarian state. Never, it could be said, was adherence to the rule of law more important than under Mr Blair, a prime minister who favoured an unrestrained approach when it came to the exercise of executive power, whether it concerned 'sexing up' the dossier to provide evidence of weapons of mass destruction in Iraq, detaining terrorist suspects without trial or ordering law enforcement officers to kowtow to the wishes of a friendly, oil-rich government. Freedom, New Labour-style, was curiously circumscribed; freedom to drink round the clock set against the erosion of the right to trial by jury, the plan to impose a national scheme of identity cards and the idea that the state should identify problem children before they were born.

The notion that the government should root out unfit parents brought a telling riposte from one critic, who believes New Labour has abandoned the party's traditionally interventionist approach to economic policy and replaced it with an authoritarian social policy (a view we share). Writing on the Spiked-online website, Frank Furedi noted that 'the turn towards the micromanagement of behaviour is symptomatic of an absence of purpose and direction. Taking the social out of policy allows government to avoid engaging with the question of what society is really all about'. He cited the government-sponsored publication, *Married Life: a rough guide for couples today:*

> It offers paternalistic advice on everything from how to buy a wedding ring to how couples should communicate with one another. Couples are advised to allocate time for each partner to communicate without interruption. The pamphlet is written in such a way that suggests that couples who are about to get married are really only children playing at being grown-ups.

The dwindling band of apologists for the government found this sort of *bien-pensant* criticism infuriating. Despite appearances to the contrary, it was not really authoritarian, merely seeking to balance freedom and security in an age when the terrorist threat was all too 'real'. Nor was the 'cash for peerages' investigation evidence that New Labour was seedy; political parties had to be funded somehow, it was said, and if no cash was forthcoming from the taxpayer, friendly millionaires would have to be milked instead. The government was grappling as best it could with thorny issues such as energy security, globalization, multiculturalism, consumer enfranchisement, global warming. Labour was much more competent than it looked. The 'third way' was working.

It took the former head of the army, General Sir Mike Jackson, to bring a much-needed dose of reality to proceedings. In a perfectly timed Dimbleby Lecture on the day after Mr Brown's 'state of the nation'-style December 2006 Pre-

Budget Report, Sir Mike laid bare what the third way actually meant to soldiers on the front line. His insistence that 'the nation must, therefore, pay the cost in treasure' (see p. 187)[4] did not seem unreasonable; it seemed a bit much to expect squaddies in Basra to risk their lives for barely more than the minimum wage when one City trader was picking up a bonus of £50 million.

The fact that Sir Mike's lecture came in the same week as the government confirmed that it would be spending more than £20 billion on a replacement for Britain's 'independent' nuclear deterrent only added piquancy to his remarks. Throughout the Blair years there was a discontinuity between the insistence that resources would get through to the 'front line' and the billions of pounds squandered on white elephants, private-sector consultants and extra layers of bureaucracy to police targets imposed from the centre. In defence, money that could have been spent on decent body armour for the troops in Iraq or Afghanistan had been blown years earlier by the commitment to buy the ferociously expensive Typhoon (previously the Eurofighter), a warplane which, in the absence of a threat from the Soviet Union, was of highly dubious military value. After the Cold War, Britain could have followed the Scandinavian model or the American one. The government could either have used the peace dividend for welfare spending or tax cuts, reducing the armed forces to little more than ceremonial organizations not really equipped, financially or psychologically, for combat; or it could have maintained defence spending at a level commensurate with fighting a real war thousands of miles from home. The Blair government made the mistake of believing that it was possible to do both.

It was, however, a similar story across the public sector. By the end of 2006, it was reported that 15 hospital trusts were technically bankrupt, bled dry by overpaid (and useless) management consultants, the Private Finance Initiative and the government's own bizarre resource accounting system, under which hospitals were doubly penalized for running a deficit. Tellingly, the television drama programme *Casualty*, which in the 1990s had regularly featured Tory penny-pinching on health as the backdrop to its soap opera plots, was now featuring demonstrations against the threat of closures to A&E departments. For the Tories this was manna from heaven. For David Cameron, one episode of *Casualty* excoriating the financial problems of the NHS was worth 100 blows landed on Mr Blair at Prime Minister's Question Time.

A junior doctor, writing anonymously, said medical staff inhabited a 'strange new world' where they were inundated by expensive and time-consuming private-sector initiatives, imposed by the government without any idea of whether there was a need for them or staff to implement them. One example, she said, was the electronic patient record, which had to be used for requesting investigations; on the face of it, an example of new technology being used to save time and increase productivity. In practice, the forms still had to be printed, thereby using exactly the same amount of paper, but because there were only two working printers in the hospital a doctor had to make a six-flights-of-stairs round trip to collect the forms every time a patient needed a blood test.

> Morale in medicine is at an all-time low. Doctors of my generation have never worked harder, and yet their pay is being cut, while colleagues who leave are not being replaced; they face an uncertain future and possible unemployment as hospital services are broken up and privatised. Most depressing of all is that our work is dictated by irrelevant and conflicting targets that render us impotent to deliver the care our patients need. This week, managers decided that 26 surgical beds must be closed to save money for the trust. This was implemented overnight and the beds physically removed from the ward.[5]

Running on empty: the Fantasy falls apart

This brings us to the crux of this book. Whether it is in the private or public sector, whether it is the trade deficit or rising carbon emissions, Britain is living well beyond its means. The common thread that runs through all the individual fantasies is excess. There is a surfeit of consumption, a surfeit of borrowing, a surfeit of speculation and a surfeit of deceit.

Our conclusion is brutally simple: there has been a long period when reality has been suspended, but a crisis is now imminent. After a decade of escapism, Fantasy Island is on the point of disappearing beneath the waves. For years, we and those who have thought as we do have been asked when, precisely, this terrible unravelling will take place. Did not the Thatcher era, which opened with several years' worth of the worst recession since the war, end on a reasonably balmy note? Did the 1990s not resemble the 1950s, with the contrast between a downbeat first half, with real hardship, and an upbeat second half, with soaring dot-com shares and much jollity provided by entertainers including the Spice Girls, Blur and Oasis?

By the early part of 2007, it was becoming clear that the unravelling had started, with interest rates and inflation on the way up along with unemployment, with debt and bankruptcy at vertiginous levels, with environmental degradation accelerating more quickly than even pessimists had feared, with strike action in the civil service, with no end in sight to costly commitments in Iraq and Afghanistan and with considerable difficulties being encountered in filling the 'throne' of creative Britain, the chairmanship of the BBC governors.

Does this have to become a full-scale crisis or could it be contained as merely a severe economic downswing? It could be, but only by relearning some traditional values: restraint, thrift and frugality. At an individual, national and global level, the message is the same: we have to start cutting our coat according to our cloth and end the delusion, cultivated by the government, that we can 'have it all'.

We have identified seven fantasies in this book, which we divide into two separate categories. Five of the fantasies – prices, the knowledge economy, the public sector, work and defence – involve pretending two opposites are not opposite at all. In all five cases, the fantasy arises not out of the choice but out of the pretence that there is no need to make a choice. The other two – debt and the environment – are showcased for two reasons: they are of a different order of magnitude and there really is no choice available. Only an abrupt reversal of direction stands any chance of avoiding disaster.

Our two separate lists may surprise some. Is not the enfeebled state of Britain's manufacturing base a cause for real concern? It may well be, and there are policies that could help. The government could have a different mixture of monetary and fiscal policy, squeezing consumer spending through higher taxes while at the same time cutting interest rates to reduce the level of the pound. While this would make exports cheaper, it would not be a real solution to the problem; that would involve understanding that in industrial terms Britain is no longer a developed but a developing nation. Rebuilding the manufacturing base requires support for strategic industries and, whisper it quietly, the sort of selective protectionism that would be feasible only if our relationship with the European Union were to be radically recast – at present, such assistance would fall foul of EU rules. The fact is, though, that any crash rethink of economic policy that is needed to turn Bullshit Britain into Productive Britain can only happen if the big fantasies are dealt with first.

It is with our five minor-key fantasies that Labour's intellectual debt to the Social Democratic Party of the early 1980s is evident. On important issues of the early 1980s – such as nuclear defence or health spending – the SDP boasted of having made tough choices that were, in reality, not choices at all. In reality, the 'low-cost' alternative to Trident and the prescribing of lower-priced 'generic' medicines proposed by the SDP were not 'tough choices' but rather attempts to split the difference. And at a deeper level, the party seemed to believe even the starkest choices could somehow be smoothed away. One of its founders, Lord Jenkins, said the SDP's own origins lay in the Britain in Europe campaign, the cross-party group of which Lord Jenkins was president, which had been set up to campaign for a 'Yes' vote in the 1975 referendum on European Economic Community membership.

Its booklet, *Why You Should Vote Yes*, makes remarkable reading today, not so much for its often-criticized failure to spell out the Community's federalist ambitions but for its apparent belief that all positions are reconcilable. Thus staying in the Community not only did not weaken ties with the Commonwealth, it strengthened them; the same went for the relationship with the United States. There was no threat to the monarchy, or to common law. Indeed, the booklet seems to have only just stopped short of claiming that, for those thinking of voting 'No', voting 'Yes' was just the same thing in terms of achieving their objectives, only better.

The same sort of double-think has been characteristic of Mr Blair's New Labour project, as with the argument that there is no essential difference between those who want to 'rationalize' A&E services in the NHS and those who oppose the plans; rationalization will lead to improved care free at the point of delivery.

In our view, real choices are available and it is time that they were made. Britain could go full tilt at trying to create a knowledge economy, with manpower and money being thrown into universities and technical education, with incentives for those studying approved subjects and financial penalties for those declining to do so. Alternatively, the choice could be to keep a grip on public spending on higher education and view the choice of degree subjects as an essentially private matter.

Similarly, we could bend policy – whether competition policy or trade policy – towards the provision of ultra-cheap goods and services, or we could take the view that stability of earnings and spending power is essential to public stability as a whole and bend policy the other way. We could have a cheap, low-grade public sector used mainly by poor people, or a costly top-quality Scandinavian-type public sector used by everyone, with tax rates to match. We could aim for high levels of job protection and for an ever more agreeable workplace, or we could deregulate the workplace and 'free' the workforce to compete with all-comers from the developing world. And we could adopt the military stance of a latter-day Prussia, sharply increasing defence spending and attempting to police the world in junior partnership with the United States, or we could reduce our defence establishment to the point where it provides little more than homeland defence, with maybe one or two specialities (hostage release, perhaps, or an obscure aspect of naval warfare) available for the use of ourselves and our allies. These would be real choices, not the fantasy choices of New Labour.

But while there are choices available on the knowledge economy, on our policies towards prices, the public sector and jobs and on defence, we have bookended these fantasies with the two master-fantasies, the one that suggests we can borrow money without limit and the one that suggests that caring for the environment is entirely compatible with endless economic growth. These super-sized fantasies dwarf the others, although both sets of illusions enjoy a mutually supportive relationship. The refusal to make choices on the smaller questions increases the pressure and the temptation to live beyond our means in financial and ecological terms. And for as long as there is no real accounting in terms of money or the environment, there seems little point in making any of the smaller decisions. But in contrast to the five smaller fantasies, there *is* no choice available on debt or the degradation of the environment. We have to get back to living within our means, starting with the paying off of accumulated debts and the repairing of environmental damage.

Blue or Brown: can either be truly green?

It will not fall to Mr Blair to make these choices but to either David Cameron – a man of whom we know little – or Gordon Brown, a man of whom we know almost too much. Mr Cameron has sought to revive the political fortunes of the Conservative Party by being a *tabula rasa*; he has wiped the slate clean of what he considers to be unwanted political baggage – the commitment to tax cuts, the hostility to immigration, a deep scepticism about 'alternative' lifestyles – and replaced it with a commitment to match Labour's spending on health and education, promises to put the environment at the centre of policy, and an image transparently stolen from the younger Tony Blair.

Gordon Brown, by contrast, is well-known to the public. As a result of the deal that handed Mr Blair the Labour leadership in 1994, Mr Brown was given almost the same free hand over domestic policy that Clement Attlee, as deputy prime minister, enjoyed while Churchill was planning the war effort. It is worth taking a close look at what a Brown premiership would be like, not just because he is Mr Blair's most likely successor but also because we know next to nothing about what any of the other possible candidates stand for.

In some ways, Mr Brown is the ideal candidate to cleanse the stables; he may be prickly and obsessive, but the longest-serving chancellor since Gladstone also has a reputation for being incorruptible; the customary way of explaining that Mr Brown was a man of unquestionable morality was to say that he had been brought up as a 'son of the manse', which sounded high-minded and upright even if few knew what it actually meant. In his last two or three years waiting for the job he considered his by right, Mr Brown talked long and seriously about the need for political renewal in Britain. What the Chancellor actually meant by this was never entirely clear; there was talk about boosting the power of the legislature at the expense of the executive, of reforming party funding and of changing the use of the Crown prerogative by the prime minister. That, though, did not really matter. The not-so-subliminal message was that where Mr Blair had played fast and loose with parliament, Mr Brown would play by the rules. And where Mr Blair had been tainted by the whiff of scandal, Mr Brown would be clean.

Mr Brown would certainly come across as an improvement. He is seen as straight and honourable, precisely the characteristics that James Callaghan brought to the job when he followed Harold Wilson into Downing Street in 1976. His proposed reforms might even help to dispel some of the widespread cynicism about politics, even though it is hard to see any of them as a 'Bank of England' moment (a reference to the sharp intake of breath when Mr Brown announced four days after the 1997 election that the Treasury was giving up day-to-day control of interest rates).

It is also likely that a Brown premiership may possibly be more willing to make some of the tough choices identified above. In terms of tax and public spending, Mr Brown would certainly wish to see Britain move closer to the European mainstream, and he meticulously planned and implemented the increase in National Insurance contributions in 2002 that enabled the government to increase spending on the NHS.

Under Mr Brown, policy making may well be thought through, rather than, as all too often under Mr Blair, made up on the hoof in a television studio. If, as seems possible, there is about to be a backlash in Britain against the live-now-pay-later culture of the 1990s and 2000s, Mr Brown might just be suited for the times, just as Margaret Thatcher was at the end of the 1970s.

Privately, Mr Brown shares the view of many on the left that Labour squandered the glorious political opportunity provided by three election victories and a demoralized opposition. It failed to bring about a fundamental redistribution of wealth and power; it failed to enhance social mobility; it failed to take the action needed to tackle climate change; and it supported a right-wing US president in pursuit of what increasingly looked like a pyrrhic victory in Iraq. Some commentators are clear that Mr Blair's support for Mr Bush should not be seen as a curious right-wing aberration to a decade of solid social democratic progress, arguing that it epitomized the main thrust of New Labour policy.

> This has been a Government that has majored on hyperbole, but in fact from the outset it was hugely timid and cravenly orthodox. Although New Labour enjoyed a huge majority, it defined its goals, in stark contrast to the 1945 Labour Government, in terms of its own re-election rather than political change. It was characterised by a profound lack of ambition, concealed by spin, forever a Government of gesture rather than substance.[6]

But all this ignores the fact that Mr Brown is not merely a hired hand on Fantasy Island, awaiting the chance to depose its current self-deluding tribal chief before hollowing out a fleet of canoes in which to ferry its people to safety on the mainland. On the contrary, he is both architect and cheerleader of the project, a true believer that fairness and enterprise, war and peace, higher taxes and lower taxes, the Swedish model and the American model can be joined together; and that the resulting jumbo chalk and cheese sandwich will be both delicious and nutritious. Furthermore, his presumed rivalry with Mr Blair has provided valuable cover for the Chancellor. On every issue, it has been assumed that he has a passionate political position; when he fails to spell out this position, it is thought this is merely the result of collective cabinet responsibility forcing him to keep his views to himself.

That he may simply view an issue in terms of personal advantage – as was routinely assumed of the likes of Harold Wilson or John Major – is rarely suggested. When, for example, he remained silent on the January 2007 row between the government and the Catholic Church over whether the latter's adoption agencies would have to place children with gay couples, few suggested Mr Brown was staying well out of a fight involving two of his support groups (Labour's backbenchers and the Catholic Church) for reasons of self-interest, nor that he may well have no view one way or another on gay adoption as it affected religious organizations. This assumption of his permanent high-mindedness has served Mr Brown well, regardless of whether it has any basis in reality.

It is also troubling that Mr Brown is a master of the oft-repeated policy announcement, of the selective use of statistics and of public spending increases counted twice and sometimes thrice. It is even more troubling that when it comes to some of the 'broad contours of policy', as Martin Jacques puts it, Mr Brown is as big a fantasist as Mr Blair. We will concentrate here on just three of our fantasies – defence, debt and the environment.

On the face of it, the question of Britain's place in the modern world ought to be easy to resolve. Mr Brown has ambitious plans for eradicating child poverty in Britain by 2020, but to have any chance of doing so he needs to spend billions of pounds in benefits for the poor. He has also been at the forefront of anti-poverty campaigns in the developing world, working hard and successfully to persuade the West to offer debt relief and more generous aid to some of the world's poorest countries. The plan is that by 2013, Britain will have raised its aid spending to 0.7 per cent of GDP, the level proposed by the United Nations in 1970 but which only countries like Norway and Sweden ever meet.

One way for Mr Brown to wage war on poverty would be to reduce Britain's military commitments to Swedish levels. That would mean no replacement for Trident, no hideously expensive new aircraft carriers, no open-ended military commitments for an under-resourced army East of Suez. As Andrew Rawnsley put it:

> Commitments will have to be reduced to match resources or resources will have to be increased to deliver commitments successfully. That is the hard choice Tony Blair has left for his successor as the Prime Minister heads for his own passing-out parade from Number 10.[7]

Mr Brown will be helped, to some extent, by the inevitability that at some point in the coming years the Americans will bow to domestic pressure to bring the troops back from Iraq and Afghanistan, thus allowing Britain to do the same. The notion that Britain has a special relationship with the United States and is obliged to stick by its ally is, however, only part of the story. The real fantasy is not really the (always) tenuous special relationship but the current belief that Britain has an indispensable role as a global policeman, akin to the dogged but indispensable role Sergeant Lewis played in assisting Inspector Morse, and that this role can be exercised on the cheap. Early in 2007, Mr Brown let it be known that he wanted to see a broadening of Labour's foreign policy, so that instead of being dominated by Iraq and Afghanistan it would become a three-legged stool, with climate change and universal education sharing equal billing with Middle East security. Yet there was not the slightest suggestion that Mr Brown would want to abandon the government's pro-American foreign policy stance; as Chancellor, almost all his intellectual inspiration has come from across the Atlantic rather than across the Channel, and he has been resolutely pro-American. All the signs are that Mr Brown, with loftier ambitions than Mr Blair for redistribution, would continue the same policy of intervention on a shoestring, with potentially the same disastrous consequences. Britain's armed forces have been stretched to the limit and sometimes beyond, in a period when the economy has had its longest period of sustained growth for decades.

Here we come to Mr Brown's difficulty in tackling the second fantasy: the necessary admission that steady growth and high levels of employment have not really been the result of smart government policies but are the consequence of a Faustian bargain between Britain's over-extended consumers and their creditors. A combination of cheap money and financial deregulation has allowed individuals to borrow lavishly and cheaply; they have speculated in the financial and property markets, often borrowing still more money as the value of their assets has risen. The collapse of communism and the emergence of China and India as providers of low-cost goods and services has meant inflation has remained low, with the domestic cost of living in the UK and the United States artificially suppressed by the determination of Asian central banks to keep their exports cheap by undervaluing their currencies.

As one senior economist at the Bank for International Settlements put it:

> Buoyed by justified optimism about some particular development, credit is extended which drives up related asset prices. This both encourages fixed investment and increases collateral values, which supports still more credit expansion. With time and underpinned by an associated increase in output growth, the process leads to increasing willingness to take on risks (irrational exuberance) which gives further impetus to the credit cycle.[8]

And, eventually, there is an almighty crash followed by the grinding sound of stable doors being bolted. Those old sweats in the City and on Wall Street who say the five most dangerous words in financial markets are 'it is different this time' are absolutely correct. Memories are short and selective; there is always a reason why the current bout of speculation is different from the mania for tulips in seventeenth-century Holland or the South Sea Bubble. The idea that there should be pre-emptive and precautionary reform to ensure that the inevitable crisis does not occur is a tough message to swallow. History suggests that there has to be a catharsis for reform to be politically acceptable, not least because in the period leading up to crisis the prevailing mood is one of denial. There was fundamental reform of Western democracies in the 1940s, for example, with controls on capital, a new international economic order, demand management policies designed to ensure full employment and the creation of welfare states. Yet it had taken a 30-year period that included two world wars, the worst depression in 250 years of industrial capitalism and the rise of murderous fascist states to create the conditions in which it was possible to formulate new ideas.

As today, the Wall Street Crash and the slump that

followed it were the products of a period when inflation was low but speculation was rampant. What's more:

> the period was characterised by rapid technological innovation, rising productivity, rapid increases in the prices of equity and real estate and strong fixed investment. Behind these developments were ongoing technical innovations in the financial sector, not least the much greater availability of consumer credit.[9]

The parallels with today's world are striking. By the time Franklin Roosevelt arrived in the White House in January 1933, pledging to expel the moneychangers from the temple, unemployment in the US had risen to more than 25 per cent and industrial production had halved. Almost one-third of US banks failed in the course of the 1930s, and the backlash against Wall Street ensured that the first decades after the Second World War were years in which the financial interest was subordinate to 'the forgotten man at the bottom of the economic pyramid'.

By the mid-sixties, finance was starting to fight against the shackles and, with the help of laissez-faire governments, by the mid-1980s it had broken free. There are now at least 10,000 hedge funds, of which 8,000 are registered in the Cayman Islands. The daily market in derivatives is worth $6 trillion, equivalent to half the annual GDP of the United States. Policy makers have started to wake up to the risks of unregulated capital markets. The Bank for International Settlements has warned that low inflation can create a false sense of security in which policy makers ignore excessive speculation in financial markets; over the past decade and a half that has been the story of the global economy. The period after 2001 saw a bubble develop in the US housing market that was the direct consequence of the excessively low interest rates sanctioned by Alan Greenspan, the chairman of the Federal Reserve, in the wake of the 9/11 terrorist attacks.

Consumers loaded up on debt in the nineties to speculate on Wall Street, and when the collapse of the dot-com bubble threatened to seize up the economy, Greenspan's solution was another bout of borrowing that had the effect of shifting the bubble from the equity to the housing market. The body that has the responsibility for policing the global economy – the International Monetary Fund – says that it has been 'quantitatively marginalized', a phrase which, translated into English, means that it no longer has the firepower to deal with a severe financial crisis. Despite being in the vanguard of the campaign for liberalization of capital markets around the world, the IMF now admits frankly that deregulation has caused problems. A study prepared for the Fund by three academics concluded: 'The authors believe that deregulation has caused national financial systems [to] become increasingly vulnerable to increased systemic risk and to a growing number of financial crises.'[10]

Le Monde Diplomatique put it rather more pithily in October 2006: 'Reality is out of control. The entire global financial structure is becoming uncontrollable in crucial ways that its nominal leaders never expected, and instability is its hallmark.'

We agree. We believe an almighty financial crash is likely and that the upshot will be a backlash against the excesses of the financial markets of a kind not seen for 75 years. There will be calls for lending to be more strictly regulated, there will be pressure for higher taxes on 'unproductive speculators', there will be demands for a tax on foreign-exchange speculation and there will be firewalls erected to prevent footloose capital from de-stabilizing democratically elected governments. All this will be highly desirable; the only pity is that reform now could avoid the crash.

Mr Brown is certainly unlikely to propose any curbs on the activities of global financial markets, not least because the UK has actually done rather well out of these conditions, at least in the short term. British speculators have proved rather better at speculation than their foreign counterparts and the winnings they have made have had the effect of making the deterioration in the trade deficit appear less serious than it is. The UK has a current account deficit of 2 per cent of GDP, which on the surface looks modest and manageable. Yet the deficit is only that small as a consequence of Britain's surplus on investment income; the deficit in goods and services is around 5 per cent, approaching the record levels seen in the mid-1970s and late 1980s.

Other countries have tended to play safe with their investments in the UK, concentrating on bonds and bank deposits. Britain has tended to go for riskier investments. One group of analysts in London said the Bank of England's polite way of describing this process was to liken the UK to a bank or venture capitalist in borrowing to invest in projects that earn a higher rate of return than the cost of funding. 'Put more simply, the UK has taken something of a gamble in its overseas investments. And so far, that gamble has paid off.'[11]

Only time will tell whether the UK can continue its hot streak or whether, as with even the best gamblers, the cards eventually turn bad with a vengeance. Mr Brown sees no reason why the City should cease to be a cash cow; indeed, Labour has been far more willing to accede to demands from the financial sector for favourable tax and light-touch regulation than it has been to lift the burden of an overvalued pound from industry. The City is seen both as a pivotal part of the 'knowledge economy' and a cluster of excellence to rivals' manufacturing prowess. Globalization, according to Mr Brown's view of the world, means that countries have to specialize in what they are good at, and what Britain is good at is finance.

Yet relying on the City (there are, to be honest, not many other clusters of excellence in the UK) would be fraught with danger, even if it did not have the effect of widening both the regional and personal inequalities in modern Britain. In its study of the UK's financial flows, Capital Economics expressed deep scepticism about the sustainability of a current account dependent on the fruits of speculation:

> This situation has only been possible due to the unusual combination of robust rates of global growth and exceptionally low global interest rates. But such a favourable environment was never likely to last forever. A sharp fall in income amidst a slowdown in the US economy could leave the UK's external position looking significantly less healthy.[12]

Britain's position is thus identical to the one of which John Maynard Keynes warned in his General Theory 70 years ago. 'Speculators may do no harm as bubbles on a steady stream of enterprise', he said.

> But the position is serious when enterprise becomes the bubble on a whirlpool of speculation. When the capital development of a country becomes a by-product of the activities of a casino, the job is likely to be ill-done.[13]

Britain has no manufacturing base to speak of and, for all the talk about the strength of the service sector, the knowledge economy and 'the creatives', the nation is more or less reliant on the spin of the roulette wheel to remain halfway solvent. This is not a position the Germans or the Japanese find themselves in. For all its alleged inefficiencies, Germany has been able to exploit the explosive growth in Asia because it has retained a formidable industrial presence. The difference between Germany's record trade surplus and Britain's widening trade deficit is that Germany has factories, Britain has *The Office*.

Virtue and necessity: from fantasy to frugality and freedom

Alarming though it is that Britain is living well beyond its means in terms of its balance of trade, this is not the main worry. Countries that live beyond their economic means can always tighten their belts; unless Karl Marx was right about the ultimate crisis of capitalism, the world will recover from even the most serious crash, given time. There are great similarities between the precarious nature of the global economy now and its state in the late 1920s; what is different is that the world is also spending its own ecological capital at an increasing rate, and from that sort of crisis there may be no coming back. As such, living within our means has to start with acknowledging what the planet can and cannot bear.

Most of us exercise caution in our everyday lives. We strap our children into car seats; we take out insurance on the contents of our homes; we put a fireguard round the hearth before we go to bed. Yet collectively we seem willing – Mr Brown included – to take the most reckless of risks with the environment. Climate change scientists believe that if global temperatures rise by more than 2 degrees centigrade above pre-industrial levels there is a high probability of a mass extinction of life on earth that will most likely include a sizeable proportion of the world's population. In Britain, the Stern Review of the economics of climate change is seen as the last word on the subject, but it has effectively given up on the 2-degree limit, putting it in a box marked 'too politically difficult'. Britain has plenty of miserable experience of allowing politics to affect big economic decisions: entry into the Exchange Rate Mechanism (ERM) at the wrong time, at the wrong rate and for the wrong reasons in October 1990 being perhaps the best recent example. The idiocies of the ERM would, however, be dwarfed by allowing politics to dictate action on climate change; perhaps learning their lesson from the Black Wednesday experience, the Tories have got it right when they say 'the politics must fit the science and not the other way round'.

The safe approach would be to start making substantial cuts in global carbon emissions immediately. Ideally, improvements in science and technology – cleaner fuels, more efficient cars, sustainable buildings – could cut pollution without the need for changes in consumption patterns. All the signs, however, are that these developments are years away; in the meantime, the consume-at-all-costs mentality has to be challenged.

But this is not quite the infringement of the consumer's human rights that some business-as-usual pundits say it is. Half a century ago, it was uncommon for anyone in the UK to go abroad for their holiday (indeed, most workers only had two or, at the most, three weeks off every year). Today, it is seen as an outrage to suggest that the tax system might be used to discourage the possible contraction of a sexually transmitted disease in a brothel in Riga or to make a family think twice about a second skiing holiday (even assuming the rise in global temperatures has left any snow on the piste).

Governments, of course, have sticks as well as carrots. New technology was supposed to mean that more of us could work from home and that executives could use video conferencing to avoid business trips for face-to-face meetings in New York and Shanghai. There is no reason why the tax system should not be used to provide incentives for this to happen.

Starting now, the government should invest heavily in Britain's environmental industries, both directly through public spending and through deliberate acts of procurement. To those who say that this smacks of green protectionism, our answer is that we have no problems with green protectionism. Green protectionism is not going to kill the planet; unrestrained globalization just might. As such, we favour actions that promote the local. The full environmental cost of flying in hothouse flowers or okra should be included in the price. Green regulations should be stiffened up so that only cars with much higher levels of fuel efficiency can be driven on British roads. Out-of-town supermarkets should be discouraged by the planning system.

Cautious though we are to use the phrase, we envisage something like a trickle-down effect, as the policies necessary to deal with one fantasy create the right framework for dealing with others. At the summit of policy making, there is a need to put the future of the planet before spurious increases in GDP. That requires us to think about consuming less, which in turn means that we will need to borrow less and the financial system will display fewer signs of instability. Green technology is not only vital for the future, it also stands to be lucrative as countries in both the developed and the developing world search for ways of meeting the challenge of climate change. It is a more sustainable (in every sense of the word) basis for the economy in the future than the creative industries.

For the past 250 years, the economic growth engendered by industrialization has meant each generation has grown up expecting to be better off materially than its parents. That is now about to change, as indeed it already has for some of those in Britain and America who have not flourished under the free-market conditions of the past three decades. If consumption is limited by the carrying capacity of the planet, as we believe it is, then the priority will be to provide for those who lack electricity, clean water and basic sustenance rather than those who have plenty. That does not necessarily mean a zero-growth economy; it does mean that progress will have to be measured by more than the number of cars in the drive. And since this process is inevitable, we may as well start planning for a more frugal future now.

As the shadows lengthen on the lawn, and the long, long summer draws to a close, the inevitable comparisons will start to be drawn with the last days of Edwardian Britain in the early years of the last century, an era whose elegance and privilege seemed destined to last forever but which was to fall in the carnage of the First World War and the horrors of the Depression. A small rich men's club tries to direct world affairs (the old European empires then, the Group of Seven now), blissfully unaware that the rules have changed and new players are on the field (Germany, Japan and the United States then, India, Brazil, China and Russia today). Far-off wars fought by superbly equipped professional troops against 'natives'/'extremists' have recently started to turn a lot nastier and much less amusing (the Boer War then, Iraq and Afghanistan now). The hitherto-unquestioned monetary pillar is creaking under unsustainable liabilities (the gold standard then, the reserve role of the dollar now). An elegant liberalism in political life, keen to square welfare with capitalism, trade unions with business, is on its way out.

But despite all this, the stronger parallel is with the sixties. There is the slow-motion disintegration of the reputation of a one-time Labour election wizard, someone who won at the polls because he was trusted by the middle class. There is the terrible quicksand of a foreign war led by the Americans, the nervous approval of the older generation for frighteningly different youngsters doing things in a completely different way (the 21-year-old Estonian web entrepreneur is today's hippy capitalist). There is the official belief that tidal levels of immigration are both symptom and cause of rude social and economic health, there is the wave of consumer products that started the decade as luxuries and are ending the decade as necessities, there is even the belief that a federal Europe is 'off the agenda' thanks to the French. The Tories have selected a leader who is as similar as possible to the Labour leader (Edward Heath then, David Cameron now). There is the enthusiasm for constitutional tinkering and the creation of vast, bureaucratic 'strategic' units, the alternation between panic and acquiescence of youthful intoxication (drugs then, binge drinking now) and the mania for the expansion of airports and the concreting over of the countryside.

We know what happened to the sixties. They hit the wall of a mighty environmental-economic catastrophe known as the Energy Crisis. Lights went out, prices rocketed, public expenditure was slashed and unemployment soared. But strange though it may seem, we believe the Energy Crisis was a wasted opportunity. There was some talk about taking the public into the confidence of politicians, of explaining the changed circumstances, of trying to get an electoral mandate for a radically different lifestyle. But before too long, the same old hucksterism triumphed, the same buy-one, get-one-free brand of economics and politics.

What will happen this time round is unclear. Many of the signs are discouraging. As problems mount, doubtless 10-point programmes will proliferate, charting the way to a socialist nirvana, a free-market utopia or any permutation in between. We have not 10 points, but two. First, on the five fantasies where we believe there is a choice – on a productive economy, prices, the future of the public sector, work and defence – then the fact that a choice has to be made ought to be spelled out to the public, with associated costs. This should be very definitely a menu with prices. On the two master fantasies, where the luxury of choice does not apply – our spiralling financial and environmental debts – the imperative of frugality needs to be explained, honestly and without equivocation. The future we envisage is thriftier; the aim is to save more and spend less. This is a future built upon restraint, given that lack of restraint has brought us to the edge of a financial and ecological abyss.

We recognize that these conclusions will not be to everybody's taste. There will be those, we are sure, who will say it is time to join the real world. The real world is loading up on debt to buy a bigger house; the real world is that dream holiday in Bali; the real world is crunchy green beans flown in from Kenya at huge environmental cost. To them we say that the belief in ever-higher levels of consumption at all costs is a delusion; it is not the path to personal fulfilment but the road to slavery. Thrift and solvency – both financial and environmental – are not disagreeable necessities but positive goods that are essential for personal and national freedom.

Indeed, both are concepts whose time is about to come. Britain's creditors will not remain patient for ever. Their displeasure may manifest itself either through higher interest rates, a decline in the value of the currency or both. Yet even were their wallets to remain ever-open, mounting levels of indebtedness are a sign of weakness and dependence in a mature and developed economy, not a sign of rude health. Consumer and mortgage credit has been piled up beyond all reason, and we will soon be at the point where we owe more than we can ever realistically pay back. Mr Micawber's dictum has been repeated so often as to have achieved the status of cliché. But funnily enough, Dickens' fictional spendthrift was slightly off the mark. The result of chronic and continued indebtedness is not misery, but servitude. Debtors cannot do all those things that modern society suggests they should: take risks, change jobs, break new ground, try to care for the environment and put aside plenty of time and effort for friendships and relationships – in short, for other people.

Thrift is not a synonym for penny-pinching, or for genteel poverty, or for miserly behaviour. It is a synonym for realistic living. We have nothing to fear from thrift and we have nothing to fear from reality. By contrast, living in debt – financial and environmental – means abandoning reality for fantasy.

It is time to wake up from the fantasy before the real world goes up in smoke.

Notes

Preface

1   Larry Elliott and Dan Atkinson, *The Age of Insecurity*, Verso, 1998.

Chapter 1: Forever Summer

1   *Guardian*, 7 July 2005.
2   *Daily Mail*, 11 May 1995.
3   Susan Crosland, *Tony Crosland*, Jonathan Cape, 1982.
4   Statistics from HM Treasury.
5   The latest figures available at the time of writing on the National Statistics website (http://www.statistics.gov.uk/pdfdir/t&b0506.pdf) relate to 2005–6.
6   In *Thunderbirds*, Universal Pictures, 2004.
7   From the album *Surfer Girl*, 1963.
8   A.J. Davies, *To Build a New Jerusalem*, Michael Joseph, 1992.

Chapter 2: The Voyage of the *Dawn Treader*

1   Austin Mitchell, *Four Years in the Death of the Labour Party*, Methuen, 1983.
2   Mark Ellen, *The Last Party*, John Harris, Fourth Estate, 2003.
3   Robert Peston, *Brown's Britain*, Short Books, 2005.
4   Anthony Seldon, *Blair*, Free Press, 2004.
5   Ibid.

Chapter 3: The Ever-Louder Tick

1 Martin Amis, *Money*, Jonathan Cape, 1984.
2 Provisional statistics from the Department of Trade and Industry's Insolvency Service.
3 Ibid.
4 Correlli Barnett, *The Lost Victory*, Macmillan, 1995.
5 Harold Wilson, 'Demos', *The Go-Ahead Year*, Book Distributors Leicester, 1966.
6 Raymond Williams (ed.), *May Day Manifesto 1968*, Penguin, 1968.
7 Anthony Buckeridge, *Jennings and Darbishire*, Collins, 1952.
8 Susan Crosland, *Tony Crosland*, Jonathan Cape, 1982.
9 Drew Middleton, *The British*, Secker & Warburg, 1957.
10 Ernest Kay, *The Wit of Harold Wilson*, Leslie Frewin, 1967.
11 Ibid.
12 Socialist Union, *Twentieth Century Socialism*, Penguin, 1956.
13 Quoted in 'The man who fell to earth', *Guardian*, 21 June 1995.
14 Tony Benn, *Against the Tide*, Hutchinson, 1989.
15 Jeremy Seabrook, 'The end of great expectations', *Guardian*, 20 July 1981.
16 Eric Deakins, *What Future for Labour?*, Hilary Shipman, 1988.
17 Figures taken from www.thisismoney.co.uk, 4 May 2005.
18 *Guardian*, 4 November 2006.
19 Robert Beckman, *The Downwave*, Milestone, 1983.
20 *Guardian*, 6 November 2006.
21 In conversation with the authors.
22 Bank of England, *Inflation Report*, 15 November 2006.
23 At the press conference at the launch of report, 15 November 2006.

Chapter 4: Bullshit Britain

1 Ian King, in the *Sun*, 5 December 2005.
2 Andrew Turvil, *Good Food Guide*, *Which?*, 2006.
3 *The Times*, 10 November 2006.
4 Charles Leadbetter, *Living on Thin Air*, Viking, 1999.
5 *The Times*,15 October 2002.
6 Paul Thompson, *Skating on Thin Ice*, University of Strathclyde, 2004.
7 James Heartfield, *Great Expectations: the Creative Industries in the New Economy*, Design Agenda, 2000.
8 Thompson, *Skating on Thin Ice*, op. cit.
9 Heartfield, *Great Expectations*, op. cit.
10 R&D figures for the financial year 2004–5 from the '2006 R&D Scoreboard', published by the Department of Trade and Industry.
11 Larry Elliott and John Chapman in the *Guardian*, 3 February 2006.
12 NESTA, *The Innovation Gap: Why Policy Needs to Reflect the Reality of Innovation in the UK*, The National Endowment for Science, Technology and the Arts, October 2006.
13 Bob Rowthorn, *UK Competitiveness and the Knowledge Economy*, Cambridge-MIT Institute, 2001.
14 Department for Culture Media and Sport, *The Creative Industries Mapping Document*, DCMS, 2001.
15 Statistics from ibid.
16 Ivor Tiefenbrun in *Journal of the Royal Society for Arts*, August 2006.
17 Bank of England *Quarterly Bulletin*, October 2006.
18 Richard Gardener, *Sterling-Dollar Diplomacy*, 1969, quoted by Heartfield, *Great Expectations*, op. cit.
19 David Puttnam, 'The creative imagination', in Giles Radice (ed.), *What Needs to Change*, HarperCollins, 1996.

20 Speech to the Institute for Public Policy Research, June 2005.
21 NESTA, *The Innovation Gap*, op. cit.
22 Ibid.
23 Heartfield, *Great Expectations*, op. cit.
24 Speech at the Edinburgh Television Festival, 2006.
25 Figures from the Office for National Statistics.
26 Statistics from BPI (formerly British Phonographic Institute).
27 NESTA, *The Innovation Gap*, op. cit.

Chapter 5: Going Once, Going Twice

1 From *The Whitsun Weddings*, Faber and Faber, 1964.
2 *Guardian*, 3 November 2005.
3 *Daily Mail*, 2 March 2001.
4 *Guardian*, 29 March 2002.
5 *Sunday Times*, 7 May 2006.
6 Dhaval Joshi in conversation with the authors, 3 November 2006.
7 *Guardian*, 1 July 1975.
8 Harold Wilson, *Final Term*, Weidenfeld and Nicolson, 1979.
9 Robert Moss, *The Collapse of Democracy*, Temple Smith, 1975.
10 President Gerald Ford, addressing the US Congress on 8 October 1974.
11 President Gerald Ford, addressing the Future Farmers of America, 15 October 1974.
12 Robin Ramsay, *Prawn Cocktail Party*, Vision, 1998.
13 Richard Clutterbuck, *Britain in Agony*, Penguin, 1980.
14 Guy Bellamy, *The Secret Lemonade Drinker*, Secker & Warburg, 1977.
15 Transport and General Workers' Union, the National Union of Mineworkers, the Union of Construction,

Allied Trades and Technicians, Union of Shop, Distributive and Allied Workers and the Associated Society of Locomotive Engineers and Firemen.

16 National Union of Public Employees, National and Local Government Officers' Association, Confederation of Health Service Employees.

17 Speaking at an International Symposium on Public Employment Labour Relations, New York. See the *Guardian*, May 1971.

18 Dhaval Joshi, in conversation with the authors, 3 November 2006.

19 *Economist*, 28 October 2006.

20 Figures from the Office for National Statistics.

21 Quoted in the *Mail on Sunday*, 23 May 2004.

22 Peter Wilby, 'Sooner or later, you pay for it', *New Statesman*, 2 October 2006.

23 Published by the Office for National Statistics, 26 October 2006.

24 *Daily Telegraph*, 26 December 2006.

Chapter 6: The Tottering Empire State

1 Jonathan Lynn and Antony Jay, *The Complete Yes Minister*, BBC, 1984.

2 Website accessed 12 February 2007.

3 Tony Blair, speaking at the 2006 Labour Party conference.

4 Peter Tymms, Robert Coe and Christine Merrell, *Standards in English Schools: Changes Since 1997 and the Impact of Government Policies and Initiatives*, Durham University, 2004.

5 Evidence to the House of Commons Select Committee on Education and Skills, *Hansard*, 7 April 2003.

6 Department for Education and Skills, press statement, 19 October 2006.

7   Alison Wolf, *Does Education Matter?*, Penguin, 2002.

8   ICM poll in the *Guardian*, 24 October 2006.

9   Due for publication in April/May 2007.

10 Quoted by Polly Toynbee in the *Guardian*, 24 October 2006.

11 *Guardian*, 24 October 2006.

12 *Guardian* leader, 18 October 2006.

13 Christian Wolmar, *Broken Rails*, Aurum, 2001.

14 David Craig with Richard Brooks, *Plundering the Public Sector*, Constable, 2006.

15 *Financial Times*, 11 January 1997.

16 *Hansard*, 12 March 1996.

17 Craig and Brooks, *Plundering the Public Sector*, op. cit.

18 Craig and Brooks, *Plundering the Public Sector*, op. cit.

19 Public Accounts Committee, press release, 3 May 2006.

20 Allyson Pollock, *NHS PLC*, Verso, 2004.

21 Ibid.

22 Reported on the BBC news website, 3 September 2001.

23 Craig and Brooks, *Plundering the Public Sector*, op. cit.

24 *Herts Advertiser*, 19 October 2006.

25 Pollock, *NHS PLC*, op. cit.

26 Reported in the *Evening Times* (Glasgow), 1 October 2002.

27 David Willetts, in conversation with the authors.

Chapter 7: Hi-Ho, Hi-Ho

1   Alexandra Jones, *About Time for Change*, Work Foundation and Employers for Work-Life Balance, 2003.

2   *Regan*, Euston Films, first broadcast 4 June 1974.

3   Stephen Fothergill, Christina Beatty and Ryan Powell, *Twenty Years On: Has the Economy of the Coalfields Recovered?*, Centre for Regional Economic and Social Research, Sheffield Hallam University, 2005.

4 Clive Jenkins and Barrie Sherman, *The Collapse of Work*, Eyre Methuen, 1979.

5 Rodney Dale and Ian Williamson in *The Myth of the Micro*, W.H. Allen, 1981.

6 Ian Angell, *The New Barbarian Manifesto*, Kogan Page, 1999.

7 Ibid.

8 Ian Angell, *No More Leaning on Lamp-posts: Managing Uncertainty the Nick Charles Way*, Villa Publishing, 2005.

9 Timothy Radcliffe, *What is the Point of Being a Christian?*, Burns & Oats, 2005.

10 Jeremy Rifkin, *The Age of Access: How the Shift from Ownership to Access is Transforming Modern Life*, Tarcher/Putnam, 2000.

11 Radcliffe, *What is the Point of Being a Christian?*, op. cit.

12 Polly Toynbee, *Hard Work*, Bloomsbury, 2003.

13 Website accessed February 2007.

14 Fothergill interviewed on Radio 4's *You and Yours*, 20 January 2006.

15 Fothergill et al, *Twenty Years On*, op. cit.

16 Ibid.

17 Figures from the Office for National Statistics website. For the purposes of these figures, 'public administration' spans local and national government.

18 Ibid.

19 Ibid.

20 Office for National Statistics, *Population Change*, 24 August 2006, available at http://www.statistics.gov.uk/cci/nugget.asp?id=950.

21 Quoted in the *Sun*, 15 February 2005.

22 Quoted by Robert Rowthorn in 'Never have we seen immigration on this scale', *Daily Telegraph*, 2 July 2006.

23 Margaret Hodge, speaking at a seminar organized by the Institute for Public Policy Research in London, 13 January 2003.

24 *Sunday Telegraph*, 20 August 2006.

25 From 1 October 2006.

26 *Guardian*, 14 June 1989.

Chapter 8: All Along the Watchtower

1 A.F.N. Clarke, *Contact*, Secker & Warburg, 1983.

2 *Daily Telegraph*, 26 December 2006.

3 Major Charlie Burbridge, quoted in *The Daily Telegraph*, 26 December 2006.

4 Peter Thwaites, *Muscat Command*, Leo Cooper, 1995.

5 Quoted in the *Daily Telegraph*, 13 September 2001.

6 Denis Healey, *The Time of My Life*, Michael Joseph, 1989.

7 Figures from the Ministry of Defence.

8 Figures from the Department for Education and Skills.

9 Colin Cross, *The British Empire*, Hamlyn, 1972.

10 Healey, *The Time of My Life*, op. cit.

11 *Homage to a Government*, January 1969.

12 Arthur Wise, *The Day the Queen Flew to Scotland for the Grouse Shooting*, Cavalier, 1968.

13 Douglas Hurd, *An End to Promises*, William Collins, 1979.

14 Lawrence Freedman, *Britain and Nuclear Weapons*, Macmillan, 1980.

15 Douglas Hurd, *Truth Game*, William Collins, 1972.

16 In conversation with the authors.

17 *Observer*, 4 May 1997.

18 Will Hutton, *The State We're In*, Jonathan Cape, 1995.

19 Dimbleby Lecture, broadcast on BBC television, 6 December 2006.

20 *Daily Telegraph*, 28 December 2006.
21 Peter Hennessy, *Never Again: Britain 1945–1951*, Jonathan Cape, 1992.
22 Tony Blair on forces radio, 7 October 2006.
23 Reported in *The Times*, 21 November 2006.
24 *Guardian*, 19 December 2006.

Chapter 9: Lonely Planet

1 From the album *Basement Tapes*, 1975.
2 Nicholas Stern, *The Economics of Climate Change*, Cambridge University Press, 2006.
3 Speaking at the launch of the Stern Review, Royal Society London, 30 October 2006.
4 Ibid.
5 *Guardian*, 2 November 2006.
6 Speaking on the BBC *Today* programme, 3 November 2006.
7 *Guardian*, 23 November 2006.
8 Speaking at the launch of the Stern Review, Royal Society, London, 30 October 2006.
9 *The Eddington Transport Study*, HM Treasury, 1 December 2006; *Barker Review of Land Use Planning*, HM Treasury, 5 December 2006.
10 Study undertaken by Transport 2000.
11 News release, 28 March 2006.
12 Speaking at the University of Kansas, March 1968.
13 new economics foundation, *Chasing Progress: Beyond Measuring Economic Growth*, nef, March 2004.
14 PriceWaterhouseCoopers, *The World in 2050*, March 2006.
15 Goldman Sachs, *The BRICs and Global Markets: Crude, Cars and Capital*, October 2004.
16 World Economic Forum, *Global Risks*, 2006.

17 Association of British Insurers, *Financial Risks of Climate Change*, June 2005.
18 new economics foundation, *The UK Interdependence Report*, nef, 2006.
19 Stern, *The Economics of Climate Change*, op. cit.
20 Ibid.
21 Ibid.
22 Ibid.
23 Paul Baer and Michael Mastrandrea, *High Stakes: Designing Emissions Pathways to Reduce the Risk of Dangerous Climate Change*, IPPR, November 2006.
24 Ibid.
25 Stern, *The Economics of Climate Change*, op. cit.
26 Baer and Mastrandrea, *High Stakes*, op. cit.
27 Ibid.
28 In the *Ecologist* newsletter, October 2006.

Chapter 10: Striking Out for the Shore

1 Jane Furnival, *Mr Thrifty's How to Save Money on Absolutely Everything*, Michael O'Mara Books, 2003.
2 David Hare, *Saigon: Year of the Cat*, Faber and Faber, 1983.
3 Statement by the Attorney General, December 2006.
4 Dimbleby Lecture, broadcast on BBC television on 6 December 2006.
5 *New Statesman*, 11 December 2006.
6 Martin Jacques, in the *Guardian*, 29 November 2006.
7 *Observer*, 10 December 2006.
8 William White, *Is Price Stability Enough?*, Bank for International Settlements, Working Paper No. 205, 2006.
9 Ibid.

10 Kern Alexander, Rahul Dhumale and John Eatwell, *Global Governance of Financial Systems: the International Regulation of Systemic Risk*, Oxford University Press, 2005.

11 Capital Economics, *Is the Current Account About to Get a Whole Lot Worse?*, Capital Economics, November 2006.

12 Ibid.

13 John Maynard Keynes, *The General Theory of Employment, Interest and Money*, 1936.

Index

Jenny was pregnant.

Mike looked down at her and the flash in her blue eyes did nothing to ease the anger bubbling and frothing inside him. It didn't help to know that even as furious as he was, he could still look at her and need her.

'No matter what you think," she said tightly, "I didn't ck you. I didn't set up a *trap* to catch the mighty and elusive Mike Ryan."

"Well, since you're so honest," he ground out, "I'll just believe you, okay?"

"You should but you won't," she told him, shaking her head, sending those curls that drove him crazy into a wild dance about her head. She underlined each of her words with a determined tap of her index finger against his chest. "Do you really think I would trap a man who doesn't want me? I've got more self-respect than that, thanks."

Jenny stood facing him, her chin lifted, eyes narrowed and hot with banked fury. She looked beautiful and strong and it took everything he had to fight down the urge to grab her and pull her in close. Jenny Marshall got to him like no one else ever had and he hated admitting that, even to himself.

* * *

A Baby for the Boss

is part of the Pregnant by the Boss trilogy—

Th

—and fat

05073322

A BABY FOR
THE BOSS

BY
MAUREEN CHILD

First Published in Great Britain 2016
By Mills & Boon, an imprint of HarperCollins*Publishers*
1 London Bridge Street, London, SE1 9GF

© 2016 Maureen Child

ISBN: 978-0-263-91844-1

51-0116

Our policy is to use papers that are natural, renewable and recyclable products and made from wood grown in sustainable forests.The logging and manufacturing processes conform to the legal environmental regulations of the country of origin.

Printed and bound in Spain
by CPI, Barcelona

Maureen Child writes for the Mills & Boon Desire line and can't imagine a better job.

A seven-time finalist for a prestigious Romance Writers of America RITA® Award, Maureen is the author of more than one hundred romance novels. Her books regularly appear on bestseller lists and have won several awards, including a Prism Award, a National Readers' Choice Award, a Colorado Romance Writers Award of Excellence and a Golden Quill Award.

One of her books, *The Soul Collector*, was made into a CBS TV movie starring Melissa Gilbert, Bruce Greenwood and Ossie Davis. If you look closely, in the last five minutes of the movie you'll spot Maureen, who was an extra in the last scene.

Maureen believes that laughter goes hand in hand with love, so her stories are always filled with humor. The many letters she receives assure her that her readers love to laugh as much as she does. Maureen Child is a native Californian but has recently moved to the mountains of Utah.

To Sarah and Dan—
Ten years is something to celebrate
As we celebrate the two of you every day
We love you

One

"I don't trust her." Mike Ryan drummed his fingertips on his desktop and glared at his younger brother.

"Yeah," Sean said on a laugh. "You've made that clear for months. What *isn't* clear is why. She's a terrific artist, meets her deadlines, is easy to get along with and a hell of a baker—she's always bringing goodies in for everyone. So how about you tell me what Jenny Marshall ever did that you're so against her."

Scowling, Mike gritted his teeth and shifted his gaze to the view out his office window. Even in Southern California, January gardens looked a little grim. The backyard of the Victorian mansion that served as Celtic Knot Gaming's office boasted dry, brown grass, leafless trees and empty flower beds. The sky was studded with gray clouds and a cold wind swept in off the ocean to rattle those bare tree limbs.

Still, looking at that dismal view was better than drawing up a mental image of Jenny Marshall. As unwilling as he was, though, that picture of her flashed across his brain. She was a damn munchkin, only standing about five foot two, but that tiny body was really packed well. She had curves that made Mike's mouth water every time he saw her—especially since he already knew just what those curves looked like *naked*. One more reason he tried to avoid running into her.

Her short blond hair was a mass of curls that ended at her jawline, stirring up a grown man's idle daydreams into fantasies of hot, sweaty nights. Instantly, he forced his mind away from the images of naked Jenny and instead thought of her eyes. As blue as the sky, bright with lies—and once, glazed with passion—for him.

Okay, that's enough of that, he told himself firmly.

"I've got my reasons," he muttered, not bothering to look at his brother again.

Sean had no clue that Mike and Jenny had met long before she was hired at Celtic Knot and there was no reason for that to change.

"Fine." Sean blew out a breath. "Always were a hardhead. Anyway, doesn't matter what the reasons are. You, me and Brady already decided this."

"Brady's in Ireland."

"Yep," Sean said, then added, "ain't technology great? You do remember the meeting we had over webcam? The one where we *all* decided who would do which hotel?"

"I remember."

"Good. Because Jenny's in her office right now, working on the designs for the River Haunt hotel." Sean met his brother's gaze. "She's already coming up with some great stuff. If we switch designers at this stage, it's going to slow down everything. Besides, Jenny's good. She *earned* this."

Mike scowled and bit back any further argument because it just wouldn't do any good. Sean was right: the plans had been made. He couldn't change them now. All of the artists for the company had already been assigned their work schedules. Most of them were finishing up the graphics for the next game to be released in the coming summer. So Jenny was the only logical choice.

Didn't mean he had to like it.

But there were deadlines to meet and no one knew that better than Mike. He, his brother and their friend Brady Finn had begun this gaming company when they were still in college. Their first game had been short on art and long on mystery and action. It had taken off faster than any of them had hoped and by the time they graduated from college, they were all millionaires.

They'd plowed their money back into the company they called Celtic Knot and within six months had released a bigger, more sophisticated game. They built a reputation for action games based on ancient Irish legends and superstitions, and their fan base swelled.

They'd bought this old Victorian in Long Beach, California, as their home base and hired the very best computer programmers, and digital and graphic artists.

They'd won awards and had legions of fans waiting for the release of their next game. And now, they were growing in another direction.

They were buying three hotels and revamping them into perfect role-playing venues for guests. Each hotel would be modeled after one of their top-selling games. The first, Fate Castle, was in Ireland. The modifications had just recently been completed and the hotel would be open and welcoming guests in March. The second, River Haunt, was in Nevada on the Colorado River and was just waiting for Mike to step up and get the renovations moving forward.

But how the hell could he do that while working one-on-one with Jenny Marshall? Answer: he couldn't. But he wasn't prepared to go into all of the reasons why with Sean. Instead, he'd simply go to Jenny. Convince her to back off this project. She was probably in no more hurry to work with him than he was with her. If she went to Sean herself and asked to be replaced, there wouldn't be a problem. Mike would offer her a raise. Or a bonus. A woman like her would jump at a chance for that—and he'd be able to get on with the hotel transformation.

"Meantime," Sean said, loudly enough to snap Mike's attention back to the moment, "I'm still talking to the toy company about the line of collectibles they're proposing based on our gaming characters."

"What do the lawyers say?" Mike asked.

"Plenty," Sean admitted. "And most of it I can't understand. I swear they teach these people to speak in tongues when they're in law school."

"Agreed. How much did you get out of it?"

Sean crossed his legs, ankle on knee. "Enough to know that if they up their offer on the licensing fee, this could be a really good thing for us."

"I don't know… Toys?"

"Not toys. Collectibles," Sean corrected. "I called Brady this morning and he's on board. So think about this, Mike. At the next gaming convention we not only have the games to push, but the collectibles. We can spin that off to board games even, for people not interested in video games."

Mike laughed shortly and leaned back in his chair. "There aren't many people uninterested in games."

"Okay, true. But we're pushing into the hotel industry, giving people a chance to live their favorite games. We could take that another step," Sean said, slapping one hand down on Mike's desk. "We can sponsor our own conventions."

"What?" Surprised, Mike just stared at him.

Sean grinned. "Think about it. Hell, Comic-Con started out small and look at them now. We could hold Celtic Knot Con—an entire convention centered around our games and products. We can host tournaments, offer prizes. Costume contests. Hell, we could run a contest offering a contract to whoever comes up with the best new beast to use in one of our games."

"Did you go surfing this morning?"

Sean stopped. "What's that got to do with anything?"

"That water's cold, probably froze a few brain cells."

"Funny."

"Don't you think we've got enough going on right now? The latest game came out in December, and the sequel to 'Fate Castle' hits this summer, not to mention the hotel business."

"Okay, we're busy," Sean allowed. "We want to *stay* busy, we have to keep thinking, expanding. Our business is based on the fans. On the way they feel connected to the scenarios we create. If we give them more, offer them other ways to connect, to feel a part of the world they love, that can only benefit us."

Mike thought about it for a minute. He could see the enthusiasm on his brother's face and knew that Sean was at least partly right. Continuing to build their brand would only solidify their position in the marketplace.

The castle hotel in Ireland already had a waiting list six months long and they hadn't even opened yet. That told Mike there was a huge market for just what Sean was describing. And little brother was right about something else, too.

"We'll talk to Brady about your convention idea—that may be a good way to go."

"Whoa." Sean grinned. "This is a moment. Maybe I should hunt up a photographer."

Mike laughed. "Okay, fine. I think you're onto something. On the collectibles, I'm on board. Tell the lawyers to work up the company's licensing offer and then we'll sign."

"Already did," Sean said.

"Sure of yourself, weren't you?"

"Damn right."

Amused, Mike said, "Okay, well, you're right about the other stuff, too. The role-playing, the contests. Ireland's too hard for a lot of people to get to. The grounds on the hotel in Nevada aren't big enough for us to hold tournaments on any kind of real scale. So the hotel in Wyoming will have to be the base for that kind of growth."

"Just what I was thinking," Sean said. "It's on a hundred and fifty acres, with lakes and forests. It's perfect for the kind of thing I'm talking about."

"Then it's handy you're in charge of that one, isn't it?"

"Also what I was thinking," Sean said with a quick, smug smile.

It was the smug part that had Mike suggesting, "You should go to Wyoming. Check it out in person."

Sean snorted. "Sure. That'll happen. It's *January*, Mike. It's snowing there. Like crazy cold snowing." He shivered. "No, thank you. Look, we bought the property in Ireland by checking it out online and that worked great."

"Yeah, but—"

"I've talked to the Realtor, had her make videos of everything. The inn itself needs a lot of work, but the property is perfect and that's more important, right?"

"Yeah, but—"

"You take care of yours and I'll take care of mine. No worries, I'll go look around in a few months, *before* we start the design stage." Sean stood up and looked down at Mike. "Right now, though, I'm dealing with the big Game Con in Chicago next month. And I've got the art on 'Banshee Screams' to oversee. I'll get to Wyoming," he said. "But it can wait until summer…" Shaking his head, he laughed and headed for the door. "A surfer. In the snow. Yeah. That'll work."

Mike frowned after him. Brady was happy as hell, working and living in Ireland with his wife and new baby son. Sean was busy making plans to be a happy, surfing megalomaniac. So, it was only Mike staring at nothing but trouble. It would take at least six months to refit the Nevada hotel. And since he couldn't find a way to get her off the project, that meant a hell of a lot of time spent with Jenny Marshall.

A woman who had already lied to him once.

Yeah. This was gonna be great.

Jenny Marshall poured herself a glass of white wine and sat down in an overstuffed chair, ordering herself to relax. But she didn't take orders well, not even from herself. Curling her feet up under her, Jenny looked out the window at the neighbor kids playing basketball in the driveway across the street.

The duplex she rented was old and small. Built in the 1940s, it sat on a narrow street a few blocks from the beach. The rent was too high, but the place itself was cozy, close to work and less generic than some cramped apartment. Here, she could garden and go to block parties and buy Girl Scout cookies and football pizzas from the kids who lived on the street. Here, Jenny felt that she was…connected. A part of things. And for a woman alone, that feeling was priceless.

She took a sip of her wine and shifted her gaze to the front yard, where bare trees clattered in the wind. Twilight fell over the neighborhood in a soft lavender glow and lamplight began blooming in her neighbors' windows. Relaxation still eluded her, but with everything she had on her mind that really wasn't a surprise.

Between her work on the upcoming game from Celtic Knot and the designs she was working on for the River Haunt hotel, there was plenty to think about. She did love her job and was grateful for it. Especially since one of her bosses would like nothing better than to fire her—or to see her drop into a black hole and simply disappear.

She frowned into her glass and tried to ignore the pain of regret that clutched at her heart. It hadn't been easy, working with Mike Ryan for the past several months. Every time they were in the same room together, she felt hostility coming off him in waves so thick it nearly choked her. The man was hard-hearted, stubborn, unreasonable and…still the one man who made her insides quiver.

She lifted her glass of wine in a toast to her own stupidity.

Seriously, hadn't she learned her lesson more than a year ago? When they met that night in Phoenix, it had been magic, pure and simple. And, like any good fairy tale, the magic had lasted exactly one night. Then Prince Charming had turned into an ogre and Jenny's proverbial glass slippers were flip-flops again.

It had all started out so well, too. The night before a big gaming convention in Phoenix, Jenny had met a tall, gorgeous man with a wicked smile and eyes as blue as a summer sky. They had a drink together in the bar, then had dinner, then took a walk and finally had ended up in her room at the convention hotel. She'd never done that before—gone to bed with a man she barely knew. But that night, everything had been...different. From the moment she met Mike, she'd felt as if she had somehow only been *waiting* for him to walk into her life. Which, she could admit now, was absolutely ridiculous. But that night... Jenny had allowed her heart to rule her head. She'd given in to the rush of attraction, that *zing* of something special that she'd only ever felt for him. And by morning, Jenny knew she'd made a huge mistake.

Sighing, she laid her head against the back of the chair, closed her eyes and drifted back to the moment when the floor had opened up beneath her feet. The morning *after* the best night of her life.

Mike pulled her close and Jenny laid her head on his chest, listening to the steady beat of his heart. Her body was loose and languid from a long night of loving. Dawn streaked the morning sky with pale rose and gold and she was nowhere near wanting to get out of bed.

This was so unlike her, she thought, smiling to herself. She didn't do one-night stands and never with a veritable stranger. But she couldn't regret any of it. From the moment she'd met Mike, she'd felt as if she'd known him forever. She didn't even know his last name, yet she felt closer to him at that moment than she had to anyone else.

"Really hate to move from this spot," Mike said, "but I've got to get down to the convention floor early."

"I know. Me, too." Jenny cuddled in closer. "My uncle needs me to set up his booth. He can't get here until to-morrow, so..."

Mike ran one hand up and down her back and his fingertips felt like tiny sparks of heat against her skin.

"Yeah?" Mike asked, his voice low and slow and lazy. "Who's your uncle?"

"Hmm?" She was nearly hypnotized by the slide of his fingers and the deep rumble of his voice. "Oh. Hank Snyder," she whispered. "He owns Snyder Arts."

Mike suddenly went still. His hand dropped from her back and she felt a hard shift in the lovely little glow they'd been sharing. Then there was a physical shift as Mike pushed to a sitting position and rolled Jenny right off his chest.

She plopped onto the bed and stared up at him. "What?"

"Hank Snyder?" Mike jumped out of bed and stood staring down at her with a wild, dark gleam in his eyes, sharp as a knife blade. With the morning light stream-ing in through the window behind him, he looked like a naked avenging angel.

The haze in her mind was clearing and a cold, sinking sensation opened in the pit of her stomach. Slowly, she sat up and tugged the blankets over her breasts. Pushing one hand through her hair, she shoved blond curls out of her eyes and met his hard gaze with a look of confusion. "What's wrong?" she asked. "Do you know my uncle?"

He snorted. "Wow. That's really good. The little hint of innocence in your voice? Nice touch."

Completely confused now, she shook her head. People should not be expected to be coherent in the morning before several cups of coffee. "Innocence? What?"

"Oh, drop it," Mike snapped and stalked across the room to snatch up his clothes. He dragged them on as he talked, flicking her quick, icy glances. "Gotta say, you were good."

"What are you talking about?" The sheet where he'd been lying only a moment ago was rapidly cooling and she shivered in response. "Good at what? You're not making sense."

"Sure. You're confused." Mike nodded. "You know, I bought the whole act last night, but trying to keep it up now, when I know who you are, is only pissing me off."

She didn't have the first clue what he was so angry about, but her own temper was beginning to boil in self-defense. How could they have gone from lovemaking, to snuggling, to spitting ice at each other all in the blink of an eye?

"Will you just tell me what's going on?"

"What I don't get is how you knew I'd be in the bar last night." He pulled his long-sleeved white shirt on and buttoned it with an almost eerie calm that belied the fury in his voice and eyes.

"I didn't know—heck, I didn't even know I was going to be in the bar last night until just before I went in."

"Sure. Your uncle," Mike said, nodding. "He had to have planned all this for you anyway."

"What does Uncle Hank have to do with us?"

He laughed but there was no charm or humor in it. "Everything, sweetheart, and we both know it. Snyder

*Arts has been trying to get us to incorporate their pro-
grams into our games for the past year and a half." His
gaze dropped to her chest, then lifted to her eyes again.
"Looks like Ol' Hank finally decided to pull out the big
guns."*

*Every word Mike said echoed weirdly in her mind
until at last, Jenny understood what he meant. What he
was accusing her of. Anger leaped into a full boil in the
pit of her stomach. Her heart pounded crazily and she
felt as if she couldn't catch her breath. Her mind racing,
Jenny practically leaped out of bed, preferring to meet
her accuser on her feet. She held the blanket up in front
of her like a shield that could somehow protect her from
the ice in his eyes.*

*"You think my uncle sent me here to have sex with
you?" God, she could barely force the words past her
tight throat. "So I could convince you to use his arts
program?"*

"That about sums it up," Mike said flatly.

*Jenny's brain burned. She was torn between insult,
fury and complete humiliation. Instantly, images of the
night before streamed through her mind like a movie on
fast-forward. She saw him, over her, staring into her eyes
as his body claimed hers. She saw herself, straddling
him, taking him deep inside her. And she felt in that flash
of heat the pleasure, the sense of completion his every
touch caused. Then the mind movie ended abruptly, and
she was here, in this sunlit room, staring at a stranger
who now knew her body intimately, but her heart and
soul not at all.*

*"Who the hell do you think you are?" she asked, voice
trembling.*

"Mike Ryan."

She staggered at the name. Mike Ryan. One of the owners of Celtic Knot. Jenny knew their work, knew the art and graphic design that went into every one of their games. She'd admired them for years, had hoped to one day work for them—which wouldn't happen now. Not only did he clearly think she was a spy—and oh yes, a whore—but she couldn't imagine herself working for a man who made snap decisions with zero thought behind them.

"Uh-huh," he said, nodding as if he'd just had every one of his suspicions verified. "So you do know me."

"Now," she said. "I didn't last night. Not when I met you. Not when we…" She pushed one hand through her hair and kept clutching the blanket with the other. Best not to think about everything they'd done because she'd do something completely stupid like blush, for heaven's sake. With her fair skin, the moment she was embarrassed, her cheeks lit up like a red light at an intersection.

"And I'm supposed to take your word for that," he said.

Her gaze sharpened and narrowed on him. "It seems you don't need anything but your own suspicions to make up your mind. You've already decided who and what I am, why should I argue with you over it?"

"You know, playing the outraged innocent isn't nearly as convincing as the seductress I met last night."

She sucked in a gulp of air and fed the flames burning in her belly. "You arrogant, conceited, smug bastard."

One dark eyebrow winged up and a look of pure male amusement tugged at the corners of his mouth. "Doing better now. The outrage almost looks real."

Her heart pounded so hard in her chest it was a won-

der he couldn't hear it. She half expected her heart to crash right through her rib cage. "This isn't an act, you jackass. Think about it. I didn't seduce you. You approached me in the bar. And nobody forced you into my bed. As I remember it you came willingly enough."

"Several times," he said, playing on her words just to irritate her further.

It worked.

"That's it. I don't have to listen to any more of your paranoid ramblings. Get out of my room." She swung one hand toward the door and stabbed the air with her index finger.

He grabbed his black jacket off a nearby chair and shrugged it on. "Oh, I'm going. No worries there. I wouldn't stay if you begged me to."

"That's not gonna happen."

He snorted again, a particularly annoying, insulting sound. Striding across the room to the door, he stopped before he opened it and looked back over his shoulder at her. "Tell your uncle I said nice try, but no cigar. Celtic Knot won't be doing a deal with him no matter how many attractive nieces he tosses into my bed."

Jenny picked up a wineglass from the room service tray they'd shared the night before and hurled it at him. He was through the door and out before the glass shattered against the wood to lie in splinters on the floor.

Jenny sighed and took another sip of her wine. She hadn't thought to even see Mike Ryan again, but then six months later, his brother, Sean, had offered her a job that was simply too good to pass up. The chance to work on the kind of art she loved was worth the risk of being around Mike every day. And frankly, by being on-site every day, she was silently telling Mike Ryan that what he'd done hadn't hurt her. Hadn't crushed her. Of course that was a big, fat lie, but he didn't have to know that. Working at Celtic Knot was a dream that only occasionally became a nightmare when she was forced to deal with Mike.

Of course now, the nightmare would be a 24/7 thing for the next few months. Yes, she was excited about being the artist to design the murals for the River Haunt hotel. But having to work one-on-one with Mike was going to make it all so much more grueling than it should have been. Still, she wouldn't back off. Oh, Jenny knew that Mike wanted her off the project, but this was too big an opportunity for her to turn tail and run. Especially, she reminded herself, since she'd done nothing wrong.

He was the one who had plenty to apologize for. He was the one who'd insulted her, humiliated her and then stomped off without so much as listening to her side of the story.

So why should *she* be the one to pay a price?

The knock on her door interrupted her thoughts and she told herself, if it was a salesman, she'd buy whatever he was selling out of simple gratitude.

She opened the door and stared up into Mike Ryan's blazing blue eyes. Without waiting to be invited in, he pushed his way past her and marched into her apartment with all the determination of Grant taking Richmond.

With little else to do but accept the inevitable, Jenny closed the door. "Well, do come in," she said, every word dripping with sarcasm. "Make yourself at home."

Features grim, eyes the color of a lake frozen over, he said, "We need to talk."

Two

Mike stopped in the middle of the room, turned and just looked at her. She wore a pale green T-shirt and faded, curve-hugging jeans with a hole at the knee. Her small, narrow feet were bare but for the pale pink nail polish. Her hair was a rumpled mass of tumbling blond curls and her wide blue eyes were fixed on him warily. She looked good. Too damned good, and that was part of the problem.

Stuffing both hands into his pockets, just to keep from reaching for her, Mike deliberately looked away from Jenny and glanced around the small living room. His gaze picked out the details even as his brain reminded him not to let her distract him. Great body, beautiful eyes and kissable lips notwithstanding, he had come here for a reason and he had to keep his focus.

The duplex was old, probably one of the original beach

cottages built in the late 1930s. Jenny's home was well kept, casual and welcoming. There were overstuffed chairs covered in a flowery fabric and a love seat boasting yellow and blue stripes. Several small tables and standing brass lamps were scattered about the room, shining puddles of golden light onto the scarred but polished wood floors and the few rugs that broke up the space. The walls were painted a soft green that reminded him of spring. There were framed paintings and photographs clustered together in no discernible pattern and on one wall, there was a mural.

His gaze caught it and held. Obviously, Jenny had painted it herself and Mike had to admit that whatever else she was, the woman was also immensely talented. The mural was a scene straight out of a fairy tale—or an Irish legend. A forest, just waking up to daylight. Fog drifted across the landscape in thin gray wisps, sunlight speared through the trees to lie in a dappled pattern on the leaf-strewn ground. There was a hint of a flower-laden meadow in the distance and in the towering trees were fairies, delicate wings looking as if they would flutter any minute.

Damn it. He hated that she was this good.

"Why are you here, Mike?" Her voice was soft, but the glint in her eye was anything but.

Good question. Mike knew he probably shouldn't have come here—they hadn't been alone together since that night in Phoenix—but he had run out of options. He couldn't tell Sean why working with Jenny was a mistake—because damned if he'd let his little brother know that he'd once been taken for a ride. In more ways than one.

But Jenny knew why this wouldn't work. All he had

to do was get her to tell Sean she didn't want the job of designing the art for the new hotel. And if Jenny herself requested that she be let out of the project, Sean wouldn't object.

Time to get to the point so Mike could get the hell out of this too-small house where her scent seemed to hover in the air for the express purpose of tormenting him. "I want you to back out of the hotel job."

She didn't even blink. "Interesting. Well, I want to be three inches taller and have smaller boobs. Looks like we're both doomed to disappointment."

Why the hell she would want smaller breasts was beyond him, but not the point. "We both know that working together for months is a bad idea."

"Agreed." She crossed her arms over her chest, pushing her breasts higher. "Maybe you're the one who should quit. Switch hotels with Sean. I *like* Sean."

"Leave Sean alone," Mike ground out.

Her oh-so-casual pose evaporated and she threw her hands high in frustration. "Please. Now you're afraid I'm going to be paid to seduce Sean?"

"I didn't say that." Thought it, maybe. Said it, no. All right, he admitted silently, he hadn't even thought it. Not really.

"What exactly *are* you saying, Mike?" She plopped both hands on her hips and the movement tightened the fabric of her shirt against the aforementioned breasts. *Distractions*, Mike told himself. *Pay no attention.*

"I'm saying leave Sean out of this," he said. "It's between you and me."

"Fine. Then *you* tell Sean he should take over the River Haunt and you do the Wyoming place."

"No." He wasn't ready to admit defeat yet. He could

still find a way to convince Jenny that this was an impossible situation and that it was up to *her* to back off.

She shrugged again, and walked past him slowly enough that the scent of her vanilla perfume flavored the breath he took and held as she made for the chair by the wide window.

"So, since neither one of us is willing to drop out of this project, I guess we're done here," she said, plopping into the chair and lifting her wineglass for a sip.

"We are far from done." Through the window behind her, he saw the street was dark, with the dim glow of lamplight shining through a neighbor's drapes.

January nights at the beach could be cold, but here in this tiny duplex, Mike felt only the heat of being near her again. Her hair shone, her eyes glittered and her mouth curved up at one corner when she spoke. She was enjoying this, he thought, and a part of him liked that about her.

Jenny Marshall didn't back down for anyone. He'd seen her go head-to-head with older, more experienced artists, defending her designs and techniques. She held her own in meetings and wasn't afraid to fight for her vision of things. But as much as he admired those traits, he wished she wasn't currently turning her admirable qualities on *him*.

"Mike, you don't want to work with me and I don't want to work with you. But we're stuck with each other." She lifted one shoulder in a half shrug. "We'll have to make the best of it."

"Unacceptable." Shaking his head, he looked away from her because the damn lamplight made her hair shine like burnished gold. He never should have come here. It had been a bad idea and if he were smart, he'd leave right now since their argument was getting them exactly nowhere.

As he sifted through dozens of pretty much useless thoughts, his gaze fixed on the magical forest mural. It was dark, mysterious, but with the fairies in the limbs of the trees, there was a sense of playfulness amid the darkness and the longer he looked at it, the more fairies he spotted. Hiding behind leaves, beside rocks, in the water of a fast-moving stream. It was hypnotic, mystical.

He shifted to look at her. "Damn good work," he blurted, before he could stop himself.

"Thanks." Surprise flitted across her face, then vanished. "But if you're wondering, I didn't *steal* that scene from any of Celtic Knot's games."

He fired a look at her that had been known to make stone-hearted business rivals quake. Jenny wasn't fazed. "I didn't say you stole it."

"Not yet," she told him, pausing for another sip of wine. "I'm sure you'll get to it. I know very well what you think of me."

"Do you blame me?" he countered. Mike pushed one hand through his hair, then scrubbed that hand across the back of his neck. Ever since he met her, this woman had had the ability to tangle him up into knots. Even knowing she was a damn liar hadn't taken away the rush he'd felt every time he thought of her.

At work, he kept his distance, knowing it was best for everyone. Coming here, into her place, being alone with her in the lamp-lit dark was dangerous. He knew it, and still he didn't leave. Instead, he took a single step toward her and stopped because her scent clouded his mind and he couldn't afford to addle his brain any more than it already was.

"That's not a fair question," she answered. "You made up your mind about me in an instant and never once listened to any side but your own."

"What other side *was* there?" he countered. "Hell, your uncle is still running Snyder Arts."

"Oh, for God's sake," she snapped, setting her wineglass onto the table with a harsh click.

"Tell me I'm wrong."

"How can I? He does own Snyder Arts. He doesn't own me."

"He's family." Mike shrugged.

"Yeah, and he thinks enough of me that he's never asked me to do what you continue to imply I've already done." She sucked in air, then blew it out. "Sean's never questioned my integrity."

"Sean's more trusting than I am."

"News flash," she muttered, then asked, "Would you lie and cheat for your family?"

"No, I wouldn't." Mike had grown up knowing exactly what kind of damage lies could do. As a kid, he'd promised himself he'd avoid lies and the people who told them. That's why he couldn't trust Jenny. First time he met her, she'd lied. No going back from that.

Her eyes flashed. "But you assume I would."

"Don't have to assume a damn thing," he reminded her.

"My God, you have a thick head." She huffed out a breath. "At least come up with a *new* crime to accuse me of. I didn't use you then. I'm not using you now."

"I'm pretty sure every thief claims innocence."

She pushed out of her chair, stalked toward him and was forced to tip her head back to meet his eyes. "Name me *one* thing I've stolen. Give me *one* reason you have the right to call me a thief."

"Fine," he said, staring into her eyes until he could actually see her anger churning and burning. "You haven't stolen anything that I know of. Yet. You're a prethief."

"Then why haven't you fired me or told Sean to?"

"I do my own firing," he said. "And if I ever have proof that you've betrayed us, then I will fire you so fast your head will spin. Suspicion isn't proof."

She laughed shortly and shook her head. Then she took a long step back, and folded her arms beneath those magnificent breasts. "Boy, you're really reaching. Being a prethief is like being prepregnant. Or prepublished. All that means is you're *not* something. Like I'm *not* a thief, so I'd appreciate it if you'd quit throwing accusations around that you can't back up."

Damn, the angrier she was, the hotter she got. Bright spots of color dotted her cheeks and her blue eyes were flashing dangerously. What did it say about him that her temper only fueled the need inside him?

Most of the women in his life agreed with him, smiled coyly, flirted outrageously and in general made sure they were pleasant company. Jenny didn't give a damn about any of that. She had an opinion and wasn't afraid to share it and that was just as sexy as the way her eyes glittered.

And sexy wasn't the point.

"We both know what's going on here, Jenny," he argued. "You might not want to admit it—and who could blame you—but the fact is, your uncle owns a company that would like nothing better than to have a contract with Celtic Knot. You meet me 'accidentally,' go to bed with me and try to convince me you're not colluding with your uncle?" She opened her mouth to argue, but he rushed on before she could. "Then months later, you come to work for us, grab a job as head designer."

"I didn't 'grab' anything," she snapped. "Sean came to me and offered me the job."

He'd never told Sean about his time with Jenny. Maybe if he had, his younger brother wouldn't have hired her in the first place. Which, Mike was forced to admit, would have been a damn shame. As much as she managed to irritate him, she was a hell of an artist.

"Sean asked, but you took it." He tipped his head to one side and studied her. "So the question is, why? You miss me? Or are you some kind of corporate spy now?"

"Now I'm a spy? Wow," she said, slowly shaking her head. "Paranoia reaches new heights."

He snorted. "I'm not paranoid if you really are a spy."

"You're amazing."

"So it's been said."

She threw her hands up. "There's no talking to you. So think whatever you want," she told him, voice as icy as her eyes were hot. "You have from the beginning."

"Right. When we met at the gaming con in Phoenix. Another coincidence?" His eyebrow lifted. "You just happened to be at my hotel?"

"Or," she countered, "you arrogant jackass, *you* happened to be at *my* hotel."

Surprise almost had him laughing. Almost. But she was too furious and he was too sure he was right. There was nothing funny about being cheated. Lied to. Old memories of his mother crying, his father shamefaced, rose up in his mind, and Mike deliberately quashed them. Not the time or the place for memories, other than the ones he and Jenny had created the first time she'd lied to him.

"Right. I went looking for you that night."

"You're the one who approached me in the bar," she reminded him. "Not the other way around."

"You were beautiful. And alone." And somehow she had looked insulated, cut off, as if she'd been alone so long that she hadn't expected anything else from her life. Intrigued, Mike had watched her sip a single glass of wine for nearly an hour, as bar patrons came and went. As the bartender flirted with her and she ignored him, apparently oblivious to her own allure.

Mike wasn't unaware, though. She was tiny, making a man want to step up and be her protector. She was beautiful, making a man want to see her smile to know what that smile would do to her eyes. And she had so many curves in all the right places, *any* man would have wanted to get her out of the short red dress and high, needle-thin heels she had worn.

How the hell could he have resisted her?

She flushed at the unexpected compliment and he watched, fascinated, as a stain of deep rose filled her cheeks. She looked away from him then as if hoping to regain her sense of balance. He knew how that felt because damned if he didn't feel off his game every time he was around her.

"Look," she said, her voice cool and even, "the past is done. All we have now is the present and the future." Lifting her gaze to his, she said, "I'm not walking away from the hotel project. Not only is it my *job*, but it's going to be fun."

"Not how it looks from where I'm standing," he muttered.

"Well that's how I'm looking at it. So you can either deal or switch hotels with Sean."

"You don't make the calls in *my* business," he pointed out, irritated that she could try and order him off his own damn project.

"Sean put me in charge of the art design," she argued. "Not you. If you have a problem with that, talk to him."

"I did." He pushed one hand through his hair and started pacing, more to get away from the scent of her than because he needed to move. "But he doesn't know what happened in Phoenix so he doesn't get it."

"So tell him," she shot back. "If you're so sure I'm a thief and untrustworthy, tell him and let him fire me."

"I'm not telling him that I let myself get used by a woman who looks more like one of the fairies she paints than she does a damn spy."

"Wow. Thief and spy," she mused. "I'm really notorious, aren't I?"

"Why the hell else would you come and work for my company if it wasn't to be a spy for your uncle? You had to know that we'd be thrown together and clearly that thought didn't bother you. The only answer I can come up with is you're still trying to use me—now *us*, for your uncle's sake." That one question had been simmering inside his brain for months. Ever since the day he'd walked into the graphic design room and seen the woman he hadn't been able to stop thinking about sitting at one of the computers.

Damn it, he *wanted* her to convince him he was wrong, that his thoughts were baseless. He wanted to know that she really was the woman she'd seemed to be when he first met her.

"Listen up, you unbelievably suspicious…*man*. I took that job in spite of you, not *because* of you. Sean offered me a great position doing something I'm damn good at and I should have turned it down because I might see *you*?"

"I don't buy it. I think I'm the reason you took the job," Mike said, his gaze spearing into hers from across the narrow room. "You were hoping to get me into bed again."

Her head jerked back as if she'd been slapped. Gulping a deep breath, she muttered, "You pompous, arrogant… You know, sex with you wasn't *that* good."

He laughed shortly. "Now I know you're lying. It's amazing what a talent you have for it."

"Get out," she said flatly, holding up both hands toward him as if warding him off. "Just get out of my house and go away. Far, far away."

Mike shook his head.

"That night we had was incredible," he said. "And I know you felt the same way."

"Please."

His body churning, his brain racing, Mike stalked back to her, grabbed her and pulled her in close. "Since you asked so nicely…"

He kissed her, drowning in the taste and scent and feel of her. Not since that hot, amazing night in Phoenix had Mike felt so completely *right* about anything. She squirmed halfheartedly against him for a second or two, as if she might actually try to deny what was happening between them as thoroughly as she'd lied about their past.

But then the moment was gone, hesitation evaporated and she wrapped herself around him, arms locked about his neck, her short, shapely legs hooked around his waist. His hands dropped to the curve of her behind and held her there, tight against the erection straining and pulsing with the need to be buried inside her.

Had he known what would happen when he'd decided to come here tonight? Had he guessed that he wouldn't be able to deny himself—as he had for months—the sheer glory of her body? Didn't matter, he told himself as his tongue swept into the heat of her mouth. Nothing mattered but the now. The feel of her surrounding him, pulling him deeper.

No other woman had ever affected him like this. It was as if his brain and his body weren't even linked. He knew this was a bad idea, but his body just didn't give a damn. All it wanted…needed was her. One more night of being in her, on her, under her.

He tore his mouth free of hers, then shifted to taste her at the pulse beat in her throat. Her heart hammered in time with his own.

"Mike…" She sucked in a gulp of air and shivered in his arms when he nibbled at her skin. "We really shouldn't do this—"

"Yeah, I know," he whispered against her neck. "Do you care?"

"No."

"Good." His grip on her tightened and she ground her hips against him, her heels digging into the small of his back. He groaned and hissed in a breath. "You're killin' me here."

She lifted her gaze to his and a slow, sensual smile curved her mouth. "Killing you, not really the plan."

"There's a plan?"

That smile widened as she leaned in and kissed him. "Oh, yeah."

He shook his head. "I don't know why…"

"Why what?" she murmured, then gasped as his hands kneaded her behind.

"Why it's *you* who does this to me," he said on another groan as his mind shut down and his body simply took the lead.

"Ditto," she whispered, then kissed the side of his neck, trailing her lips and the edges of her teeth along his skin.

"Oh, yeah." He held her tighter to his groin. "Bedroom. Where?"

"Down the hall," she whispered, her breath blowing hot against the dampness of his skin. "Hurry."

"On that." Thankfully, her place was so small, it didn't take him long to carry her into the bedroom. Like the rest of the apartment, the room was tiny. A double bed, covered by a brightly colored quilt, stood against one wall. Pale yellow curtains were parted over a window that opened onto the backyard where a soft, violet glow heralded twilight.

A narrow cushioned chair sat alongside the bed, and the dresser on the opposite wall boasted a wide mirror that reflected the two of them as Mike dropped her onto the mattress.

He stretched out over her, braced himself on his hands at either side of her head and bent to kiss her. Jenny's hands scraped up and down his arms as her mouth fused to his. God, she tasted good. Almost as good as she felt.

Quickly, he pulled her shirt up and off, then sent it sailing to a corner of the room. With just her lacy white bra standing between him and what he most wanted, Mike couldn't wait. He flicked the clasp open, then slid the straps down her arms. His gaze locked on the feast that was Jenny Marshall. He groaned and bent his head to take first one hardened nipple and then the other into his mouth.

Her hands fisted in his hair, holding him to her as his teeth and tongue lavished attention on those full, beautiful breasts. She came up off the bed when he suckled her and the groan that shot from her throat seemed to roll around them, echoing off the walls and ceiling.

Not enough, his brain screamed at him. *More. Take more.*

He dropped his hands to the snap and zipper of her jeans and undid them quickly. With her help as she wriggled eagerly beneath him, he scraped the worn denim down her legs, taking the flimsy scrap of lace panties with them. Then she was there before him, naked, willing, as desperately hungry for this as he was, and Mike couldn't wait another second to claim her.

"Too many clothes," she muttered as she ran her hands over his chest in frantic strokes, unbuttoning his shirt as she went, tearing at the tiny white buttons, muttering, "I hate buttons, why are there so many buttons?"

"No more buttons," he said tightly as he shrugged out of his shirt and tossed it over his shoulder. "I'll make a note."

"Good, good." Her fingers stroked his skin then and each tiny stroke of her nails felt like fire dragged over flesh, burning, branding.

He took a breath and held it, calling on every ounce of control he'd ever possessed, knowing it wouldn't be enough. If he didn't have her soon, the top of his head would explode. But Mike dragged it out. It had been too long since he'd had his hands on her and he wanted to savor the moment.

He ran his hands down her body, breast to the heat of her and back up to her breast again. He explored every curve, every line, and with each caress he gave her, she reached for him, fingers grabbing at his shoulders, trying to pull him in closer, tighter. Her hips arched and rocked when he dipped one hand to the heart of her and cupped her heat.

"Mike!" Her head dug back into the mattress as she lifted her hips into his touch. "If you don't get out of those slacks and come to me soon, I—" She broke off, dragged in air and whimpered when he drove first one finger and then two into her damp heat. "Mike, please!"

He worked her, driving himself and her to the edge of control and beyond. It took everything he had to keep from giving her just what she wanted. Just what he wanted. But first, he would torment them both. It had been a long year and a half.

His thumb brushed over that one tiny bud of sensation and the deliberate caress had her shout his name. Again and again, he touched her, deeply, outside, inside, across that sensitive piece of flesh until she groaned and whispered broken pleas for a release that he kept just out of reach. Her eyes glazed over, her body continued to twist and writhe, chasing a climax he refused to give her too early.

Then he couldn't bear it anymore. Pulling away from her, he stood, stripped out of the rest of his clothes and kept his gaze locked with hers as he did. She licked her lips, rocked her hips again in silent invitation and held up her arms to welcome him.

"Almost," he murmured and she groaned again, frustrated. Until he knelt on the floor and dragged her body toward him. When she was close enough, he covered her heat with his mouth and felt the crash of the climax that slammed into her. She reached down, held him to her as her body convulsed. His tongue flicked over her, into her and he tasted her as she exploded, crying out his name over and over like a mantra designed to prolong the pleasure rocking her.

When she was limp and her gasping breaths were shuddering in and out of her lungs, he joined her on the bed and she rolled into his arms. One leg tossed across his hip, she brushed the tip of him against her heat and Mike almost lost it. Then she slid her hand down and her fingers wrapped around his hard length, working his flesh as expertly as he had hers.

He hissed in a breath, squeezed his eyes shut for a moment and then opened them again to look down into hers. "Tell me you've got condoms."

"Yeah, oh, yeah. Bedside drawer." She wiggled her hips, grinding her body against his. "Hurry."

"Right." Mike didn't think about why she had condoms. About the other men she must have invited into her bed. None of that mattered now. All that was important was this moment. He grabbed a condom, tore it open and sheathed himself, then looked back to the woman waiting for him.

She was like a damned nymph, straight out of one of the fantasy games his company designed. Like one of her drawings—blond curls rumpled, blue eyes heated and languid all at once, curvy body lush and waiting for him.

"Now, Mike. I need you inside me, now."

"Yes, now." He pushed deep into her heat with one long stroke. Her body bowed beneath him, her legs hooked around his waist, pulling him tighter, deeper. He stared into her eyes, eyes that held what seemed to him the mysteries of the universe, and watching her, took what she offered. He rocked his body into hers, over and over, setting a breathtaking rhythm that she raced to meet.

Again and again, they parted and came together, each of them driving the other higher, faster. He heard her ragged breathing, felt the frantic slide and scratch of her nails at his back. The race for completion was all. They looked into each other's eyes, fierce now, impatient for what they knew was coming.

"Mike," she cried, gasping. "Oh, Mike!"

She grabbed his shoulders and held on as wave after wave of sensation crashed through her body, making her tremble and shudder violently in his arms.

He watched her eyes flash with satisfaction only seconds before his own body splintered and jolted into a wild pleasure that left him feeling jagged and shaken. Locked together, the two of them slid over the edge, riding the thunder and crash of completion. And willingly, Mike tumbled into the dark, locked in the arms of the one woman he couldn't have.

Three

Dawn crept into the room and stretched out long, golden fingers across the bed where Jenny lay beside Mike. For more than a year, she'd thought about him, wished things had been different, wanted him. And now he was here, sleeping in her bed, and she knew that as the sun rose, their time together was running out.

Nothing had changed between them. Not fundamentally. They hadn't settled the issues that had separated them for so long before falling into bed—they'd simply ignored them in favor of the desire arcing in the room like summer lightning. Basically, they'd taken a long time-out. She smiled to herself at the thought.

Turning her head on the pillow, she studied Mike, using the moment to really look at him while he was completely unaware. He didn't look young and innocent in his sleep, she thought. He looked sexy. Dangerous. Like the hard man he was. And yet... She curled her fingers into her palm to keep from reaching out, stroking his beard-shadowed jaw.

Jenny's heart took a slow tumble. Pitiful, she told herself with a heavy, inward sigh. How could she feel so much for a man who thought of her as a thief and worse? And why did she *care* what he thought about her?

"You're thinking too loud." He opened his eyes and stared at her.

"A lot to think about," she said just as quietly.

"I suppose," he agreed, one corner of his mouth lifting into a seductive smile. "But we don't have to think about it right this minute, do we?"

Under the blanket, Mike reached for her and slid one hand along her curves. Jenny held her breath as his hand glided up from her hip, along her ribs to cup her breast. She sighed when his thumb brushed across her nipple. No, they didn't have to think. Didn't have to let this night end just yet. The sun was coming up and soon enough, they'd have to face the real world again. The world where the two of them stood on opposite sides of a wall Jenny had believed would never be breached.

But for now...

"No," she said, moving into him, "there's no rush to start thinking."

He kissed her and as she fell into the swirl of sensations, Jenny put everything else out of her mind.

An hour later, though, she knew it was over. Even with his weight pressing her into the mattress, even with his body deep inside hers, she felt Mike pulling away from her. As physically close as they were at that moment, there was a distance between them that lovemaking couldn't bridge. All this time with him had actually managed to do was enforce the lines separating them. To make things worse, now it would be even harder to work with him over the coming months.

He rolled to the side and went up on one elbow. Shooting a quick glance at the window and the rays of sunlight peeking through, he shifted his gaze back to her and said, "I should go."

"Yeah." Jenny looked at him and sketched this view of him into her memory. Hair mussed, a shadow of whiskers and that amazing mouth of his quirked into a rueful smile. If she'd had any sense at all, instead of trying to build a memory, she would have been attempting to put this time with Mike out of her mind completely.

She wasn't sure where they would be going from here, but she knew that whatever connection they'd found, however briefly, was gone. Over.

"Look," he said, gently pushing her hair back from her face, "last night was—"

"A mistake, I know," she finished for him, since it was easier to say it than to hear it.

He frowned, rolled off the bed and grabbed his clothes, pulling them on while he talked. "Can't really call it a mistake since it was something we both wanted."

How did he do that? she wondered. He was right there, within reach, and yet he'd pulled so far away that he might as well have been in a different city. A cold ball of regret dropped into the pit of her stomach.

"Last night didn't change anything, Jenny."

She nearly sighed because she knew exactly where this conversation was headed. "I know, you don't trust me."

"You lied to me the first night I met you."

"I didn't lie," she argued tiredly. God, she hated having to defend herself over and over to a man who refused to see past his own suspicions. How could he sleep with her, make love with her and not have the slightest clue who she really was? "Since I've worked for Celtic Knot, haven't I done a good job? Have I ever let anyone down? Doesn't that count for something?"

"Yeah, it does," he said shortly. "You know it does. But it can't change the past." His features tightened and his mouth thinned into one grim line as he held up one hand for peace before she could respond.

"Let's not," he said. "You have done good work for us, Jenny. That's why we've got a problem now. You're the logical choice to do the work on the River Haunt hotel, but if we have to stay on the project together it's going to be more difficult than it has to be."

Shaking her head, she only stared at him. Difficult? Like going into the office every day and feeling him watching her warily? Like knowing that he was waiting for her to screw up? To prove that she was exactly the liar and cheat he took her for?

She pushed off the bed and quickly snatched her robe off the end of the bed. They weren't going to argue about the past, fine. But she was more than ready to fight for the present and her own future. And damned if she'd do it naked. Slipping the robe on, she belted it tightly, then shook her hair back and turned to face the man who continued to haunt her. "It's not a problem for me, Mike. I'm going to do a hell of a good job on that hotel. And it doesn't have to be difficult if you'll just trust me to do what I'm best at."

For a second she thought he might argue that point, but instead, he blew out a breath and shoved one hand through his hair. "All right. We do the hotel. We do the job. Then we're done."

Eager, wasn't he, to push her aside and keep her there? But even he had to realize that he'd said pretty much the same thing about being done with her more than a year before. And yet, here they were, facing each other across yet another rumpled bed.

Still, it's what she wanted, Jenny reminded herself. A chance to prove herself on the hotel project without being at war with Mike, because it really would make things harder. So why, she wondered, did she suddenly feel so terrible now that he was offering her just that? She scrubbed her hands up and down her arms as if to chase away the bone-deep chill crawling through her, but it didn't help.

"We keep...this," he said, waving one hand at the disheveled quilt and the still-warm sheets, "between us and do what we have to do."

Another secret, then, Jenny thought. But probably better that the people at work didn't know what was going on between them. Since even *she* wasn't sure what exactly it was they shared, beyond the burn and desire.

Nodding, she asked, "Do we shake hands on it?"

For the first time that morning his lips curved in a half smile. "I think we can do better than that."

He walked up to her, cupped her face between his palms and bent his head for a kiss. His mouth was firm, soft and left hers all too quickly. She really was an idiot, Jenny thought as her insides jumped and her heart galloped. The kiss meant nothing. *She* meant nothing to him and oh, boy, was that a hard thing to acknowledge. But she knew it was only hunger that burned between them, nothing more. Yet she looked into his eyes and found herself wishing things were different. Wishing for—

"I'll see you at the office?"

"Yeah," she said abruptly, cutting off her own thoughts before they could lead her down completely ridiculous paths. "I'll be there."

"All right, then." He turned away to grab his jacket off the floor. Shrugging it on, he looked back at her and said, "In honor of this new cooperation between us, I'd like you to go to Laughlin with me in a week or so. Check out the new hotel. I want to walk the property, get a feel for it before we start the renovations."

"Good." She forced a smile that she hoped looked more convincing than it felt. "It would be good for me to get an on-site idea for the placement of the murals."

"Okay." He tugged the jacket into place. "We'll go out a week from Monday. Figure to stay at least overnight. I'll have Linda make reservations at the River Lodge."

Her stomach jittered. Laughable really, because what virtue was she suddenly so worried about? But the two of them were practically combustible, so was it really wise to invite more temptation? "Overnight?"

He shrugged. "We'll take the company jet into Vegas, and drive into Laughlin from there. I want enough time to explore the place. Staying over is the only solution."

"Right." Overnight. Did that mean they'd be sharing a bed again? Was he expecting that? Well, if so, he was doomed to disappointment. Jenny wasn't going to let this spiral into an affair that would leave her broken and miserable when it ended. Better to end it now. And much better to let him know just where she stood on this before they went any further.

"I won't be sleeping with you again."

One dark eyebrow winged up. "I didn't say you would be."

"Just saying," she went on, shaking her head, "I'm not interested in an affair and I'm not going to keep sleeping with my boss."

A dark scowl marred his face briefly. "This wasn't about boss and employee. It never was."

She shivered under his steady stare, but lifted her chin to ask, "Then what was it about, Mike?"

"Need," he said simply, biting the single word off as if it tasted bitter.

There it was. Plain and simple. He didn't care about her, Jenny told herself. Probably didn't much like her. He certainly didn't trust her. She hated to admit that he was right about this, but she knew that hunger had drawn them together and then that same vicious desire had pulled them back in when they'd both believed it was done between them.

So no more. Of anything. They would have to work together for the next few months and sex—especially *great* sex—just complicated everything.

Over the next few days, Jenny almost convinced herself that nothing had happened between Mike and her. She spent her days concentrating on the art ideas for the new hotel. Using the photos and 360-degree videos provided by the real estate company, Jenny laid out her plans for the work to be done. But she couldn't really be sure of anything until she saw the place firsthand.

"Have you got the sketches for 'The Wild Hunt' done yet?"

She glanced up from her computer screen to look at Dave Cooper, the new head of graphic design. When her old supervisor, Joe, had left to take a job with one of the big Hollywood studios, they'd all missed him. But Dave had slid right into the position as if he'd always been there.

"You'll have them by tomorrow," she said. The next game they were working on was already taking shape and so far, Jenny loved doing the art for it. A wild hunt, complete with faery warriors, pookas and the supernatural beings that hunted them. No doubt, it would be another winner for Celtic Knot and she really enjoyed being a part of it.

"I think you'll like them." She'd been refining her sketches for the past few nights, polishing them so no one could say she'd neglected this project in favor of the art for the new hotel.

Dave grinned, eased one hip against the edge of her desk and pushed his glasses higher up the bridge of his nose. In his late thirties, he looked like a typical computer geek—tall, thin, with big brown eyes behind thick, black-rimmed glasses. He had a generous smile and a puppylike enthusiasm for the work. "I always like your stuff, Jen. I read your notes on the ideas you have for the drawings and I think they'll be great."

He was so nice, Jenny thought. It was a damn shame that all she felt for him was friendship. Life would have been much easier if only she'd been attracted to someone like Dave.

"Thanks." She smiled at him. "I'm glad you stopped by. There's something else I'd like to run past you."

"Yeah? What's up?"

"You know in 'The Wild Hunt,' there's the magical wolf terrorizing the village?"

"Yeah." Joe grinned wider and nodded his head eagerly. "Early renderings are awesome. Eric Santos worked it so that when the wolf transforms into a Black Knight, he retains the teeth and the yellow eyes. Truly excellent."

Eric did great work. He had an eye for detail that skipped most artists as they usually looked at the big picture and left the so-called inconsequential bits for the interns to fill in or expand on. Eric didn't work like that, though, and neither did Jenny, so she had a lot of respect for him.

"Sounds really great," she said, meaning it. "Can't wait to see it. But what I wanted to ask you about is, I've got this idea for another hero in the game program."

He frowned a little, clearly puzzled. "Another hero? We've already got Finn MacCool as the hero. He's the ancient Irish warrior. What're you thinking?"

Actually, she'd done a lot of thinking in the past few days. Trying to keep her mind busy and off Mike Ryan, Jenny had indulged herself with searching out Irish myths and playing with possible story lines. She'd even turned a few sketches into an abbreviated storyboard to pitch to Sean and Mike at some point. But her idea for "The Wild Hunt" was just a little something extra and if she ran it by Dave first, he'd let her know if it merited being presented to the Ryans.

"I was thinking that even a legendary hero like Finn MacCool could use a little help."

"Okay." Dave pushed his glasses up higher as they slid down his nose. "What've you got?"

"I was thinking it might be a nice twist to have a Wise Woman in the mix."

"Wise Woman?"

"You know, it's what they called witches back in the day."

He laughed. "Really? Interesting. Okay. Tell me."

Encouraged by the way he was giving her his complete concentration, Jenny started talking. Reaching into her top desk drawer, she pulled out a few sketches she'd made the night before. Handing them to Dave, she talked while he looked through them.

"She can live in the village. Almost like an Easter egg surprise, she wouldn't be activated unless the gamer hit a certain point on the quest."

Jenny paused, waited and was rewarded when Dave said, "Keep going."

"Okay." Tapping one finger on a storyboard of "The Wild Hunt," she said, "Here, in the timeline of the story, Finn finds a sword in a cave at the base of the cliffs. The gamer has to collect twelve rune clues to free the sword."

"Yeah…"

"Well, I was thinking, what if we laid down fifteen rune clues? Twelve to free the sword and allow the gamer to take Finn into combat with the wizard. *But*, if he finds all fifteen, then he unlocks the Wise Woman. She could help Finn defeat the forest demons and—"

"Be a love interest that maybe we could carry over into the sequel," Dave finished for her, studying the sketches of the witch. "That's excellent, Jenny. It adds another layer and rewards the gamer for collecting all of the runes." Nodding to himself, he added, "Game rules say twelve unlocks the sword, fifteen unlocks magic." He laughed to himself again and kept nodding. "Yeah, that'd be great. We make three of the runes really difficult to find so that players have to work for it if they want the extra. Most will just go for twelve and the sword, but the hard-core gamer will want to go for the magic. I like it." He lifted his gaze to Jenny's and added, "You should take this to the Ryans. Get their okay. They'll love it."

"Um…" she said, pleasure sliding away at the thought of talking to the Ryan brothers together. Sean would be okay. He was nice, reasonable and he liked her. Mike on the other hand… "Why don't you do it? You're the head of my department."

He looked surprised. "It's your idea, Jenny, and it's a great one."

"Yeah, but—"

"Don't be dumb," he said and dropped the sketches onto her desk. "Sean's in Mike's office. You can pitch it to both of them at the same time. The sooner you get this to them the better. Programmers will need more time to set up the extra layers."

"I know, but—"

Dave chuckled a little. "Since when are you shy? Come on, take your idea to the bosses, impress the hell out of 'em."

Still shaking his head, he wandered off to check on a couple of the other artists. Jenny watched him go, then dropped her gaze to the Wise Woman sketches. It *was* a good idea, damn it. And if she and Mike weren't…she didn't know what they were exactly, but if they weren't in such a weird space, she'd have no trouble at all taking her ideas to the Ryan brothers. They were always open to the employees coming to them with suggestions.

She was the head artist now, so she shouldn't be wary of facing her bosses. This was her job, and hadn't she made a point out of telling Mike that nothing was going to stop her from doing her job?

Nodding to herself, she gathered up her sketches and headed out of the office.

* * *

Mike and Sean were going over the figures sent by the collectibles company. "The licensing fee is good, but did you take a look at their latest batch of figurines based on that kids' movie?"

"Yeah," Sean said with a wince. "I admit, they're not great."

Mike snorted. "'Not great' covers a lot of territory. This can be narrowed down to crappy."

"Okay, yeah." Sean tossed the pictures back on his brother's desk. "If they couldn't get the talking frog and the Princess Knight right…"

"Exactly," Mike agreed. "Those are easy. What'll they do to our banshees, warlocks and Irish warriors?" Shaking his head, he continued, "Brady and I both went along with this idea of yours, Sean. But if this is what the collectibles are going to look like, I don't know if it's a good thing."

"True." Sean crossed his legs, propping one ankle on his knee. "There are other companies we could try."

"Is it worth it?"

"I think so," Sean countered. "If we get into the collectibles market, it's going to push our name recognition even higher and affect game sales. We could pull in gamers who haven't tried us yet."

Mike frowned and tapped his fingertips against the desk. It was hard to keep his mind on business. Even now, while his brother continued to talk about his plan, Mike's mind drifted to the woman working on the floor above him.

Three days since his night with Jenny and he'd hardly been able to shake thoughts of her for five minutes at a stretch. He'd convinced himself that spending the night

with her had been a wise choice. A way to not only ease
the ache for her but a chance to push away the memories
of that one night in Phoenix.

Well, that had worked, but now it was memories of a
night in Long Beach that tormented him. Rather than getting her out of his mind, that night had only entrenched
her there.

"Are you listening to me?" Sean demanded.

"What?" Mike scowled and shot his brother a hard
look. "Yeah. Sure."

"Uh-huh." Sean smirked at him. "What did I just
say?"

"Collectibles. Gamers. Blah, blah. Pretty much what
you've been saying for months."

"Right. So what's going on with you?"

"Nothing," Mike said, picking up a pen and twirling
it idly between his fingers. "I'm busy."

"Yeah," Sean said, "me, too. So what's going on?"

"Who're you all of a sudden?" Mike asked. "Mom?"

"Hah. If I was Mom I'd get an answer to my question."

True. Peggy Ryan was tough and had a way of getting
her family to confess all. Which, Mike reminded himself,
wasn't always a good thing. She'd once pried truths out
of her husband that had changed the way Mike felt about
his father forever. It was the day that Mike learned how
much damage liars and cheats could do.

And that thought steeled his spine and firmed his
resolve to get past whatever it was he was feeling for
Jenny. Liars had no place in his life and damned if he'd
forget that.

As if his thoughts had conjured her, a perfunctory
knock on the open door announced her presence. Mike
looked at her, his gaze locking with hers, and he felt a

fast jolt of awareness tangled up with a bone-deep need that just never seemed to drain away. "What is it?"

She blinked at the brusque tone, then deliberately looked away from him to Sean. "I had an idea I wanted to run past you. For 'The Wild Hunt.'"

Sean glanced at Mike, then shrugged and said, "Sure, Jenny. Come on in."

He waved her into a chair and she sat, still avoiding looking at Mike directly. "I was talking with Dave, showed him a few sketches, and he said I should bring it to you guys."

Mike watched her lips move, heard her voice, but couldn't concentrate on what she was saying as she explained her idea for a new character to drop into "The Wild Hunt." Instead, his brain insisted on dredging up images from the other night. How the hell could he focus on work with rich, sexual memories flooding his brain and torturing his body?

"Those are great," Sean was saying. He leaned close to Jenny to look at the sketch she held and a flash of irritation shook Mike in response.

Why the hell did Sean have to practically drape himself over Jenny's shoulder to get a look at her sketch pad?

"Let me see," he said abruptly, breaking up what looked to him like a too-cozy scene.

Sean passed the drawings over and said, "I think she's onto something. I like the idea of a powerful woman coming to the aid of the beleaguered hero." He grinned. "Might get more female players out of it, too."

Nodding, Mike scanned the drawings and once again was forced to admit just how talented Jenny Marshall really was. The sketches weren't complete, more of a bare-bones idea for a new character, but even at that stage, he could see the beauty that would pop through when it was finished. The witch was tall, powerful, magical, a perfect addition to the game cast.

He slanted a look at Jenny and found her watching him, waiting for whatever he was going to say. And in her eyes, he saw resignation, as if she was expecting him to shoot down her ideas. Well, hell, he might have some issues with her, but he wasn't an idiot.

"This is good work."

"Wow, high praise," Sean muttered and earned a quick, grateful grin from Jenny.

Mike ignored a new flash of irritation and kept talking. "I'll keep the high praise for when I see the fleshed-out ideas. But for now, I agree. It's a good addition to the game."

A slow, pleased smile curved Jenny's mouth and everything in Mike warmed, softened. The effect this woman had on him was dangerous. And it didn't seem to be dissipating any.

"Thank you," she said simply. Her eyes shone with a deeper gratitude that only Mike was aware of. It made him feel like a damn bully to know that she had fully expected him to shoot down her ideas just because they were hers.

He handed the sketches back and turned to his brother. "What do you think? Can we come up with a new story line and get it to the writers by the weekend?"

"Probably," Sean said, then shrugged. "But what's the rush?"

Mike slanted a look at Jenny. "Because Jenny and I are headed to Laughlin to check out the new hotel. We're leaving on Monday. Be gone a couple days."

She shifted a little uneasily in her chair and Mike

caught the motion. He could only hope Sean hadn't. Sometimes, Mike's little brother saw too damn much.

"Well, then," Sean said and stood up. "I'll talk to the writers, get them to amend the script. Meanwhile," he added, "if you could finish out those sketches, that'd be great, Jenny."

"I can have them to you in an hour," she said, rising and heading to the door.

"Great. You want to start on the storyboard changes now, Sean?"

"Should we call Brady before making a final decision?"

Mike thought about it, then scrubbed one hand across the back of his neck. "No. We'll tell him about it at our next conference call, but he'll be on board."

"Okay." Sean headed out. "I'll get the stuff together."

"Be right there," Mike called after him. When they were alone, he stood up and asked, "Leaving Monday work for you?"

"Oh," Jenny said, giving a quick look over her shoulder as if to make sure the hallway behind her was empty. "So you *are* going to ask me? I thought you were just handing out a royal decree."

Mike grimaced and stuffed his hands into his pants pockets. "We talked about going to the hotel."

"Yeah, but you didn't give me a specific date," she countered. "And I was supposed to have dinner with my uncle on Monday."

Everything in Mike fisted at the reminder of Hank Snyder, her uncle and the owner of Snyder Arts.

"You don't have to make that face," she told him. "You might not like my uncle," Jenny added, "but I love him. He's my family."

"That's the problem, isn't it?"

"For you, yes."

A couple of people walked down the hall, their voices raised in argument.

"Zombies have to die when you cut their heads off."

"In real life, not in the gaming world, hello?"

"We have to at least try to be realistic, don't we?"

"You want realism, then our zombies have to eat brains, not just bite people…"

Their voices faded as they went into the break room and shut the door after them. A moment later, Jenny chuckled. "Zombies in real life." She looked up at Mike, the smile still curving her mouth. "We have weird lives."

All he could see was that smile and after a second or two, he returned it. "Yeah, I guess we do. So. Monday?"

"I'll be ready," she said, all trace of amusement disappearing. "Should I meet you here?"

He shook his head. "I'll pick you up at nine. We'll take the company jet to Vegas."

"Okay." She took a breath, blew it out. "Now, I'd better go see about finishing the images of my Wise Woman."

Mike crossed the room and propped one shoulder against the doorjamb. Watching her go, he wondered if, when all this was done, seeing her walk away from him would be his clearest memory.

Four

"I'll only be gone overnight, Uncle Hank."

"With *him*," Hank Snyder muttered under his breath.

Jenny sighed and let her head fall back. It was Monday morning; Mike would be here in a few minutes and she still had to finish packing. But as her uncle went on a long-winded rant, she realized having to listen to this was her own fault.

She never should have confessed to her uncle what Mike had accused her of a year ago. But in her defense, she had really been upset, and Hank had dropped by her apartment just when she was in the middle of a good rant. So instead of shutting up, she'd spewed everything at the feet of the man who'd raised her.

Naturally, his first instinct had been to go to Celtic Knot and punch Mike Ryan in the mouth. Thankfully, she'd talked him down from that. But he hadn't forgiven and he hadn't forgotten. In fact, Hank had tried to talk her out of going to work for the Ryan brothers on the principle that she should simply stay the hell away from Mike altogether. But Jenny had refused, then and now, to let Mike Ryan's presence dictate how she ran her life and career.

"He is my boss," she finally said.

"Doesn't have to be," Hank told her, and Jenny's hand fisted around her phone. "You could come to work for me. You know that."

Snyder Arts was a small company with an excellent arts program. The program itself simplified digital and graphic arts design and implementation. They sold retail and to companies looking to refine their own graphic art departments. Which is why Hank had tried to make a deal with Celtic Knot in the first place. He'd thought—and *rightly*, Jenny acknowledged—that his program would streamline the gaming company's art and design division.

And since Jenny now knew *both* companies well, she understood that if Mike weren't so hardheaded, even he would have to admit that her uncle's program would make the work easier for his own artists. But Mike being Mike, he would never let himself see that. Especially since he believed that Hank had tried to use Jenny to worm a contract out of Mike.

She sighed and leaned against the bathroom door. "I do know that, Uncle Hank. And I appreciate it. Really. But I'm not interested in R & D or in sales and marketing. I'm an artist and I'm good at what I do."

"You're the best, honey," he said on a belabored sigh. "I just don't like you being upset is all. And I really don't like you having to deal with a man who thinks so little of you."

"It doesn't matter what Mike thinks of me personally," she said, though in her head she was chanting, *Liar, liar, pants on fire*. "I like my job. And this trip to Laughlin will be fast and all business. I want to scope out the hotel in person so I can start planning the murals."

"Never could argue with you once you had your mind set on something, could I?"

Jenny smiled. "Nope."

"Fine, fine. You just be careful and you let me know when you're home safe."

"I will." Then Jenny listened as her uncle talked about what was happening at Snyder Arts. His R & D department was coming up with some interesting things. Jenny knew how important his company was to him. Until she had come into his life and he had taken over as her guardian, that company had been his entire world.

But the main point in all this was Hank didn't need a deal with Celtic Knot to make Snyder Arts profitable. Their bottom line was very comfortable. Okay, not billionaire comfy, but still. It was laughable that Hank would have needed her to coax Mike into some kind of deal even if it hadn't been insulting on the face of it. Snyder Arts didn't need Celtic Knot and Mike had to know that, in some part of himself. He was just so down-to-the-marrow suspicious and hard, he'd never admit it.

While Hank talked, she smiled to herself and quickly packed away her hair products and makeup, zipping them into a small purple bag. She walked into the bedroom, tucked the bag into her suitcase and sat on the edge of the bed.

Now she was packed and ready to go. Well, as ready

as she could be. Two days alone with Mike would be either a misery or wonderful—and that would turn into misery later. The man wanted her, that was plain enough. But he didn't want to want her and she had no idea how to get past that. Or even if she should try.

Jenny had spent a lifetime knowing that she wasn't wanted. Heck, her own parents had walked away from her and never looked back. She was twelve when they decided they didn't really want the burden of a child and were bored with being parents. They'd dropped her off with Hank, her mother's older brother.

Hank was a widower who had buried himself in his company at his wife's death. Barely home back then, he'd had to shift his entire life around to accommodate Jenny. And she'd known it. She'd tried to be as invisible as possible so that he, too, wouldn't decide to walk away.

Even as a kid, Jenny had known that Hank didn't really *want* her. Taking her in had simply been the right thing to do. But Hank had always been kind and supportive, and she was still grateful to him for so much.

"You're not listening," Hank said with a short laugh.

Caught, she said, "I'm sorry, Uncle Hank. My mind wandered."

"That's fine. I know you're getting ready to leave."

True. Mike would be arriving any minute. Well, there went the knots in her stomach, tightening viciously enough that it was hard to breathe.

"I'll just remind you to be careful."

"I will, promise." Jenny glanced out the window, saw Mike's car pulling up and said, "I've really gotta go."

Her uncle hung up, still muttering direly. Jenny tucked her phone into her pocket, zipped her suitcase closed and told herself to relax. Not that she was listening, but she had to try. Outside, Mike stepped out of his car, looked at her apartment and for just a second, Jenny felt as if he were looking directly into her eyes. That was stupid of course, but it didn't change the zip of heat that raced through her.

This was probably a mistake. Two days. Alone. With Mike Ryan.

No way this was going to end well.

Traveling with a gazillionaire was eye-opening.

Even at the small airport in Long Beach, people practically snapped to attention for Mike Ryan. Baggage handlers hurried to stow the overnight bags they both carried, then the pilot stepped out onto the stairway to welcome them aboard personally.

Once they'd boarded the private jet, Jenny curled up in a buttery-soft leather seat and sipped at the fresh coffee served by a friendly attendant. Mike concentrated on work, staring so hard at the screen of his tablet, Jenny was almost surprised he didn't burn a hole through it. But left to herself, she watched the clouds and enjoyed the all-too-short flight.

In less than an hour, they were landing in Las Vegas. There again, people scrambled to make Mike's life easier, smoother. A rental car was waiting for them and after forty minutes on a nearly empty highway flanked on either side by wide sweeps of desert, they were in Laughlin, Nevada.

Laughlin was sort of the more casual, fun, younger sister of Las Vegas. There were plenty of casino hotels, but there was also the Colorado River. In the summer, the town was booming with water-skiers and boaters and everyone looking for a good time on the water. Then the hot desert nights featured riverside dining or visits to the casinos where top-name acts performed on glittery stages.

Jenny had been there before, though the last time had been five years ago for a bachelorette party. Remembering, she smiled. That party was the reason she'd had condoms in her bedside drawer a week ago when Mike had shown up at her apartment. As a party favor, the condoms had seemed silly at the time, but now, Jenny could appreciate the gesture because without them, she wouldn't have had that spectacular night.

The town had grown a lot in five years. There were new casinos springing up everywhere along with housing developments and shopping centers just out of sight of the big hotels.

In late January, the weather was cool and the river ran high and fast. Jenny stood on the shore and looked upstream toward the heart of the city where big hotels lined the Riverwalk—a wooden boardwalk that stretched the length of hotel row. At night, she knew, there were old-fashioned streetlights sending out a golden glow along the walk. There were restaurants and bars, where a couple could sit and talk and look out over the water.

The Ryans had made a good choice in building their hotel here. All in all, Jenny told herself, if she had a choice, she would come to Laughlin instead of Vegas. It was smaller, friendlier and offered a variety of things to do.

She shrugged deeper into her navy blue jacket as a hard, cold wind carrying the sharp tang of sage blew in off the desert. There were clouds on the horizon promising a storm, but for the moment, the sky was a bright blue and all around her, trees dipped and swayed in the wind. Jenny walked out onto the boat dock and watched as the river churned and sloshed below her.

"It's a good spot."

She turned her head into the wind to look back at the shore. Mike was headed her way, hands tucked into the pockets of his black leather jacket.

Nodding, Jenny shifted her gaze to the river again. "I was just thinking that. There are so many trees on the grounds, you could almost forget you're in the desert."

"Yeah, now," he said, a chuckle in his voice as he came closer. "Wait until summer."

She smiled. Temperatures in the desert regularly topped out at one hundred twenty and more during the summer. But as the locals liked to say, *It's a dry heat.* "Agreed. But you can go in the river to cool off."

"Or the hotel pool," he said as he joined her at the edge of the dock.

"True."

Upstream, there were flat-bottom boats, owned by the hotels, taking tourists for river rides. The windows and gold trim on the hotels winked brightly in the sunlight. But here, standing in the shadows of the nest of trees edging the river, it was as if they were alone.

"I wonder why the previous owners couldn't make the hotel work," she mused aloud. "It's a great spot. Wonderful views, plenty of trees, a gorgeous pool—"

"No gambling."

She looked at him. "What?"

"The hotel." Mike squinted into the sun. "The old owner didn't approve of gambling so the hotel didn't offer it." He shrugged. "A hotel with no casino in a gambling town isn't going to survive. Plus, he didn't have smoking rooms, either."

"That's important?"

"Again, a gambling town. People come here looking to relax, throw a little money down a rat hole..." He looked at her. "They're not interested in being snubbed because they smoke. Or if they can't find a slot machine anywhere on the premises."

"Good points." He was always thinking and she shouldn't have been surprised to know that he'd done his homework on the previous owner's failures and come to his own conclusions. Mike Ryan always had a plan. "So, you'll have gambling?"

He gave her a fast grin. "Not a regular casino, no. But we'll have some custom-made slot machines if people are interested. Based on the game, of course."

"Of course." She smiled and looked up at him. He was so tall, so broad shouldered. His dark hair ruffled in the wind and his blue eyes were narrowed on the distant view, as if he was staring off into a future that lay waiting for him to conquer it.

Oh, she really had to stop.

"Still," Mike said, grabbing her attention again, "the River Haunt isn't going to be your standard hotel. It's being designed to appeal to gamers—not gamblers."

"Gamblers like games, too."

"Yeah," Mike said. "But they're more interested in risking their money for the chance of a big reward. A gamer wants to beat his time, beat the game." He turned and looked back up the rise to the hotel that now belonged to Celtic Knot. "The people who come here are going to be looking for the experience. The opportunity to pretend they're a part of the game they love. Gambling doesn't have anything to do with that."

"But you'll have a few slot machines just in case."

He winked at her. "Doesn't hurt to cover all bases."

Pleasure rushed through Jenny at that friendly wink.

She liked this. They were talking. About important things, and he hadn't taken a single shot at her yet. No insults, no disapproval. Maybe it was being away from their everyday routine, but whatever the reason, she was enjoying it. And maybe, she thought, these two days with Mike wouldn't be as hard as she'd thought they would be.

"I'm guessing you'll have smoking rooms, too, then," she said with a smile.

"Absolutely," he said. "I'm not going to cut anyone out of coming to the hotel." He shook his hair back when the wind tossed it across his forehead. "It's ridiculous for any business owner to discriminate against possible customers."

"Agreed," she said. Half turning, she looked back at the hotel sitting at the top of a low rise.

It was old, but sturdy. Paint that had once been a deep brick red had faded in the sun until it looked almost pink. The building sprawled across the property but Jenny knew that compared to the rich new hotels farther downriver this place was small. Only a hundred and fifty rooms, the soon-to-be River Haunt hotel would be exclusive and that would appeal to the gamers who would flock here.

There was a wide porch that swept along the front of the building, and floor-to-ceiling windows provided a great view of the river and the purple smudge of mountains in the distance. The now pink paint was peeling and the plain boxlike structure wasn't exactly appealing, but she knew that Mike would be changing it all up. The rehab wouldn't go fast, but she could imagine it all as it would be in a few months.

Like the setting of the "River Haunt" game, the main building would be made to look like a weathered, deserted cabin. A cabin where ghouls, ghosts, zombies and other assorted supernatural beings assembled and tormented the gamers who fought to defeat Donn, Lord of the Dead.

The guests at the River Haunt hotel would be treated to rooms and suites decked out with top-of-the-line gaming systems, flat-screen TVs and enough gaming tokens and symbols to make them feel as though they were a part of their favorite game. The latest Celtic Knot hotel was going to be huge.

"It'll be a lot of work," Jenny said thoughtfully.

"It will."

She turned and flashed him a quick smile. "But it's gonna be great."

"Damn straight."

His gaze locked with hers and for one bright, amazing moment, Jenny felt like they were a team. In this together. And in that impossibly fast heartbeat of time, she really wished it were true.

They were making the most of their two days in Nevada.

Mike spent hours with his contractor, Jacob Schmitt, going over the plans for the River Haunt. The two of them walked the hotel, checking out the rooms and talking to the skeleton staff who remained on-site.

Mike appreciated good work and loyalty, so when he was given the opportunity to keep on some of the hotel employees, he did. He wasn't a soft touch, though, so in interviews with the hotel manager, and the heads of the other departments, he'd quickly weeded out the people who were simply dead weight.

Maybe the previous owner's standards had been lax,

but Mike had no intention of paying people to do nothing. But he was also ready to pay top money for the right kind of employee. Which was why he'd fired the previous manager and promoted that man's assistant, Teresa Graves.

Teresa was a middle-aged woman with a no-nonsense attitude and an unerring ability to cut through the bull and get the best out of the people who worked for her. With his new manager's help, Mike wanted to keep the skeleton crew in place during the transition. He didn't want the hotel sitting empty and deserted while it was being rehabbed. It seemed like too much of an invitation to vandals and or thieves.

Having people there was important enough that he was offering bonuses to the workers who were willing to actually *live* in the hotel so that someone besides the security people he'd hired were around 24/7. With a working kitchen, a pool and plenty of guest rooms to choose from, it was no hardship for those who chose to stay. Plus, they were paid enough that they didn't have to look for another job while waiting for the hotel to reopen.

"I figure we'll do the pool last," Jacob said as they walked through the main lobby and out onto the sun-splashed deck. "Leave it as is so your people can use it while we work. And this way, with all the construction going on, we don't risk breaking up the new tiles you wanted in the pool surround."

Mike studied the architect's line drawings for a long moment.

"That's a good idea," he said finally. "Pool's going to be the last thing we need done anyway."

"Yeah, and these tiles we'll be laying in the deck and surround aren't something we want scratched up." Jacob yanked his battered blue ball cap with a faded Dodgers patch off his head and rubbed the wild scrub of gray hair that sprung up as if freed from prison. "Just like you wanted, the tiles actually look like rough wood—gives the feel of the forest floor."

Mike glanced at the man and smiled. "You know the 'River Haunt' game?"

"I should," the other man said. "My son plays the damn thing every chance he gets." Chuckling, he added, "I swear, I hear banshees wailing in my dreams."

"That's good to hear, too," Mike said, and gave the other man a friendly slap to the shoulder.

"I'll bet." Jacob Schmitt turned slowly to take a look around the property. "This is a perfect spot for what you're wanting. My opinion, the last owner didn't make enough of what he had. But his loss—your gain."

"That's what I think, too."

"You know, my son's already nagging at me to bring him to the hotel for a long weekend."

Mike followed the other man's gaze and realized that he was anxious to get this hotel up and running, too. He couldn't wait to see how it all came out. "Tell you what," Mike said. "You bring the job in on time and on budget, you and your family can stay a week, on us."

The older man's bushy gray brows shot high on his forehead as he gave a wide smile. "My son will think I'm a god."

Mike laughed. "Anything I can do."

Eager now, Jacob pointed to the sketch of the pool area. "You can see this wall behind the pool will be a series of ledges, each of them planted with flowering plants that will trail down to the edge of the pool itself."

Mike listened as he looked at the ink drawings, bringing it all to life in his mind. He had a good imagination and used it to mentally change the plain, kidney-shaped pool into the fantasy spot he wanted.

He could almost see it. A waterfall would cascade at one end of the pool and behind that waterfall would be a swim-up bar where guests could be served as they hid behind a froth of water. There would be lounge chairs in deep forest green and tables that looked like the twisted limbs of ancient trees. The flowering vines Jacob described would be a curtain of green in the desert heat. It was a very good representation of the kind of scenery found in the "River Haunt" game.

Hell, Mike thought he could practically hear the groaning zombies approaching. He'd like to show the sketches to Jenny, get her opinion. After all, she was here to work, he reminded himself. But she was inside, scouting out the right places for the murals she would design and paint.

"I've expanded the dock," the contractor said, getting Mike's attention again, "so you'll have room for both of the boats you're planning for."

"That's good. We want to offer late-night cruises as part of the experience."

"It's pretty out here at night," the contractor said with a nod as he lifted his gaze to look around. "Far enough away from hotel row, you can see the stars like you never would in the city."

"Yeah?" It had been a long time since Mike had even taken the time to look up at a night sky. But it was part of the whole experience his guests would have. "What did you think of the idea for the animatronics?"

Jacob chuckled and tugged his hat back into place. "I

think it's gonna scare the hell out of your guests," he said. "But I suppose that's why they're coming here, isn't it?"

"It is." Mike nodded to himself and glanced toward the riverbank that stretched along the front of their property. Plenty of thick, high bushes and trees to hide the mechanics of the banshees and river specters who would be made to move in and out of the shadows as the gamers drifted by on the water. He could practically see how it would play out and he was anxious to get it all going.

"We're working with the engineers to make the housings for the creatures to move on as well as the shells they'll retreat to so they're protected from the elements," Jacob said.

"You can hide the housings well enough they won't be seen?"

"Absolutely."

It all sounded good. Hell, perfect. With any luck at all, the hotel would be finished and ready to welcome guests by summer. Hot desert nights, dark skies, perfect for scaring the hell out of people.

"I've got the best crew in Nevada," Jacob assured him. "We'll get it all done just the way you want it."

Nodding, Mike said, "I'll be making trips out to check on things, but Ms. Graves, the new manager, will be the point person on this. You go to her with any issues if you can't get hold of me. She'll make sure I'm kept up to date."

"I'll do that, and don't worry, it's going to be something special when it's done."

"Agreed," Mike told him, then turned back to the hotel. "Let's go through the kitchen work that needs doing. I want to hear about any potential problems."

"Well," Jacob said as he fell into step beside him,

"we've got a few of those, too. But nothing to be worried about."

Mike only half listened as they headed inside. He had researched every aspect of this rehab. He knew Jacob Schmitt would deliver good work done at a fair price. He knew Teresa Graves could be trusted to keep on top of the day-to-day issues that were bound to crop up. And he was sure that the security company he'd hired would protect his property.

Of course, the only thing he wasn't sure of in all this was Jenny. He hadn't seen her since the conversation on the dock hours ago. Probably best to keep a distance between them, but damned if he didn't want to go find her. Talk to her. Look at her.

And more.

Yeah, not going there.

"Right, Jacob. Let's get back to work."

Five

Jenny's imagination was in overdrive. She'd brought her ideas for murals with her and she'd spent the past two hours walking the halls and the big rooms on the main floor, plotting just where she'd put them.

The restaurant was perfect for a wide mural on the back wall. She would paint it as if there was a path leading from the room into the forest itself. Sort of a trompe l'oeil, giving the guests in the room the feeling that they could simply step into the painting. Of course, being gamers, they would know what lurked in that forest, she thought with a smile, so maybe they wouldn't want to follow the path.

On the opposite wall, there were tall windows, displaying the view of the tree-laden yard and the river beyond. Those she would surround with deep green vines, twining down the wall to pool on the floor.

She took a deep breath and simply sighed at the pleasure of having so many blank canvases just waiting to be turned into fantasies. Her hands actually itched to take hold of her brushes. God knew, she loved her job, but having the opportunity to paint rather than generating images on a computer was just…fun.

Grinning, she left the dining room and walked into the lobby. She had a great idea for the main entrance to the hotel and knew that it was only because she'd been here to see it in person that the thought had occurred to her. She wanted this painting to make a statement. To show the gamers and other guests that from the moment they walked into the hotel, they were stepping into another realm.

The lobby area was another big, gorgeous space that only needed some attention to really wake it up and make it special. And Jenny was just the artist to do it. There were a few crewmen in the room already, tearing out the old reception desk. It was white and sterile and too contemporary-looking for what the Ryans had in mind, so it had to go.

"Excuse me," she said and waited until one of the men turned to look at her to ask, "who do I speak to about the color of paint I want on this entry wall?"

"Oh, that'd be Jacob." A guy in his thirties with big brown eyes, a heavy mustache and deeply tanned skin smiled at her, touching off a dimple in one cheek. "I think he's in the kitchen with the boss."

"Okay, thanks." She started that way, but stopped when the man spoke again.

"You're the artist, right? Jenny?"

Jenny turned to face him. "That's right."

"Nice to meet you. I'm Rick."

He really was cute and that dimple was disarming. His jeans were worn and faded, and his white T-shirt strained over a build that was truly impressive. And Jenny was pretty sure Rick knew exactly how good he looked. There was something in his stance—as if he were posing for her admiration—and in the knowing gleam in his eyes that told Jenny he was used to women curling up at his feet and staring up at him adoringly.

Hard to blame them.

"Hi, Rick," she said. "Good to meet you, too. I'm going to be doing the murals for the new hotel. Well," she hedged, "not me all on my lonesome. It would take me ten years to do all of them myself.

"But I'm doing the designs and supervising the artists we'll bring in to finish the job."

He nodded as if he cared and she knew he didn't. Please. Were most of her gender really so easily manipulated by a gorgeous face and the appearance of interest in what they were saying?

"So what color do you want for that wall?" he asked.

She glanced at the wall in question. It was the first thing you saw when you walked into the hotel. Right now, it was cream colored, with sun stains from where framed paintings had once hung. But when Jenny was finished with it, it was going to be...mystical.

When she spoke, she wasn't really talking to Rick-With-Dimples. Instead, she was describing her vision to herself, sort of putting it out into the universe.

"Deep purple," she said, tipping her head to stare at the blank space as if she could see the wall changing color as she spoke. "I want it the color of twilight just before darkness falls. There will be stars, just barely appearing in the sky, with dark clouds streaming past a full moon, making them shine like silver." She sighed and continued, "There'll be a forest beneath the stars and moonlight threading through the trees. And in the shadows, there will be the hint of yellow eyes, red eyes, staring out at you, and you won't be sure if you see them or not.

"But the night will draw you in, make promises, and you'll dream about that forest and the eyes that follow you as you walk."

She fell silent and was still staring at the blank wall when she heard Rick say, "Damn, lady, you're a little spooky, you know that?"

She laughed, until Mike's voice came from right behind her.

"You have no idea."

Whipping around, she looked up into Mike's eyes and noticed the all-too-familiar flare of anger. Well, for heaven's sake, what had she done *now*?

"Don't you have work to do?" Jacob asked Rick and he immediately left, doing his best to look busy.

"Thanks for the tour, Jacob," Mike was saying. "We'll meet up here again tomorrow."

"I'll be here," the older man said, with a nod acknowledging Jenny. "You make a note on the paint colors you want where, miss, and I'll make sure the painters get the message."

"Thank you. I'll have them for you tomorrow, then."

"That's good." Jacob looked back at Mike. "The crew starts on the main floor in the morning. You and I can look at the upper floors and talk about what you want."

"See you then." Mike took Jenny's elbow and began steering her toward the front door.

She pulled free though, because A, she wasn't going

to be dragged around like a dog on a leash. And B, she needed her purse.

"Just wait a minute," she snapped and marched across the front room like a soldier striding across a battlefield. Snatching up her black leather bag, she slung it over her shoulder and stomped right back to Mike. "*Now* I'm ready."

He gritted his teeth. She could see the muscle in his jaw twitching and she almost enjoyed knowing she had the ability to irritate him so easily. Of course, she'd enjoy it even more if she knew what exactly she'd done to make him walk as if there were a steel spike between his shoulder blades.

Without waiting for him, Jenny walked out the front door, down the overgrown walk and stopped at the passenger door of the shiny red rental car to wait.

He looked at her over the roof of the car and demanded, "What the hell were you doing?"

"My *job*," she shot back, then threw the door open and slid inside.

He did the same, slammed the key home and fired the engine. Neither of them spoke again on the short drive to the hotel where they'd be spending the night.

When they got there, Mike turned the car over to the valet and Jenny was inside the hotel before he caught up to her. Again, he took hold of her elbow and pulled her to a stop.

"Will you quit doing that?" Her gaze shot from his hand on her arm up to his eyes.

"Quit walking away from me."

"Quit being a jerk and I'll quit walking away."

"You make me nuts," he grumbled.

"I think you were born that way," she said, "but Sean

seems perfectly reasonable, so it's probably not hereditary."

All around them, tourists swarmed through the lobby
and into the casino. Bells, whistles and loud bursts of
laughter played backdrop to their hurried, angry whis-
pers.

"I'm not having this conversation here."

Jenny flinched at the cold, sharp edge of his voice.
"I'm not having it at all."

"Yeah you are. We'll talk about it upstairs. Your room
or mine?"

"Ha!" She laughed shortly. "Despite that charming
invitation, I think I'll pass."

"We talk privately," he said, lowering his voice until
it was a hush, "or we do it right here in the middle of
the damn hotel."

"Fine. Upstairs. My room because I want to be able
to tell you to leave."

He snorted, took her elbow in a grip firm enough she
couldn't shake him off and steered her to the bank of elevators. One of them opened instantly as soon as Mike
stabbed the call button. The two of them stepped into
the open car as soon as it emptied and were joined by a
half-dozen other people.

The elevator was crowded and the piped-in music was
straight out of the 1980s. Mirrors on the walls made it
seem as if there were fifty people crammed together, but
the only person Jenny really looked at was Mike. He was
at least a head taller than anyone else and in the mirror,
his gaze shifted to hers and held. The car stopped, people
got off, got on, and then they were moving again. Conversations rippled around them, but Jenny hardly heard
them. All she could focus on was the glint in Mike's

eyes and the grim slash of his mouth. Finally, though, they hit the eleventh floor. Jenny stepped off and Mike followed after.

The hallway was dimly lit and narrow, and with Mike right behind her, felt even tighter. She reached her door, slid the card key through the slot and opened it. Jenny'd left her drapes open, so afternoon sunlight swamped the room as she walked to the bed and tossed her purse down on it.

Mike closed the door and was walking toward her when she turned to face him.

"What the hell was that all about?"

"What was what about?" Jenny threw both hands high and then let them fall.

"You and the carpenter." Mike bit the words off. "When I walked into the lobby, you were flirting and he was drooling, so I ask again, what the hell was that about?"

Sincerely stunned, Jenny gaped at him for a second or two. "Flirting?" she repeated as anger bubbled and churned in the pit of her stomach. "I was talking about *paint*. About the mural I want on the wall in the lobby."

"Yeah, I heard the end of the performance." Mike cut her off with a wave of his hand. "Deep, breathy voice going all dreamy and soft. Hell, you had that carpenter standing there with his mouth open and his eyes bugging out."

"Dreamy? Soft?" Had she really sounded like that, she wondered, then shook her head to dismiss the question. Didn't matter if she had, Jenny thought. She hadn't been flirting, she'd been sort of lost in her own vision.

Mike inhaled sharply and said, "You sounded just like you did when you woke up in my arms."

Now it was her turn to drag a deep breath into her lungs. Reminding her of their most recent night together wasn't playing fair. "You're wrong."

He took a step closer, grabbed her upper arms and pulled her up against him. Jenny's heart leaped into a gallop and as he was holding her so tightly to him, she felt his heart raging in the same rhythm.

"I know what I heard," he said, staring down into her eyes. "What I saw."

She fought the natural impulse to wrap her arms around his waist and hold on. To go up on her toes and kiss him. To feel that rush of incredible sensations one more time. Instead, she reminded herself just how little he really thought of her. Of the fact that he didn't want her—it was only desire driving his reactions.

"I wasn't flirting," she told him. "But even if I had been, what business is that of yours? You're my boss, Mike, not my boyfriend."

"I am your boss," he agreed. "And I don't want you playing with the crew. I want them focused on the work, not you."

Stunned all over again, Jenny demanded, "Can you hear yourself? Do you even realize when you're being insulting? I mean, is it just instinct or is it deliberate?"

"Insulting? I walk into a room in my new hotel and find you practically salivating over some guy with a tool belt and a set of dimples, and I'm insulting?"

"You are, and what's worse is you don't see it," Jenny said and slapped both hands against his hard chest to shove her way free. He let her go. Taking a few steps away from him just because she *really* needed the distance right now, she faced him and said, "I'm here to do my job, Mike. You're my boss, not my lover."

"I remember it differently."

She flushed. *Damn it.* Jenny could actually feel heat race into her cheeks and could only hope that with the sunlight behind her, her face was in shadow enough that he wouldn't notice. "A couple of nights together doesn't make you my lover. It makes you…"

"Yeah?"

"A mistake," she finished. "Isn't that what you yourself called that first night? Oh, *and* the last one we spent together?"

He shoved both hands into his pockets and stared at her with an intensity she could feel. "I did. It was. That doesn't mean I enjoy standing by, watching you work some other poor guy into a frenzy."

"I had no idea I had so much power," Jenny said, shaking her head in disbelief. "Didn't realize I was so oblivious, either. I didn't see Rick—"

"Hmm. First-name basis already, huh?"

She ignored that and punched home what she most wanted to say. "I didn't see Rick in a frenzy—but you surely were."

"I was angry, not in a frenzy."

Was he jealous? Was it possible that Mike Ryan had seen her talking to Rick and had felt territorial over her? If he had, what did that mean? "Really. Angry that I was 'flirting' with someone other than you?"

"That you were flirting on the job, that's all," he said, and pulled both hands from his pockets to fold his arms across his chest. "Don't read more into this than there is."

"I don't think I am," Jenny said, moving close to him again. This was the weirdest conversation she'd ever had. Just a week or so ago, she'd pledged that she wouldn't be sleeping with Mike again. She already knew that this was a ticket to disaster. That the man had believed her to be a thief. Maybe he still did, she couldn't be sure. And yet, here she was, surrendering to the very need and hunger that had led her to his bed in the first place.

No. She couldn't. Not again. She would not allow herself to willingly walk right into more pain. With that thought firmly in place, she stopped where she was, looked up at Mike and said, "We're not going to do this again. I won't go to bed with you again."

"I didn't ask you to."

Now she smiled sadly. "Yeah, you did. In everything but words."

"Now you're a mind reader?"

"I don't have to be," Jenny told him and took a breath, hoping to ease the gnawing inside her. "I just know what happens when the two of us are alone together."

Seconds ticked past and the silence was heavy with a kind of tension that nearly vibrated in the air. Jenny held on to the ragged edges of the control that was rapidly slipping out of her grasp. If he pushed back, if he kissed her, then she'd be lost and she knew it.

"Damn it," he finally said in a gruff whisper. "You're not wrong." His gaze dropped from her eyes to her lips and back again. "I saw you with the carpenter and... Never mind. Like you said, none of my business."

Jenny nodded and said, "Let's just forget today, okay? We'll get the job finished tomorrow, then go home and things will get back to normal."

His blue eyes flashed with emotions that came and went so quickly, she couldn't identify them all, and maybe that was for the best.

"Normal." He nodded sharply. "Fine. We can finish

up at the new hotel by noon, probably. Then we'll head home and forget the whole damn trip."

Her heart gave a tug that unsettled her, but Jenny only forced a smile, keeping that small sliver of pain to herself. He wanted to forget the whole trip. Forget being with her, even that way-too-short moment they'd shared on the dock, where they'd talked like friends—or maybe more.

Forgetting wouldn't be easy, Jenny told herself, but it was the one sure path to sanity. Holding on to what she felt for Mike—feelings she didn't want to examine too closely—was only going to add to the misery later on. She had to find a way to let go of what-might-have-beens and focus instead on the cold, hard facts.

The man she wanted didn't want her beyond the nearest bed.

And that just wasn't good enough.

"So," Mike said, interrupting her thoughts, "I'll see you in the morning, then. Nine o'clock. Be ready to go to work."

"I will be." Once he was gone, Jenny dropped to the edge of the bed like a puppet whose strings had been cut.

This would be so much easier if only she didn't care.

Mike spent the evening working in his suite. He figured if he kept his mind busy with figures, budgets, plans for the future of their company, he'd have no time to think about Jenny. Or how she'd looked when he heard her describing the painting she wanted to do. He wouldn't hear the magic in her voice or see the interest in that carpenter's eyes when he watched her.

And he wouldn't keep seeing the look on her face when he had acted like some kind of demented comic-strip moron by accusing her of flirting with the guy. Hell, even if she had been, like she said, it was none of his damn business. But it sure as hell felt like it was. He'd hated watching that other man so focused, laser-like, on Jenny's face. Hated that he'd blamed *her* for whatever *he* was feeling.

"I don't know what's going on here," he muttered darkly, "but I don't like it." He'd always been in control. Of his feelings, his emotions—until Jenny. And what that meant, he didn't have a clue.

Mike scrubbed one hand across his face, pushed out of the desk chair and walked to the terrace. When his cell phone rang, he dragged it out of his pocket as he opened the sliding door and stepped into the teeth of a cold desert wind.

He glanced at the screen, then answered. "Hi, Mom."

"Hi. How's Vegas?"

"Laughlin."

"Same diff," she said and he could almost see her shrugging. "Sean told me you're out there inspecting the new hotel. What's it like?"

He dropped one hand on the iron railing, squinted into the wind and looked down to watch the river below froth beneath the hulls of flat-bottom boats taking tourists on a short ride. Neon fought against the stars for supremacy and won. On the Riverwalk, golden lamplight sifted onto the people strolling in and out of the shadows beside the river.

"It's run-down and sad right now, but I think it'll come together."

"Of course it will," his mother assured him. "My sons always do what they set out to do."

Mike smiled to himself.

"Sean says Jenny Marshall has some great ideas for

the artwork, too." She paused for a moment. "He says you and Jenny are there. Together."

"Does he?" Shaking his head, Mike ignored the blip of interest in Peggy Ryan's voice. He had to wonder if all mothers were as determined as his own to see her children married, with kids.

"Yes, he told me that you and Jenny would be working together for months on this new hotel…"

"Don't start," he warned her, amusement softening his words.

"Well, why shouldn't I?" she demanded with a huff. "You're not getting any younger, you know. And I've met Jenny. She's a nice girl. Talented. Pretty, too."

All true, he thought. She was also smart, opinionated, desirable and oh, yeah…untrustworthy. He scowled and remembered how cozy she'd looked with the damn carpenter today.

"Mom…"

"You can't fault a mother for hoping," she said, cutting him off before he could tell her to dial it back.

"Not interested in getting married, Mom," he said flatly. And she should know why, but he'd learned over the years that Peggy Ryan wanted nothing more than to forget the day that had changed everything for Mike.

There was a sigh in her voice when she said, "Fine. You are so hardheaded. Just like your father."

His frown deepened, but he didn't say anything. His mom didn't notice, or chose not to notice, because she rushed right on.

"I wanted to remind you, your dad's birthday is next week, and I want you and Sean both to show up, okay?"

Mike took a breath and blew it out. No way to avoid it and he knew it. But he never really looked forward to spending time with his father. It was…awkward. Uncomfortable.

Not that it had always been. Up until the year Mike turned thirteen, he'd thought of his father as his hero. Big, strong, with a wide smile and a kind nature, Jack Ryan was the kind of father most kids dream about. Jack had taught both of his sons to surf. A Little League coach, he'd spent hours at batting cages with them.

But the year he was thirteen, Mike had discovered that the father he idolized was also a liar. And that discovery had colored his image of his father ever since. He hadn't been able to forget or forgive. Jack had tried to close the distance between them many times, but Mike couldn't do it.

Memory was sometimes a hard thing and the images from the day when his father tumbled off that pedestal were as clear now as they had ever been.

"Oh, Mike," his mother said on a sigh, "I'm so sorry. You can't possibly know how sorry I am."

Mike stiffened. "You didn't do anything wrong, Mom."

"Yes," she argued. "I did. And I truly wish I could take it all back. Change that day."

"Yeah, well, we can't do that." Mike's hand tightened around his phone. "So let's just leave it in the past, okay?"

"I really wish you would, sweetie," Peggy said, then sighed again. "But fine. For now, I'll move on."

"It's appreciated."

"But I want you at your father's birthday dinner, Mike. No excuses. Sean's already promised to be here."

Of course he had. Sean didn't know what Mike did. He'd never told his younger brother about their father's fall from grace. Protecting Sean? Maybe. And maybe it was just that the thought of even more people knowing was too hard to take. Either way, though, Sean remained in the dark and that's how it would stay.

"Fine. I'll be there," he said, knowing his mother wouldn't stop until she'd gotten him to agree.

"Thanks, sweetie. We'll see you then." She paused. "Oh, and say hi to Jenny for me."

He hung up on her laughter. Shaking his head, he leaned his forearms on the terrace railing and watched the people below. Then he saw her. Jenny. Everything in him fisted as he watched her walk, alone, through the night, moonlight and neon playing in her hair.

Six

Normal was relative.

Jenny reminded herself several times during the following week that she and Mike were supposed to be back to "normal." And she supposed they were. For them.

The first day back, they stayed out of each other's way. But soon enough, work made that ploy impossible. While Jenny continued to work on the sketches of the Wise Woman for "The Wild Hunt" game, she was also going over her plans for the paintings at the new hotel. She'd taken so many pictures of the place, it was easy enough to figure out what she wanted where—it was simply time-consuming.

Then Mike got bogged down with calls from the contractor and plumber and electrician and the work on the game wasn't getting done, so Jenny volunteered to help. With her handling the Nevada hotel, it gave Mike time he needed to work with Sean and the marketing department on the cover design and the publicity campaign designed to push the game during release week.

Naturally, Jenny spent a lot of time in Mike's office fielding phone calls that she then had to tell him about, so they ended up spending hours together every workday. Yet what should have made them closer was instead highlighting the tension building between them.

Like now, Jenny thought as she sat down in front of Mike's desk. He was on the phone with one of the bloggers who posted about Celtic Knot, so Jenny had a minute to indulge herself in watching him.

His features were stony—his businessman face, she thought. Cool. No-nonsense. Unforgiving. His voice was clipped as he told the man what he wanted and expected, and Jenny had no doubt the blogger would do whatever Mike said. He had a knack for getting his way.

And for just a second, she wished *she* was his way.

Then he hung up and she forced her mind out of the lovely little daydreams it preferred and back to the business at hand.

"So, what've you got?" he asked, idly flipping a pen over and over between his fingers.

"Jacob says the painters can start next week," she said, checking her tablet and scrolling down to tick off information she had to give him. Jenny had spoken to the lead contractor so many times that week, she was beginning to think of the older man as family. "He also says the hotel employees you have living on-site have been helping the construction crew—lifting and toting mostly, but Jacob says they're really doing a lot to keep the work on schedule."

"Interesting," Mike admitted. "That wasn't part of our deal."

"Apparently, they got bored with just waiting for the new hotel to open." She shrugged and suggested, "They don't need to go out and find a new job, so maybe they're willing to help out, get the hotel open that much quicker. According to Jacob, they're doing a lot of the scut work, freeing up the crew to do the rehab."

Nodding, Mike said, "Make a note of the names of the guys who are doing the helping. We'll make sure they're paid for the extra work."

"Already done," she said.

He smiled and tossed the pen to the desk. "I like self-starters, people who are willing to step in and do what needs doing without being asked. Keep their names handy. We'll look at promotions when the hotel's up and running."

"I've got the list for you and the departments they worked in at the old hotel. I figured you'd want to do something like that."

"Impressive," he said with a nod of approval. "Are you sure you're an artist, not an admin?"

Surprised at the compliment, Jenny laughed. "Oh, artist, for sure. I don't mind helping you with this stuff, but if I had to keep track of everyone in the free world every day, it would drive me crazy."

"It does," Mike admitted. "I've been riding herd all week on bloggers, beta testers, the marketing guys and the design team working on the game cover. Sean hates the cover, I'm okay with it, but since neither of us is *happy* with it, they've got to go back to square one."

"What're they putting on the cover?"

"The forest, hints of a warrior stepping out from the trees, full moon…"

"Sounds a lot like the cover for 'Forest Run.'"

"Yes! That's exactly what I said." He shook his head, jumped up from his chair and paced to the window overlooking the yard and the blue, cloud-studded sky. "We need it different enough that people won't think they've already got it and similar enough that they know they'll be getting the same kind of fantasy they've become accustomed to."

"Hmm…" Jenny's gaze tracked him as he shifted impatiently from foot to foot at the tall window. If her gaze also dropped briefly to enjoy the view of his very nice behind, who could blame her? "What if we did something with the Wise Woman and the warrior together on the cover?"

He looked at her over his shoulder. "Go on."

"Maybe lightning flashing in the sky." Jenny closed her eyes briefly and could almost see it. "Magic shooting from her fingertips, wind lifting her hair, light gleaming off the warrior's sword…"

"I like it," he said, voice softer that it had been.

Jenny opened her eyes and looked into his and for a second or two convinced herself that she saw something…special. Then the moment was gone again because really, she shouldn't torture herself like that anyway.

"I'll give your ideas to the design team."

"Thanks," she said, pleasure making a warm knot in her chest.

"Hey, it's nice to talk to someone who doesn't need constant monitoring. Sometimes all I want to do is skeet shoot my cell phone."

"Understood. Completely." Didn't need to be monitored? Did that mean he was actually starting to trust her? *No*, she told herself, *don't get crazy*.

Going back to her tablet, Jenny continued. "We might as well finish this up. The engineers are on-site, working on the mechanisms for the river ghosts and ghouls. They say it'll take a couple months to get everything to be perfect, but again, according to Jacob, the engineers are excited."

"Okay, what else?"

"After all the positive stuff, there's a downside."

"Naturally," Mike said on a sigh. Easing one hip down onto the corner of his desk, he waved a hand. "Let's hear it."

"Jacob—wow, I've talked to him a lot this week—says there's a problem with the pipes."

"Great. What kind of problem?"

"The kind that means laying down new pipe. Mainly, the problem is the kitchen and the pool area. He says they'll probably last another five years, but after that, you'll need to redo the whole thing."

He laughed shortly, a scrape of sound with no trace of humor behind it. "Brady redid an entire fifteenth-century castle and those pipes were fine. I'm in charge of a hotel built in the 1950s and it's crap. What's up with that?"

Jenny shrugged. "Apparently castle pipes are made to last?"

"Apparently. Okay, what else does Jacob say?"

She winced a little. "He says to remind you that if you wait to do it, you'll need to pull out all the new tiles in the pool surround and take out a wall in the kitchen to get to everything. He suggests you do it all now."

"Of course he does," Mike said on a laugh. Then he

sighed and rubbed the back of his neck. "How the hell did we not find out about this problem during the inspection?" he muttered.

"Jacob says it's impossible to find stuff like this until you start getting beneath the surface." Jenny took a breath. This was going pretty well. They were in the same room and not sniping at each other. All she had to do was keep the focus on work and they'd be okay.

Of course, looking at him, it was hard to keep *thinking* about work. What she wanted to do was reach up and smooth his hair off his forehead. Step closer and feel his arms come around her. Lay her head on his chest and listen to his heartbeat.

And oh, dear God, she was sliding into a pool of something warm and tempting and way too dangerous. With that thought firmly in mind, she lifted her chin and stuck to business. "He says they didn't find the problems until they ripped out the kitchen floor to lay down a new subfloor before the tiles."

Mike nodded thoughtfully but didn't speak so she kept going.

"It's like all those rehab shows on HGTV. Couples buy this great house and they're redoing it and they find hideous things under the floor and behind the walls." She shuddered. "Makes you want to build new and avoid any old houses like the plague."

One dark eyebrow lifted and his mouth quirked. "Your apartment is an old one," he reminded her.

"Don't think I don't worry about that every time I see the people on TV finding mice and who knows what behind the walls." She shook her head hard and shivered again. "I try not to think about it."

"Don't blame you." Briefly, his eyes were warm,

nearly friendly. Then it was as if a shutter dropped down and suddenly, those blue eyes were cool and dispassionate again.

Jenny smothered a sigh.

"Jacob's right," Mike said finally. "We do the work now, make sure it's right. I want this hotel to be top-of-the-line all the way. No holding back. I'll call him, take care of it."

"Okay, good."

"Anything else?" He reached behind him for a bottle of water. Uncapping it, he took a long drink.

Jenny swallowed, too. Ridiculous that watching a man taking a drink could make her palms sweaty. Clearing her throat, she checked the tablet again. "Oh. Yeah. I talked to the interior designer you hired to furnish the hotel. She's not sure if you want contemporary furniture or something more—and I quote here—'antiquey' for the bedrooms."

"Antiquey?"

She shrugged. "Her word. I told her I thought you'd want something that feels old, almost otherworldly if she can manage it, but that I'd talk to you to make sure."

"You're right," he said and pushed off the desk. "I'll talk to her, but yeah, that's just what I want. Nothing fancy or fussy, but solid, heavy pieces that could be from the past or from the fantasy world we're re-creating."

"I think that's perfect."

Again, his mouth curved slightly and Jenny's heart did a slow tumble in her chest. It was ridiculous just how susceptible she was to this man.

"Good to know you agree," he said. "Because I need you to go with me to look at some furnishings. The designer's going to do most of it. She'll text me pictures of what she finds for approval, but Brady told me about a few places near here that had some great stuff he actually bought and had shipped to Ireland for the castle."

"He had stuff shipped? All the way to Ireland?"

"Well," he said, smiling a little, "not really. He had the movers stack it on the company jet and we flew it over ourselves. Still, would've been easier to buy it all there, but he found some nice stuff. Told me to check it out."

"Okay, when do you want to do that?"

"Next week's fine. We've still got plenty to arrange before then and…" he paused. "Aren't your new drawings of the Wise Woman due in tomorrow?"

"Yeah, they're nearly ready," she said, feeling a slight twinge of guilt. Usually, she turned her work in early, but she'd been so busy with everything else…

"If you need an extra day or two, don't worry about it." He walked closer. "I know you've been busy, picking up the slack on the hotel work."

"I don't mind helping."

He looked down at her. "And I appreciate it."

Her mouth was dry; her heart was pounding. She stared into his blue eyes and felt heat slide through her in a thick rush. Just being close to Mike was enough to weaken her knees—and her resolve. This was so not a good idea.

A quick knock sounded on the door and Sean walked in, already talking. "Hey, Mike? You're not going to believe what—" He stopped, looked from one to the other of them and asked, "Am I interrupting something?"

Mike took a single long step back, shook his head and said, "No. We were finished. Weren't we?"

Jenny shifted her gaze from Sean back to Mike and saw in his eyes that whatever had been looming between them was gone now. Probably a good thing, she acknowledged silently, but oh, she really wished Sean hadn't shown up.

"Yes," she said, when she found her voice, "we're finished."

And as she left the brothers alone, she thought those words had an eerie finality to them.

"Interesting," Sean mused as soon as Jenny had slipped off down the hall. He turned to look at his brother. "Something you want to share with the class?"

"No," Mike said shortly, hoping that Sean would let it go. But of course he didn't.

"I knew there was something going on between you two."

"You don't know anything about it," Mike insisted and walked around his desk to sit down.

"Oh, please. Am I blind?" Sean laughed and dropped into the chair opposite his brother. "That was an almost-kiss moment."

"Butt out, Sean."

Ignoring his brother, Sean continued. "Things were tense as hell between you guys before you went to Laughlin. When you came back it was tenser." He paused. "More tense? Whichever. You know what I mean."

"Yeah, I do, and I wish to hell you'd get what I mean when I tell you to back off."

"Oh, I get it," Sean assured him. "I'm just not listening. So tell me. What's with you and the oh-so-delicious Jenny Marshall?"

Mike's gaze snapped to his brother's. "Watch it."

"Oooh," Sean mused, grinning now. "Territorial. A good sign."

Well, walked right into that, didn't you? Mike's brain whispered.

"Damn it, Sean, stop." Mike tapped a few keys on his laptop, hoping to look too busy to sit and talk to his brother. "What did you come in here for in the first place?"

Still grinning, his brother eased off. "I wanted to tell you about the Wyoming property."

Mike frowned. "A problem?"

"Not with the place itself," Sean told him. "The sale went through, it's all ours. My problem is with the contractor."

"I'm having some issues there myself," Mike said, thinking about all the problems involved in getting a hotel up and running.

"Yeah, but your contractor's a guy. You can talk to a guy."

"Who's yours?"

"Supposedly the best one in the area. A woman. Kate Wells." Sean shook his head, jumped from the chair and paced the short distance to the window. "It's the middle of the damn winter and she wants to get started on the inside of the hotel. Says why waste time? Says she can't have the crew out working in the snow, but her schedule's clear now, so she wants to take her guys inside and start the renovation early."

"That's a problem?" Mike leaned back in his chair and tried to keep his mind on Sean's issues. Not easy when Sean was right about the almost-kiss moment. Seconds ago, he'd been about to—what? Kiss Jenny? Grab her, hold her? Close the office door and lay her down across his desk?

Damn it. Now he was hard and hot and it was even more difficult to focus on Sean.

"Sounds like a good plan to me," Mike said. "I like that this Wells woman has a good work ethic. Eager to get started, get a jump on things. Hell, she could have half of it done by the time the snow melts."

"Yeah?" Sean turned to look at him, exasperation clear on his face. "To get her started, I have to go the hell out there and work with her on the plans. Go through the hotel, see what's what, just like you did in Laughlin."

"Ah." In spite of everything else that was crowding his mind, Mike had to smile. "That's what this is about. You don't want to go to Wyoming."

"Of course I don't," Sean snapped. "There's *snow* there. Lots of it. Have you looked outside *here* today?" He waved one hand at the window behind him. "Blue skies, puffy white clouds, *sun*. It's almost eighty today. You know what it is in Wyoming? I do. I checked. It's twenty-eight. That's the *high*."

Mike chuckled and at his brother's glare, tried his best to muffle it and failed. "It's not forever, Sean. You go out, do the work, come back. At the most, you'll miss a few days of surfing. You'll survive."

"Thanks for the support," his brother muttered. "I'd have to take one of the artists to look the place over for murals, too. Hey." His face brightened. "Think Jenny'd be interested in a quick trip to snow country? Her sketches are great, she'd probably be a big help—"

"No." Mike cut him off before he could get going. Damned if he was going to sit back and have Jenny fly off to Wyoming with Sean. They'd be alone on the plane, at the hotel… No.

"Well, that was decisive."

"Just get one of the others to go with you."

"Not going to be easy to coax someone off a beach and into a snowbank."

"We've all got our problems," Mike told him, and instantly, his mind shot back to Jenny.

The problem there was he couldn't stop thinking about her, wanting her, needing her. And he knew damn well that there was no place in his life for her. He already knew that she was a liar. Okay, fine, she hadn't lied *lately*. But that didn't mean a damn thing. All it told him was that more lies were coming. When? What kind? And how the hell could he be so damn interested in a woman he *knew* he couldn't trust?

Sean came back, sat in the chair again, braced his forearms on the desk and leaned in. "Talk to me, Mike. What is going on with you? What's the deal with Jenny?"

Tempting to confide in Sean, but at the core of it, Mike wasn't a big sharer. He kept his thoughts, his emotions, locked down tight. Not many people got past the wall he'd built around himself. He loved his brother, but there were some things a man just didn't discuss. With anyone.

Shaking his head, Mike scraped one hand across his face. "Nothing I want to talk about, okay?"

Sean watched him for a long minute before saying, "All right. But I'm here when you want to talk. Remember that."

"I will."

"Okay," Sean said. "You're going to Mom and Dad's tonight, right? Not backing out?"

From one problem to another. Mike had considered blowing off his father's birthday dinner. He didn't need the aggravation piled on top of everything else going on. All he needed was to stoke the fire burning at the back of his brain. But if he didn't show up, his mother would make him pay. Somehow. Didn't seem to matter how old you were, your mother retained power over you. And Peggy Ryan had no difficulty wielding that power.

"Yeah, I'm going."

"Wow, feel the enthusiasm."

Mike glared at him. "I'm going. Should be good enough."

"You keep saying things that make me want more information," Sean told him, leaning back in his chair. He kicked his feet up and crossed them on the corner of Mike's desk. "You don't want to talk about Jenny. How about you tell me why you're always pissed at Dad."

"Not going there, either."

"You are not an easy person to have for a brother," Sean told him with a shake of his head. "You've got more secrets than the CIA."

"And the nature of a secret is, it's not talked about."

"That's what you think," Sean countered. "You know I could find out. I could just go to Mom."

"Don't." He didn't want his mother reminded of old pain. Didn't want her to have to tell her other son the things she'd inadvertently told Mike so many years before.

"Just 'don't'? That's all I get? What the hell, Mike? You've been at war with Dad for years and you won't say why." Sean braced both hands on the edge of the desk. "If you know something I should, then tell me."

Mike studied his brother for a long minute. During that short period of time, his brain raced through the familiar scenarios he knew he would be facing over dinner. Strained conversations, his mother trying to be overly bright and happy, his father sending Mike covert glances.

It wouldn't be pleasant. Wouldn't be easy. But he would play the game for his mother's sake.

As far as his little brother went, though, there was just no reason for Sean to have to battle the same emotions that Mike did when the family was together. "Sean, believe me, you don't want to know. So just let it go, all right?"

For a second or two, Sean looked as though he'd argue, but finally, he nodded and stood up. "Fine. But try to remember. I might be your younger brother…but I'm not a kid you need to protect."

Maybe not, Mike thought, but there was no reason to shatter his illusions, either.

A few hours later, Jenny jolted out of the movie she was watching when someone knocked at her door. Wearing her flannel sleep pants and a white tank, she was curled up on the couch with a bowl of popcorn and a glass of wine. Not working. Trying not to think. Just immersing herself in a few harmless explosions on the television.

She wasn't expecting anyone, so naturally, her very excellent imagination conjured up images of roving pirates, rabid serial killers or maybe even an escapee from a mental institution, all crowded together on her tiny front porch.

She wasn't the nervous Nellie type, but when she was alone at night, she often thought about getting a dog. A big one. But for now, she got up, looked out the curtains and sighed, both relieved and annoyed.

Mike.

At least he wasn't a marauder, but why did he have to show up when she looked hideous? No makeup, her hair a messy tumble of curls and wearing her *Star Wars* flannels? And what did it matter? she asked herself. He'd made it clear he wasn't interested, so let him see the real her...flannel jammies and all.

She opened the door and looked up at him.

"You don't ask who it is before you open a door?" he demanded, blue eyes flashing.

"Wow. Hello to you, too."

"Come on, Jenny. You're a woman living alone. Be smart."

"I looked out the window and saw you."

"Oh, that's all right, then."

"Thanks very much." One hand on the open door, one on the jamb, she asked, "What are you doing here, Mike?"

"Honestly," he said, "I don't know. Just had dinner with the family at my folks' house and didn't want to go home yet. I drove around for a while and ended up here."

Fascinating.

He wore a black jacket over a white shirt, open at the collar, with black jeans and boots that looked as if they'd seen a lot of miles. His hair had been ruffled by the wind and his eyes looked...empty. His features were tight, his shoulders tense, and Jenny thought he was on the verge of leaving. She didn't want him to.

"Do you want a glass of wine?" she asked.

His gaze fixed on hers. "That'd be good. Thanks."

Polite, but distant. That, plus a little outright suspicion, she was used to. Tonight, though, there was a sadness about him that she'd never seen before and Jenny felt a flicker of worry she knew he wouldn't appreciate.

He stepped inside, and she closed and locked the door behind him.

"You were at your parents' house, you said. Are they okay? Sean?"

He looked at her. "Yeah. They're all fine."

She tipped her head to one side and studied him. "You're not."

He laughed shortly and scraped one hand along his jaw. "I don't like being read that easily, but no, I guess not."

It was the first time she could ever remember seeing Mike Ryan vulnerable in any way. Normally he was so in charge, so much the stalwart head of a billion-dollar company, that seeing his features strained and closed off was unsettling. She'd rather have him raging at her than see him looking so lost.

"I shouldn't have come here—" he said abruptly.

But he had, Jenny told herself. For whatever reason, he'd been upset and he'd come to *her*. That had to mean something, didn't it? "Stay. Take off your jacket. Sit down. Have a glass of wine, Mike."

It took a moment or two, but he finally nodded and said, "Okay, thanks."

He shrugged out of his jacket and draped it across the back of a chair, then looked around the room as if seeing it for the first time. It wasn't his first visit, though. He'd been here before. The night they'd— Whoops. Probably not a good idea to think about that right now.

Mike stood in the middle of the small living room, glanced at the popcorn and her wineglass and then shifted his gaze to hers. "Movie night?"

She shrugged. "I just wanted to relax, you know. A lot going on right now…"

"Tell me about it." He sat on the couch, took a handful of popcorn and watched the movie playing out on the screen.

She went to the kitchen to get him that wine, then walked back to the living room and handed him a glass of chardonnay. He took a sip, gestured with the glass toward the TV and asked, *"Die Hard?"*

She smiled and sat on the other end of the couch. "It's my feel-good movie. You know, Christmas, good guys beating the bad guys…"

"And lots of stuff blowing up."

"Exactly." She grinned and sipped her wine.

"I didn't know you liked action movies."

"There's a lot you don't know about me."

"And some I do," he said, a frown flattening his mouth.

"Or think you do," she countered. She wasn't a liar and a thief, and she felt that somewhere inside him, he knew that or he wouldn't have been sitting on her couch.

"Touché." He nodded, glanced at the television again. "One guy going against a whole crew."

"To save his wife," she said with a satisfied sigh. "It's romantic."

He chuckled. "Romance and bombs?"

"Works for me."

His gaze shifted to the flannel pants she wore. "Darth Vader pajamas?"

She grinned. "They're cozy." And were a gift from her uncle Hank, but she doubted he'd want to hear that.

"I don't know what to think about you, Jenny," he said.

"Good. I'm glad. That means you're not entirely sure you should think what you used to think because now you think your thinking might have been wrong."

He blinked at her, then shook his head. "I actually followed that."

Turning his head again, he stared at the television. In the flickering light, darkness passed over his features, highlighting the shadows crouched in his eyes.

"Why are you really here, Mike?"

Slowly, he looked back at her. "You know why."

There was that wild flutter and rush of anticipation moving through her stomach again. She took a swallow of wine to ease her suddenly dust-dry throat, then set the glass on the table in front of her.

Jenny knew exactly what he was talking about. She'd felt it in the office today. Before Sean came in, there had been a slow, simmering burn between Mike and her, and that fire was still there, hot as ever. Acting on it would be a huge mistake. But *not* acting on it was driving her crazy.

"Yes," she said softly, holding his gaze with her own. "I know."

"So the question is," Mike asked, voice low and deep and intimate, "do you want me to leave?"

"No."

"Thank God." He set his glass down and reached for her.

Pushing the popcorn out of the way, Jenny went into his arms; all the while her mind called out a warning she refused to heed. She didn't want to be wise. Didn't want to be smart. She wanted Mike and that just wouldn't change.

But it was more than that, she admitted silently as Mike's mouth claimed hers. She leaned into him, opened to him, and felt the heat within build into something that was both wilder and more…steady than anything she'd ever known before.

Her breath caught, as understanding dawned. Her mind spun and she clung to Mike because he was the only steady point in her universe.

She loved Mike Ryan.

Her brain went into overdrive in the span of a single heartbeat. The months of working at Celtic Knot, watching Mike work with young artists, encouraging them. Seeing his dedication to his work, his brother and friend. Knowing that he didn't trust her, but having him give her the opportunity to work on his hotel in spite of it all.

He didn't trust her.

Didn't love her.

There was misery lying in wait, and Jenny knew it. But her whole life had been spent wanting the very feelings that were crashing down around her right now.

So she'd risk the pain to have this one moment—even if Mike never knew what was shining in her heart.

Seven

A few days later, Mike was at his desk when the video chat bell on his phone went off. He hit Answer and his brother's face appeared on the screen.

"I hate Wyoming."

Mike laughed. Sean looked haggard, on edge. His eyes were narrowed, whisker stubble covered his jaws and the scowl he wore looked as if it had been permanently etched into his face.

"Don't hold back, tell me how you really feel."

"Funny." Sean glanced over his shoulder, then back into the camera. "It hasn't stopped snowing since I got here. There's like three feet of snow piling up out there and it's still coming down. I don't think it'll ever stop."

"Sounds cold."

"Hah! Beyond cold. Beyond freezing. I'm wearing two sweaters *inside*."

Chuckling, Mike asked, "What's it like when you're not bitching about how cold you are?"

Sean sighed then grudgingly admitted, "It's pretty. Lots of trees. Lots of open land. And who knew the sky was so big when you get out of the city?"

Mike smiled. He'd discovered that for himself when he and Jenny were in Laughlin. Of course, allowing Jenny into his mind meant opening himself up to the memories that never really left him. Her smile. Her eyes. The feel of her skin against his. The soft sigh of her breath as she surrendered to him. Stopping in at her house after work, spending the evening watching movies, making love, talking about the work, the hotel. Talking about everything except for the fact that he couldn't trust her.

Pushing those thoughts away, he asked, "What's the hotel itself like, Sean?"

"Big. Cold. Empty." Sean blew out a frustrated breath and pushed one hand through his hair. "But the bones are good. A lot of work to do to turn it into a 'Forest Run' fantasy."

"And is Kate Wells up to the task?"

"To hear her tell it," Sean muttered. "Anyway, there's a hundred and fifty guest rooms and they all need work."

"If we go with your idea to hold our own game con on the property, we'll need more rooms. Are there other hotels close by?"

"No. We're ten miles from the closest town and it's got two B and Bs and one motel right off the highway."

It was Mike's turn to frown. "Sean, we can't go with a big conference if there's nowhere for people to stay." He took a breath and spoke again before Sean could suggest camping. "And don't say people can pitch tents."

Sean laughed. "Just because I like camping doesn't

mean I want strangers staying all over the property. Anyway, there's a bigger city about twenty-five miles from here, with more hotels and Kate—the contractor—had another idea on that, too."

"What's she thinking?" Mike picked up his coffee and took a long drink.

Sean's frown deepened. "Is that a cappuccino? You bastard."

"I'll enjoy it for you."

"Thanks." Shaking his head, Sean said, "Kate thinks we should put in some small cabins, behind the main lodge, staggered back into the forest. Give people more privacy, a sense of being out in the open..."

Mike nodded, thinking about it. "It's a good idea."

"Yeah, I know."

"Yet you don't look happy about it."

"Because she was so damn sure she was right," Sean told him. "It's hard agreeing she was."

"Sounds like you're having a great time," Mike said with another deliberate sip of his hot coffee.

Sean's eyes narrowed into slits. "This woman is the most hardheaded person I've ever dealt with and that includes *you*."

"As long as she does good work, that's all you should care about."

"Yeah, yeah. She wants to get her crew in here next week and start in on the rehab and I don't see a problem with it." He paused and ran one finger around the collar of his black sweater. "As long as I can oversee it from California."

"Okay, but since you didn't take any of the artists with you, what'll she do about the painting we'll need done?"

"Come on," Sean said. "I couldn't bring an artist out

here when everyone's doing the final run on 'The Wild Hunt.'"

True. It was bad timing all the way around, really. Sean had had to get to the next hotel and every artist in the company was focused on the finishing touches of the game that would be released next.

"Anyway," Sean continued, "how hard is it to leave walls blank? They can paint it white or something and then when we bring the artists in, they can change it to whatever."

"That'll work. You still coming home tomorrow?"

"That's the plan, thank God," Sean said. "Kate's outside, bringing her truck around. Naturally, it's still snowing."

"If it makes you feel any better, it's seventy-five here today."

"Great. Thanks. That just caps it." A door slammed somewhere. Sean looked to one side and shouted, "What?"

"What is it?" Mike asked.

"Karma probably," Sean told him, his expression disgusted. "Kate just heard on the truck radio that the pass down the mountain is closed. I'm snowed in."

Mike tried not to, but his brother looked so furious and frustrated, he couldn't hold back the laughter. Even as Sean gave him a dirty look, Mike held up one hand and tried to stop laughing. "Sorry, sorry."

"How is this funny?" Sean demanded. "I'm trapped in an empty hotel with a crabby contractor and a mountain of snow outside the door."

"Clearly," Mike said finally, "it's only funny from California. But have you got food, heat?"

"Yeah," Sean said, then spoke to someone in the room with him. "Come here for a minute. Meet my brother."

A second or two later, a woman popped onto the screen. Pretty, with a heart-shaped face and a wide mouth, she had black hair and eyes as blue as Sean's. She was wearing a baseball cap pulled low on her forehead and what looked like a heavy green sweater.

"Hi, I'm Kate and you're Mike," she said, words tumbling over each other. "Nice to meet you, but we don't have a lot of time to talk. There's firewood outside, we need to bring it in before the rest of the storm hits. Don't worry, though. There's plenty of food since I make sure my crew is fed while they work and we've been out here this last week taking measurements and getting ideas about the work."

"Okay." Mike threw that word in fast, thinking he probably wouldn't have another chance to speak. He was right.

"The storm'll blow through in a day or two and the plows will have the pass cleared out pretty quickly, so you can have your brother back by the end of the week."

"Okay…"

Sean grabbed the phone and told Kate, "I'll be right there to help. Yeah. Okay." When he looked back at Mike, he was shaking his head. "I was this close—" he held up two fingers just a breath apart "—from getting outta Dodge. Now I don't know when I'll get out. Tell Mom not to worry and don't bother calling me. I'm going to shut off the cell phone, conserve power."

"Okay." In spite of the fact that he'd been amused only a few minutes ago by Sean's situation, now Mike wondered. "You sure you'll be all right?"

Sean laughed now. "I'm the outdoors guy, remember? There may not be any waves to surf out here, but I'll be fine. I've been camping in worse situations than I've got here. At least we have a roof and plenty of beds to choose from. I'll call when I can. Just keep a cappuccino hot for me because I'll be back as soon as I can."

"I will. And, Sean?" Mike added, "Don't kill the contractor."

Smirking, Sean said, "I make no promises."

Two weeks later, Jenny was fighting a resilient flu that just refused to go away.

Every morning her stomach did an oily slide toward rebellion and every morning she fought it back. She was simply too busy to let some determined bug knock her flat. So she went to work, forced herself to eat and by evening was usually feeling if not great, at least better. Until the next day when it would all start again.

Hunched over her tablet, Jenny made notes on the hotel murals, then shifted files and added a few more finishing touches on the Wise Woman sketches for "The Wild Hunt." The witch was great and the addition to the script had really given the game that extra punch.

She'd even played the beta game the day before herself just to see how difficult it really was to find the extra runes that would free the witch. It was a challenge. So she knew the hardcore gamers among their fans were going to love it.

Yawning, she shut down that program and called up the list of artists and painters she'd developed. She'd need to hire at least three or four people to help her with the murals and would have to check out their qualifications first.

Sunlight slanted in through the windows of the graphic arts department and all around her conversations and ripples of laughter rang out. Fingers hit keyboards, rock music played softly from one of the cubicles, and here and there in the room people bent their heads together to go over the work.

None of the distractions bothered her because Jenny was used to working with background noise. She'd never yet met an artist who did their best work in sterile silence. So while her friends and colleagues worked the games, Jenny went to artists' websites.

She looked at portfolios, studied techniques, then checked the artists' bios and read about their backgrounds. Artists were usually solitary people, but she needed those who could work with others and take instruction. That was the hard part and she knew it. Most artists treasured their own vision of whatever they were working on at the time and didn't much care for someone else coming in and telling them what to do next.

But in this case, whoever was hired had to be willing to go along with the plans for the murals and portraits. They had to stick to the creative brief that Jenny was still finishing and not waste time arguing over the direction of the project.

She yawned and scrolled through the bio of a Nevada artist who specialized in fantasy paintings. His work was stellar but the smugness of his bio convinced Jenny he wasn't a team player.

"Next," she muttered and closed the page before moving on to another name on her list. She only needed to find one more artist and then she could get moving on the actual painting on-site.

"Hey, Jen—"

She looked up and smiled at Casey Williams. New to the company, Casey was a talented intern. She'd only worked at Celtic Knot for a couple of months, but she'd slid right into the mix as if she'd always been there. About twenty-five, Casey was married with a baby son. She had long dark hair that lay in a single braid across her shoulder. Her T-shirt was bright red, her jeans were a faded gray and her flip-flops revealed the green polish on her toes.

"What's up, Casey?" Jenny smothered another yawn behind her hand.

"Dave wants to know if you've finished tweaking the Wise Woman—"

"Yes, just a few minutes ago. I'll email the file to him."

"Cool. And I just want to say, I love your vision of her." Casey's hands were gripped together at her waist. "I saw the prelim sketches and they're amazing. It was a great idea to include her as a surprise for gamers. But the images are what really grabbed me. She's powerful and beautiful and— You don't look so hot."

Jenny laughed shortly. And here she thought she'd been so good about covering up how miserable she felt. "Thanks."

"No." Casey backtracked fast. "No, I mean, you look like you still don't feel well."

"Actually, I really don't," Jenny said, shaking her head, then regretting the abrupt motion because it wobbled her already unsteady stomach a little. For days, she'd been dragging around the office, trying to concentrate on the work even while her body continually reminded her she should be home in bed.

"Um…" Casey glanced around her, as if checking to make sure no one could overhear them. Then she sat down on the edge of a chair and leaned in closer. "I know we don't know each other very well yet, so this is prob-

ably out of line. But you've been feeling sick for a week
or more now, right?"

"Yes…" Jenny said, wondering where this was going.

"I know this is none of my business." Casey took a
breath and then let it go. "But I know the signs because
I lived them myself a year ago."

Confused, Jenny asked, "What're you talking about?
What signs?"

"Is it possible," Casey asked gently, "that this isn't the
flu? That maybe you're pregnant?"

Shock held Jenny in place for a slow count of ten. Her
mind, however, was racing. Thinking. *Counting.*

"Oh, my God." Panic rose up and choked off the nau-
sea in the pit of her stomach. She did some fast calculating again, running through the numbers, the weeks, the
possibilities. And ended up wheezing for air.

"Yeah," Casey whispered, nodding in understanding,
"that's what I thought."

Oh, God, how far out of it was she that another woman
was the one who had to tell her she was pregnant? How
had she missed this? But even as she asked herself that,
she knew the answer. She hadn't figured it out because
she hadn't wanted to. Her relationship with Mike was
so…tricky, a pregnancy was going to change everything.

Casey was still talking; excited, comforting, worried,
Jenny couldn't be sure. All she really heard was a buzz
of sound from the other woman. It was as if Jenny's
head were filled with cotton, muffling everything but
the pounding of her own heart.

Pregnant? By her *boss*?

It was more than possible, she knew. Instantly, her
mind dragged up images from over the past few weeks.
Incredible sex, sharing moments with Mike that she

wouldn't trade for anything. They'd used protection of course, but no contraception worked 100 percent guaranteed. Would Mike believe that, though? No, he wouldn't.

Oh, God.

She blinked and the office came back into focus. She looked at Casey, and saw the woman's encouraging smile. All around her, life went on as usual, with no one but Casey aware that Jenny's world had just taken a major shift. She took a breath, tried to calm down, but that wasn't going to happen. Not until she knew, for sure. She could suspect she was pregnant, but until she knew without a doubt, she wouldn't be able to think clearly. Wouldn't be able to face Mike, with this suspicion simmering in her bloodstream. She had to know. Now. Suddenly, she couldn't sit there a moment longer.

Jenny grabbed her purse out of her desk drawer, then lunged to her feet. "You know, I really think I should just go home early."

"Are you worried?" Casey asked gently. "About how your boyfriend's going to take the news? I was nervous before I told my husband." She smiled to herself. "There was no reason to be. He was excited. Happy."

Mike wouldn't be. But Jenny couldn't say that because no one in the office knew she and Mike were together. Oh, this just got more and more complex.

Still, she forced a smile she didn't feel and lied to the nice woman still watching her. "I'm sure you're right and he will be. But right now, I think I just need to lie down for a while."

"That's a good idea," Casey said and stood up, too. "Take care of yourself and if you need anything—" She shrugged. "Call me, okay?"

"Sure. I will. Um, thanks, Casey."

"No problem. Drive safe."

Drive, Jenny told herself as she left the office and headed for the parking lot. Straight to a drugstore where she'd buy a few pregnancy tests and take them all. For the first time in her life, she was actually hoping she had the flu.

She didn't.

An hour later, Jenny looked at the five test strips lined up on her bathroom counter. Every last one of them was positive. She hadn't trusted one kind of test, either. She'd bought different ones, tried them all. And they all proved her suspicions right.

"I guess that's it, then," she murmured, lifting her gaze to her own reflection in the bathroom mirror. "I'm going to have a baby. Mike's baby."

Both hands covered her flat belly as if cradling the child within. She waited, meeting her own eyes in the mirror, trying to decipher the myriad emotions racing through her. Sure, panic was in there, but it wasn't uppermost in her mind. First and most important, there was *excitement*.

This wouldn't be easy, she admitted silently, but nothing great ever was. There was a lot to think about, to plan for. First, of course, she had to tell Mike. She wouldn't even try to keep this from him, even knowing how he was going to react.

Her heart hurt as she thought about the confrontation that would come soon. He'd never trusted her and this news was going to convince him that he had been right about her all along. She still had to tell him that she was carrying his child. Even if he wanted nothing to do with her afterward. Even if he walked out and never looked back.

She took a breath to steady herself, but the twinges of pain still squeezed her heart. Mike wasn't going to be happy. But Jenny was. There had never been a future for her and the man she loved, but now when he walked away, she would have something of him, forever. A baby. Her own child. Her own family. Someone to love. Someone who would love her.

She hadn't planned this, but now that the baby was here, she wouldn't change it, either.

"I promise, I want you," she whispered, voice soft with wonder as her palms stroked her belly. "You'll be loved and you'll never have to worry about me walking away. About being left alone. You'll be safe, I swear it."

She lifted her chin, stiffened her spine and resolved then and there that no matter what Mike said, what he tried to make her feel, she wouldn't lose this excitement. This sense of pure joy that was already whipping through her like lightning strikes. She hadn't expected this pregnancy, but she would never regret it.

She would give this child the life she had always wanted. It would grow up loved and secure and it would never, ever doubt its mother's love.

Jenny took a steadying breath and tried to steer her celebratory thoughts back down into more immediate concerns. Like facing Mike—and the possibility that she would have to change jobs. Even if he didn't fire her and who knew, he very well might, working at Celtic Knot over the next few months could be very uncomfortable.

But before she made any decisions, she had to tell Mike.

Jenny watched her reflection wince. That conversation wasn't going to be pretty. He would never believe she hadn't planned this pregnancy. And any semblance of warmth that had sprung up between them over the past few weeks was going to dissipate.

She hated knowing that. Hated understanding that her time with Mike was going to end. But not only did she love the man, she *knew* him. So she had to prepare herself for the fact that once he knew the truth, all of her fantasies would be over.

When her cell phone rang she went out to answer it. Seeing Mike's name on the screen didn't even surprise her. Of course he would call when she was thinking about him. Of course she wouldn't have time to get used to this staggering news before having to tell him and weather the inevitable fallout. But maybe it was better this way. Worrying over the coming confrontation would only tie her up in knots anyway.

Steeling herself, she answered. "Hi, Mike."

"Jenny, are you all right?" She closed her eyes at the sound of his voice. At the concern ringing in his tone. "Casey says you went home sick."

Sick. Well, technically, her stomach was still feeling a little iffy, but it was so much more.

"I'm okay, but, Mike," she said, mentally preparing herself for what was to come, "we have to talk."

An hour later, Mike stood in her living room staring down at the five test sticks she'd laid out on the coffee table. Brain burning, heart pounding, Mike stared at the evidence in front of him and still couldn't quite bring himself to believe it. He took a few deep breaths, willing himself to calm down, to beat back the sense of betrayal and suspicion that slapped at him.

"Pregnant?" He shifted his gaze to the woman across

the room from him. Her blond hair curled around her head. Her blue eyes were wide and shone with an innocence he couldn't trust. She wore those silly flannel pants and a yellow tank top that bared her shoulders and hugged her generous breasts. His gaze dropped to her belly briefly as he tried to imagine a child—*his* child—nestled inside.

He couldn't do it.

"How the hell did that happen?"

Her eyebrows lifted. "Really?"

He pushed both hands through his hair and scrambled for patience. "I know *how*, so don't get cute. But we used a condom. Every time."

"I know," Jenny said, wrapping her arms around her middle almost defensively, "but nothing's a hundred percent."

"Well, they damn well should be," he argued. What the hell as the point of using a damn condom if they didn't do their job? "Unless…" Mind clicking along, racing down dark, twisted, tangled roads, he said, "You had those condoms in your drawer."

"So?"

He didn't answer that question. Instead, he turned and stalked into her bedroom, tore open the drawer and grabbed one of the condoms still there. Had they been damaged somehow? Had she found a way to sabotage them so… He saw the date stamped on the bottom of the foil.

"What're you doing?" Jenny asked as she came into the room behind him.

"I thought maybe you'd done something to these," he muttered, turning to look at her, still holding the damn condom. "I don't know, poked holes in them with a needle or something."

She gaped at him. "Are you serious?"

He ignored that, just as he paid no attention to the look of astonishment on her face. She wasn't an innocent and he should have remembered that before allowing himself to slide into an affair that could only end badly. "Turns out you didn't have to. How the hell long have you had these things?"

She blinked in confusion, then said, "What does that have to do with anything?"

"Just answer the question."

Frowning at him, she said, "They were party favors at a bachelorette party I went to five years ago."

"Five years." Nodding, he curled his fingers around the condom package and squeezed.

"Does that matter?"

A short, sharp laugh shot from his throat. "Yeah. It matters. Especially since they *expired* five years ago." He couldn't believe this.

"What do you mean?" She practically pried his fingers apart to snatch the packet from him. "Condoms can *expire*?"

"You thought they lasted forever?"

"No," she said, "I never thought about it. Why would I? It's not like they have to be refrigerated or anything. Who would expect they could go bad? They're in their own little foil packs for heaven's sake."

"That's just perfect," he muttered and thought back to the first night with her here, at her house, and how damned grateful he'd been that she had condoms on hand. He'd never checked them out. Never thought to make sure they were good.

He scrubbed both hands across his face and told himself this was what he got for going against his own instincts. He'd wanted her. Had to have her. Even knowing that she was a liar. Now he was paying the price for following his own needs.

"It's probably why your friend gave them away as party favors," he muttered darkly. "Because they were no good, she got 'em cheap.

"But why would you hold on to them?"

"I didn't think about it," she said with a shake of her head. "I just tossed them into the drawer and never gave it another thought."

"Perfect," he muttered, scraping one hand across his face.

"You knew they were no good," he said, voice deep, dark. Anger bubbled in his gut until it was a thick, hot brew that spilled through his veins. "You knew what would happen if we used them and you were good with that, weren't you?"

"Are you serious?"

"Damn right, I'm serious." He crowded in on her, forcing her to back up until her legs hit the mattress and she plopped down onto it. "This was all a setup, wasn't it? Right from the beginning."

"What *all* are you talking about?" she demanded, glaring up at him. "You mean, you coming to my house, willingly going to my bed? That *all*?"

"Us meeting in Phoenix. You coming to work at Celtic Knot. It's all been building to this, right? Why the hell else would you come to work for me after what happened when we met?"

"You are seriously paranoid," she snapped, tossing her hair out of her eyes so she could glare at him.

"Right. I'm paranoid, but you're pregnant, so maybe I'm not crazy, huh?" He leaned over her until their faces were just a breath apart. The smell of her invaded his senses and threw gasoline on the fire inside him. Even furious, even staggered by her news, Mike could admit to wanting her. To needing her. And that fried him.

"All you needed to do was get me in here, to use the damn useless condoms so you could get pregnant." He was so angry, the edges of his vision were blurred. His breath came fast and hard, his heartbeat thundered and desire tangled with fury until his whole body practically vibrated.

She shoved at him and he backed up just far enough for her to clamber off the bed and gain her feet again. "My God, do you really think you're that great a prize? Do you know how many times you've insulted me by calling me a thief? And that's supposed to endear you to me somehow?"

"Yet you slept with me anyway and here we are," he reminded her, in spite of the sparks flashing in her eyes.

"You're right," she said, sarcasm dripping from her words. "How clever I must be. And psychic as well to *know* that the great Mike Ryan would one day deign to visit my little apartment. Would allow me to seduce him with my trickery and feminine wiles. How brilliant of me to have faulty condoms so I could fool him into impregnating me. My God, I'm *amazing*."

It sounded ludicrous even to him, but Mike couldn't let it go completely. His mind worked, with two opposing voices shouting, demanding to be heard. But the calm, cool, rational part of him was buried beneath the facts he couldn't forget. She'd lied to him the first time he met her. She'd come to work at his company in spite of that.

She'd wormed her way onto his hotel design team. She'd made herself *important*. But he'd kept her on. Hadn't told Sean to fire her. Why? Because she had gotten into his blood whether he'd wanted her there or not.

Now she was pregnant.

He looked down at her and the flash in her blue eyes did nothing to ease the anger bubbling and frothing inside him. It didn't help to know that even as furious as he was, he could still look at her and need her.

"No matter what you think," she said tightly, "I didn't trick you. I didn't set up a *trap* to catch the mighty and elusive Mike Ryan."

"Well, since you're so honest," he ground out, "I'll just believe you, okay?"

"You should but you won't," she told him, shaking her head, sending those curls that drove him crazy into a wild dance about her head. She underlined each of her words with a determined tap of her index finger against his chest. "Do you really think I would trap a man who doesn't want me? I've got more self-respect than that, thanks."

Jenny stood there facing him, chin lifted, eyes narrowed and hot with banked fury. She looked beautiful and strong, and it took everything he had to fight the urge to grab her and pull her in close. Jenny Marshall got to him like no one else ever had and he hated admitting that, even to himself.

Shaking his head, he took a mental step backward and told her, "It's not going to work. You're not getting money out of me and I won't marry you."

Her head jerked back as if he'd slapped her, but she recovered fast, he had to give her that.

"I don't want *anything* from you. As for marrying me?

Who asked you to?" she demanded and whirled around. She left the bedroom, walked into the living room, and he followed because what the hell else was he going to do?

She stopped in front of the windows and with the last of the sun's rays silhouetting her in gold, she looked at him and said, "I wouldn't marry you on a bet, Mike. You think I'd actually trap a man who doesn't want me into a marriage that would be a misery? No, thanks. I don't need you to take care of me or my baby, Mike."

Now it was his turn to feel insulted. Whatever he did or didn't feel for Jenny, she was carrying *his* kid and she'd better get used to that from the jump. "You can't keep my child from me, Jenny, so don't even try."

"Who said I would?" Shaking her head, she said, "You keep putting words in my mouth. So why not just stop trying to think for both of us? Telling you about the baby was the right thing to do. If you want to see our child, that's your choice. But you don't call the shots here, Mike, and I think you should leave."

He didn't want to. But staying here angry wouldn't help the situation any. He needed some air. Needed to think. But when he walked out of her house and heard the door slam shut behind him, Mike acknowledged that the real problem was that he needed her, too.

Eight

"You're pregnant?"

Jenny sighed and waited for her uncle to finish ranting. Right after Mike left, she had driven south to her uncle's house on Balboa Island. She'd needed…support, and she'd known she'd find it here. At least, she would once her uncle was finished calling down curses on Mike Ryan's head.

Her gaze tracked the older man as he paced around his living room. Just as when she'd told Mike about the baby, she'd come expecting this exact reaction. The man had never forgiven Mike for accusing Jenny of trying to use him. And this situation wasn't making her uncle any fonder of Mike Ryan.

"He turned on you, didn't he?"

Jenny winced and her uncle saw it. His gaze narrowed and his features tightened into lines of fury.

"I knew it. That son of a bitch."

She sighed a little.

"When you told him about the baby, he accused you of trying to trap him into marriage, didn't he?"

Well, she could lie to her uncle or she could tell the truth and confirm his opinion of Mike. Jenny thought about it for a second, then decided she didn't need to protect her baby's father. "Yes, he did."

"Still thinks you're trying to wangle a deal for Snyder Arts?"

"I guess," she said on a sigh.

"Idiot," Hank muttered.

Before he could get going again, Jenny started talking. She wanted to say something that she should have said years ago. "Uncle Hank…"

The tone in her voice must have alerted him to a change in subject. He looked at her, concern shining in his eyes. "What is it?"

Lamps on the tables tossed golden light around the room. Outside, lights in homes and boats flickered in the darkness. This was home. Had been since she was a girl. And the comfort she felt here was something she was still grateful for.

She smiled a little. "I wanted to tell you something. When I first realized I was pregnant, I thought about all the responsibilities lying ahead. And I understood how you must have felt when my parents foisted me off on you."

"When they—"

"I just want you to know that I don't blame you for not wanting me, back then. I mean," she hurried on as Hank's forehead furrowed and his eyes narrowed, "I was twelve and you were alone and had your life and I was a—"

"Gift," Hank finished for her while she searched for the right word. "You were a gift," he repeated as if making sure she understood exactly how he felt. "My sister and her husband were fools then and they're fools now—wherever they are. They didn't know what they had in you."

Stunned silent, Jenny could only watch him as he approached and cupped her face in his big hands.

"You opened up my life, Jenny. Of course I wanted you. You're my family. You've been a joy, always. You're my *daughter* more than my niece. And now, you've given an old man something to look forward to—you're going to make me a grandfather."

Her vision blurry from behind a sheen of tears, Jenny could only look up at the one steady presence she'd known her whole life.

"No more of this not-wanting-you stuff, okay?" he asked. "Don't you ever even think it. Understand?"

She nodded because she didn't trust herself to speak. Her heart was too full to allow for mere words to explain what she felt.

"Good," he said with a sharp nod. "We've got that settled once and for all. But as for Mike Ryan…"

"Uncle Hank, this isn't all on Mike. I'm a big girl—"

"You're too trusting and he's a man used to taking what he wants. That's the issue here," Hank muttered darkly. He paced again as if he couldn't stand still another minute. "Thinks because he's richer than Croesus he can just call the tune everyone's supposed to dance to."

Jenny rolled her eyes and he saw that, too.

"I'm wound up and I know it," he said, "but with reason."

"I appreciate it, really I do," Jenny told him and

walked across the comfortably furnished and oh-so-familiar room to his side.

Nothing in this house had changed in decades. There were comfy chairs, heavy tables and a stone-faced fireplace. The cream-colored walls were covered with paintings by local artists—and a few of Jenny's early works. He had a housekeeper who'd been with him for thirty years and ran the house like a general his battalion.

"You're going to have the man's baby, Jenny. He should offer to marry you. It's what's right—not that Mike Ryan would know that."

She blew out a breath as she looked into the older man's worried eyes. Uncle Hank was tall and lanky, with thick gray hair, steely blue eyes and a stubborn jaw that was now set as if he were ready to bite through a box of nails. He had been the one steady influence in her life and he was the only family she really had. Her parents had disappeared from her life so many years ago, Jenny had no idea if they were living or dead. Hank, though, had always been there for her.

Even though, despite what he had just said, she couldn't imagine it had been easy for him to take on a twelve-year-old girl out of the blue.

She had known even then that she was his duty. She hadn't believed he'd really wanted her—why would he? His life was simple, uncomplicated. Why would he take on a twelve-year-old with abandonment issues voluntarily? But he'd taken her in, cared for her, seen her through school and dating, and even hired Jenny for her first real job as a summer intern at Snyder Arts. Hank had been the one to give her pastels and inks and sketch pads. He'd seen her raw talent and encouraged her to grow it. She would always owe him for that and for so much more.

"I don't need him to marry me," she said softly, laying one hand on her uncle's arm.

"'Course you don't, but he should have offered, damn it, not made you feel like a cheat or worse."

"I don't want a man who's forced to marry me because of circumstances." She remembered the look on Mike's face before he left. The harsh words they'd thrown at each other, and though it tore at her to admit it, Jenny knew that it was over between them. A low, throbbing ache settled into her heart and she had the distinct feeling that it would be there with her forever.

"So you'd have said no if he'd asked?"

"Yes," she said and knew he didn't really understand. In Hank's world, a man took care of his responsibilities. But what he didn't get was that Jenny didn't want to be the duty Mike picked up and carried under duress. If he didn't love her and want her, she didn't want him, either.

She still loved him, though, damn it. Even hearing his accusations hadn't been enough to kill off her feelings. Did that make her crazy or just stupid? She didn't know. All Jenny could hope was that the love she felt for Mike would slowly fade away.

Besides, she hadn't really been surprised when Mike didn't want her. No one ever really had. Until today, she would have said that not even her uncle had wanted her.

And she would never allow her child to feel that way.

"Mike Ryan." Hank shook his head and gray hair sproinged out around his head until he looked like a taller, more handsome Albert Einstein. "What were you thinking, honey? You know that man isn't to be trusted."

"Funny," she mused. "He says the same about *me*."

Hank stabbed his index finger toward her. "That tells you everything you need to know about the man. You're the most honest person I've ever known. If he can't see that, it's a lack in him, not you."

Warmth trickled through her. "Thanks, Uncle Hank."

"You don't have to thank me for the truth, honey," he said, shoving both hands into his pockets. "And I'm sorry to be carrying on so, but it just pops my corn that the man has taken advantage of you this way."

Jenny's mouth quirked. He sounded as if he thought she was a vestal virgin tempted out of her temple by Blackbeard.

"Uncle Hank…"

"Fine, fine." He lifted both hands. "You're a grown woman and you don't need your old uncle spouting off when you've got plenty to think about on your own."

"Thank you, though," she said, putting her arms around his waist. "For the outrage. For the support. For loving me."

True to form, Hank stiffened a little, as he always had. Hugs seemed to flummox him a bit, as if he wasn't quite sure what to do in response. And Jenny had often wondered what his late wife had been like. If she'd lived, would he be more comfortable with displays of emotion? He gave her a few awkward pats on her shoulder, then eased her back so he could look into her eyes.

"Are you all right with this?" he wanted to know. "I mean, you're healthy? You're going to be okay?"

"I'm fine and yes, I'm going to be great." She smiled. "I want this baby, Uncle Hank."

"Then I'll do whatever I can to help you, honey."

She smiled again. Hank wasn't the most outwardly

affectionate man, but he was loyal and kind and dependable. If he made a promise, he kept it.

"What're you going to do about your job?" he asked.

"To tell you the truth, I don't know." She bit at her bottom lip as she thought about it. "Working with Mike for months will be impossible now. Especially once word gets out around the office—and it will—that I'm carrying his child."

Hank frowned and looked as though he wanted to say something else, but he kept his silence and Jenny went on.

"But I'm not going to do anything about it right now. I've got the hotel in Nevada to finish."

"You're still going to do it?"

"Absolutely," she told him. Not only was she too invested in the project to give it up now, but being in Laughlin working would keep her from having to deal with Mike every day. "It's a fabulous opportunity and I don't want to give it up. I've got the whole thing planned out and letting someone else take it over is just impossible."

"Always were stubborn," he muttered.

"Wonder where I got it," she countered and went up on her toes to kiss his cheek.

He looked pleased but baffled.

"Come on in and eat, you two. Dinner's going cold on the table."

Jenny looked over at Betty Sanders, housekeeper, cook and, as Uncle Hank liked to call her, his nemesis. She was short and thin, disproving the theory that a great cook had to be big. She wore jeans and a sweatshirt and had her long gray hair in a braid wrapped around the back of her head like a halo.

Jenny appreciated the offer, but she wasn't all that hungry, either. "Thanks, Betty, but—"

"If you're going to have a baby, you're going to feed it. Now come in and sit down." Betty had helped raise Jenny and had run Hank's house and life for too long to stop now.

"Might as well," Uncle Hank said with a shrug. "You know she won't quit hounding you until you do."

"True." Jenny walked with him into the dining room, glad to be here in the home she'd loved growing up. Out the windows was a view of Balboa Bay, with beautiful houses lined along the shore and boats tied up at the docks.

When she first came here, Jenny had spent a lot of time down on the dock, watching the boats sail past, wondering if her parents would come back, if Hank would send her somewhere else. She'd felt lost and alone until the day her uncle had come out, sat down beside her and said, *If you're going to be spending so much time out on the dock, I'd better teach you how to sail.*

He took her out on his boat that very afternoon and for the first time in her life, she'd felt the amazing freedom in skimming across the water's surface, feeling the wind stream through her hair. He'd let her steer the boat, putting his big hands over hers on the wheel and explaining the harbor and the neighborhood that was now hers. That's when she'd understood that she was there to stay. Hank had given her everything in that one afternoon.

At the round oak table in the dining room, all three of them sat down and dug into the hearty bowls of homemade potato soup. While they ate, they talked, and Jenny was glad her uncle seemed to be calming down.

"There's just no point in worrying over what is," Betty

said, with a warning look at Hank. "Jenny's fine and she'll keep being fine with or without a man."

"'Course she will," Uncle Hank shot back. "That's not the point."

"It's exactly the point," Betty argued. "Why would you want her to have a man who doesn't really see her for who she is?"

"I want him to do the right thing, is all."

"The right thing is to walk away if you can't care."

Jenny felt as if she were at a tennis match. Her head swiveled back and forth as she followed the heated conversation that swirled around her as if she wasn't even there. Through the windows, she could see tiny white patio lights strung across the pergola, blinking like fireflies.

"I'm just saying she shouldn't have to do all of this alone," Uncle Hank muttered with a nodding glance at Jenny.

"She's not going to be alone," Betty snapped. "She's got us, doesn't she? We don't count?"

Jenny smiled, reached out and covered Betty's hand with her own. Betty was right. She wasn't alone. She had family. A family that Uncle Hank had given her. She grabbed for her uncle's hand, too, linking the three of them.

"She's right, you know," Uncle Hank told her, with just a touch of discomfort. "You've got us. For whatever you need."

"Thank you," she said, as warmth spread through her. He'd given her a real gift today. He'd let her know that her early fears in childhood hadn't had a basis in reality. He had wanted her. Still did. And now, he was making another choice, Jenny thought. A deliberate one, to once again be there—not just for her, but for her baby.

"Jenny," Betty said, giving her hand a quick pat, "you should think about moving back home."

"What?"

"That's a good idea," Uncle Hank piped up. "Never did like the idea of you living alone."

"Nonsense, why shouldn't she live alone?" Betty countered. "You're living in the dark ages, Hank. What I'm saying is, with a baby coming, she should come back home where she will have all the help she needs."

Both of them turned to look at Jenny, waiting for her response. Though she really appreciated the thought, Jenny wasn't ready to give up her little apartment and go running back home. Maybe that would change later on, when the baby's due date was closer, when she began to worry about being able to handle everything on her own.

But for now... "Thanks," she said, meaning it completely. "I appreciate that a lot, really." She looked from one to the other of them. "But I'm fine for now. I have my work and my own space."

Betty and Hank exchanged a knowing look, then her uncle turned to her. "Okay, but..." He paused and with an embarrassed shrug added, "You should remember that you've got a home here. People ready to help."

Jenny's eyes filled with tears but she blinked them back because she knew if she cried, Uncle Hank would panic. Instead, she squeezed his hand and whispered, "Thank you, Uncle Hank."

He squeezed back briefly. "No need to thank family."

Betty gave a loud sniffle, then snapped, "All right, now, that's enough of that. Soup's getting cold and, Jenny, you need to eat. That baby doesn't need a skinny mama."

Smiling to herself, Jenny did as she was told.

* * *

Mike spent the next few days at home. He couldn't go to the office because there, he'd have to deal with Jenny and he needed some damn time to come to grips with what had happened.

A baby.

Because of faulty condoms, he was going to be a father and he couldn't quite wrap his head around that one simple fact. Mike had never considered having children. To his mind, being a father meant being married and he'd never do that. Never give another person the ability to cut him off at the knees. To bring misery and—

Hell.

He left the silence of the house and stalked across the stone patio that led down a wide sweep of lawn toward the cliff. Beyond those cliffs was the Pacific and as he stared out at the ocean, glittering brightly beneath the morning sun, he squinted to see the handful of sailboats skimming the water. Closer to shore, there were a few surfers waiting for a decent wave.

The sound of the ocean reached him and the steady pulse of water against rocks seemed to steady him. He'd bought this house mainly for the view. It was too damn big for a man alone and he knew it, but until today, the quiet and the…emptiness really hadn't bothered him much.

Now, though, he looked at the pristine backyard and pictured a swing set there. He turned and stared at the shining windows and imagined Jenny in one of them, smiling down at him as she held their child in her arms.

Shaking his head, he rubbed his eyes and told himself he was just tired. Not surprising since he hadn't gotten much sleep over the past few days. How could he when memories of Jenny kept intruding? He saw her as she was the night he'd come to her after a miserable dinner at his parents' house. In her flannel pajama bottoms and slinky tank top. Saw her eyes as she leaned into his kiss. Heard her sighs as he entered her.

"How the hell is a man supposed to sleep when his own mind is working against him?" he demanded of no one.

"It's a bad sign when you talk to yourself."

Mike spun around to see Sean strolling out of the house and down the patio toward him. "When did you get back?"

"Last night," Sean said, shaking his head. "It was a hell of a storm. Kept us locked down for way too long." He tipped his head back, stared up at the blue, sunny sky and sighed. "It's good to be back in the sun. Man, I thought I'd never get warm again."

Mike gave him a halfhearted smile. It shamed him to realize he hadn't given Sean a thought in days. His own brother trapped in a snowstorm and he hadn't wondered once how he was doing. But now, it was good to steer his brain in a different direction. "You didn't kill the contractor, did you?"

Sean shot him a look, frowned and said, "No. Didn't kill her."

Mike frowned, too. "Something going on there?"

"Not a damn thing," Sean told him, then changed the subject abruptly. "I don't want to talk about Kate Wells, all right? Went by the office this morning. Glad to see everyone got the final changes in on 'The Wild Hunt.'"

Huffing out a breath, Mike realized he hadn't paid attention to that, either. One of their biggest games getting ready to roll onto the assembly line and he hadn't bothered to dot the i's and cross the t's.

"Jenny's Wise Woman character turned out spectacularly. Dave showed me the final sketches. That woman is talented."

"Yeah." Mike turned his face into the wind. Jenny was talented. And beautiful. And exasperating. And *pregnant*.

Sean was still talking. "Linda told me you haven't been in to the office in days. You sick or something?"

"Or something," Mike said. "You want some coffee?"

"Got a cappuccino on the way over." Sean grinned. "It was worth waiting for. But you're stalling. What's going on, Mike?"

He shoved his hands into the back pockets of his faded jeans and rocked on his heels. He hadn't told anyone about Jenny. About the baby. If Brady had been here, instead of in Ireland, Mike might have spilled the whole thing. But now, Sean was here and he found he needed to say it all out loud.

"It's Jenny," he said, looking at his brother. "She's pregnant."

A second or two ticked past as Sean simply stared at him, a befuddled expression on his face. Then a slow smile curved his mouth and he said, "I *knew* there was something going on between you two. And there's a baby? That's great, right?" He rushed across the patio and gave his brother a brief, hard hug. "I like Jenny a lot," he said, stepping back and grinning. "And everybody's noticed the red-hot chemistry between you two."

Mike went still. He'd been sure that what was between Jenny and him was a secret. Private. "Everybody noticed? You mean people at work know about—"

"Well, they don't *know*, but sure, there's been some talk." Sean shrugged. "Mostly the women. They really notice the stuff that sails right over most guys' heads."

"Great. That's great." Just what he wanted. All of his employees knowing about his private life, speculating, maybe even making bets on what would happen next.

"What's the problem?" Sean asked. "It's not like it would have stayed a secret for long. Not with Jenny pregnant. And here's another question. If she's pregnant, why is she out working on the hotel in Laughlin and you're not with her?"

"She's in Laughlin?"

"Yeah. Linda says she went out yesterday. She didn't want to take the jet, so she drove, hauling all of her paint supplies with her." He paused. "And you didn't know anything about this, did you?"

"No." Mike wasn't happy about it, either. She could have told him she was driving out alone to Laughlin. He thought about that long, lonely road through the desert. Hell, there were sections where you could go for *miles* with nothing but sand on either side of your car. "She didn't tell me."

"Why wouldn't she?"

Mike snapped his brother a hard look. "None of your business."

"What'd you do, Mike?"

"I didn't *do* anything," he argued, feeling defensive even though he knew there was no reason for it.

"Yeah? The woman you're crazy about is pregnant with your kid and you look like you want to punch somebody." Sean tipped his head to one side and said, "Why don't you spill what's really going on?"

"She did this on purpose," he muttered.

"Wow. She *forced* you to have sex with her?" Sean snorted. "You poor guy."

"Shut up, Sean."

"Do you get how ridiculous you sound? Get over yourself, Mike. She didn't trick you. Or trap you. Hell, you're not that great a prize."

"Thanks. So glad you're home." Mike scrubbed one hand across the back of his neck and remembered that Jenny had said the same damn thing to him not so long ago. But you'd think his own brother would be a little more supportive.

"Come on, Mike. Condoms leak. Nothing's perfect." Sean slapped Mike's shoulder. "So you gonna marry her or what?"

"No, I'm not marrying her."

"Why the hell not?" Sean threw both hands high, clearly exasperated. "She's gonna have your baby and you're obviously nuts about her."

"I need more coffee." Mike walked away from his brother to the glass-topped table at the edge of the patio. There, he poured a cup of coffee from the thermal hot pot his housekeeper had brought out. He took a sip and let the heat slide through him.

"What's going on?" Sean followed him. "I can't believe you won't marry her. This is your kid we're talking about, Mike. Marrying her is the right thing to do and you know it."

His head was pounding, brain racing. Sean's haranguing wasn't helping with the headache throbbing behind his eyes. He hadn't slept, hadn't been able to think clearly in days, and now he'd found out Jenny was in Laughlin—without bothering to tell him.

"What do you think Mom and Dad'll have to say when they find out?"

"They should understand better than anyone." Mike's gaze shot to his brother's and before he could stop himself, he was blurting out the secret he'd held since he was thirteen. "I'm not marrying anybody, you understand? I won't risk being lied to, cheated on. You think I want to take a chance on ruining my own kid's life?"

"What the hell are you talking about?"

Too late to pull it back now, Mike told his brother about the day his own image of the perfect family had been shattered. "When I was thirteen, I came home from baseball practice and found Mom crying," he said tightly. "I was worried, thought maybe Dad had been in an accident or something."

"What was it?"

He could still remember it all so clearly. Sunshine pouring through the kitchen window. His mom sitting at the table, head in her hands, crying. He'd never seen her cry before and it scared him.

Mike set his coffee cup down, crossed his arms over his chest and said, "She grabbed me into a hard hug and she told me that Dad had cheated on her. That she found out he'd been out with some woman."

"No way." Sean's eyes went hard and cool and flat.

Mike knew how he felt. Back then, it had seemed to Mike as though the floor had opened up beneath him. He'd worried about his mom, wondered if his dad would ever come home again. Would they get a divorce? Who would he live with? A thirteen-year-old kid shouldn't have to think about any of it. Shouldn't have to learn so suddenly that his parents were flawed. Human.

"She never would have let any of it slip if I hadn't

caught her in a vulnerable moment," he said, and knew it for truth since his mom had apologized over and over again over the years. "Dad lied. To her. To us. He was a liar and a cheat and ever since that day, I can't be around him without remembering our mother crying."

Sean looked away toward the ocean and Mike finished. "I won't get married, Sean. I won't put my faith in someone only to be lied to and cheated on. Not gonna happen. I won't risk my kid being destroyed by lies."

After a moment or two, Sean turned his head to look at him and Mike read the fury in his brother's eyes.

"You had no right," Sean said tightly. "No right to keep this from me. I'm a Ryan, too."

"Why the hell should you feel as crappy as me?" Mike argued. "You didn't have to know and a lot of the time I wished to hell I didn't know."

"And you make the choice for me, is that it? You decide what I should know, what I should think?"

"That's not it," Mike said.

"Sure it is," Sean snapped. "You don't even see it, do you? You've been mad at Dad for years for lying. Every time you talk about Jenny, you call her a liar, say you can't trust her. But you've been lying to me since we were kids.

"So what's the difference, Mike? Are you the only one who gets to lie? Do you get to decide which is a good lie and which is bad?"

Mike had never thought about it exactly like that until now and he didn't know what he could say to the accusation. His father's lies had destroyed Mike's image of a happy family. Mike's own lies of omission were to protect Sean from the same hurt Mike felt.

And yet today, Sean was slapped with not one, but two sets of lies.

"You ought to take a good look at yourself, big brother," Sean said quietly. "Whatever was between our parents back then? They fixed it. Healed it. In case you hadn't noticed, they're still together, stronger than ever."

Truth could hit as hard as lies.

"So don't kid yourself. This isn't about Dad. Or Jenny. This is all on you, Mike. You're the liar now." Sean turned and walked away, stalking across the patio and into the house.

Alone in the yard, Mike felt the ground he'd built his life on tremble beneath his feet. Sean was right, he realized. Which meant that Mike was wrong. About a lot of things.

Nine

Laughlin in February was pretty.

The summer heat was still a few months off and the river was quiet but for the inevitable tour boats and an occasional Jet Ski. There were a lot of snowbirds in town, older people coming in to escape snow country with a few months in the desert. Tourists were always there of course, and every day, pontoon boats full of visitors to the city slowed to watch the progress being made on the River Haunt.

True to his word, the contractor, Jacob Schmitt, was keeping to schedule. He had men working on both the hotel facade and the interior, where Jenny spent most of her time. There was the constant drone of saws and the slamming of hammers, not to mention shouted conversations and laughter ringing out all around her.

But she was still glad she'd come. Being in the desert, away from the office for a while, had been a great idea. In Nevada, she didn't have to deal with the worry of having to face Mike again so soon after their confrontation. It hurt, knowing that their connection was over. But it would be even more painful if she had to see him every day. To be reminded of what they might have had.

No, what she needed was a little space, a little time, to get used to the idea that she was going to be a single mother.

She'd always wanted to have kids—lots of them. But in her secret dreams, she also had a husband who loved her. That little dream wasn't going to come true, though. Remembering the look on Mike's face when she told him she was pregnant was enough to convince her of that. Even if she didn't also have the memory of him accusing her of trying to trap him into marriage.

Pain and anger twisted into a knot that sat like lead in the pit of her stomach.

"He really is an idiot," she muttered, swiping a paintbrush loaded with deep violet paint across the entryway wall. Why couldn't she have fallen in love with someone—*anyone*—else? Why did Mike Ryan have to be the only man for her?

Jenny sighed and finished covering the wall with the paint she'd chosen for the biggest impact. Once it was dry she'd lay out the lines for the forest, the moon and the hints of figures she wanted lost in the trees. It would take a few days, but that was okay with her.

She had driven out here with a plan to stay for at least a week. Heaven knew there were plenty of hotel rooms to choose from and she wouldn't be lonely, either. Not with the security people and the hotel employees staying here, as well.

Besides, being on-site, she could oversee the other artists she'd hired to help with the murals. There were three of them, all talented, but artists were temperamental people and just as likely to go off plan and add their own visions to a design. But that couldn't happen here. The designs had all been approved by Mike, Sean and Brady already, so there was no deviating from them.

"Hey, Jenny!"

She looked up at the friendly shout. Tim Ryerson, one of the hotel employees, stood at the front door. "What's up, Tim?"

"Some of us are going into town for lunch. You up for it?"

They were all being so nice to her, but what Jenny really wanted was quiet and some time to herself. "Thanks, but I think I'll stay here and get started on the dining room mural."

"You're allowed to have fun, too, you know," he said with a sad shake of his head.

"Thanks, but for me, this *is* fun."

"Okay, then." He shrugged good-naturedly. "Can we bring you back anything?"

"A burger," she said quickly. "And lots of fries."

She was starting to get her appetite back—at least in the afternoons—and she wasn't sure if that was a good thing or not. She was so short that if she kept eating like this, by the time the baby was born, she'd look like a soccer ball.

"You got it. Later."

Once he and the others had gone, the hotel fell into blessed quiet. Lunchtime was the one time of the day she could count on a little peace. Even the crew's ever-playing radio was silent as the men left to get something to eat. She had the place to herself for the next hour and Jenny relished it.

Leaving the main wall to dry, she walked into the dining room and studied the long partition that separated the room from the kitchen. She'd have Tony and Lena work this wall, setting out the characters and scenery from the "River Haunt" game that would bring the room to life. Christa could work on the vines that would trail around the windows at the front of the room. If they all worked together, they could knock this out in a few days and move upstairs to the hallways. According to the plans, there would be vines, flowers and a banshee or two in each of the long halls, and haunting trees, bent in an invisible wind, painted on to the elevator doors.

She looked around the dining room and saw it as it would be when finished. As in the castle in Ireland, this dining hall would consist of long, banquet-style tables and benches, forcing guests to intermingle during meals. The gamers who came here would huddle together, talking scores and routes and walk-throughs of the game itself.

Guests who were unfamiliar with the game would soon be drawn into the fantasy world of Celtic Knot and the plush environment of the hotel. Once again, Jenny was impressed by the foresight of the Ryans and Brady Finn. By expanding their company into other realms, they were going to build the brand that was already becoming known around the world. To have a small part in this expansion was both exhilarating and sad. Because she knew without a doubt that this project would be one of her last for Celtic Knot.

In the quiet, her mind drifted to thoughts of Mike and she wondered what he was doing. If he even knew she was gone. And if he would care. If only he'd trusted her. Believed in her. Her heart ached when she remembered the expression on his face when he learned about the baby.

He'd come to her concerned that she wasn't feeling well and then left her, convinced that she was trying to use him. How could it all turn so bad so quickly? Why couldn't he see that she loved him? That if given the chance, the two of them and their child could have something wonderful? Was he so hard, so accustomed to shutting down his heart to keep possible pain at bay that he couldn't risk it for a chance for happiness?

Her own pain blossomed in her chest until it squeezed her heart and she had to force herself to stop thinking of what-ifs and of Mike, because there was no help there. Nothing was going to change and it was best if she got used to that as soon as possible.

Patting her belly, Jenny whispered, "Don't worry, baby. We're going to be okay. You'll see." She got back to work, pushing thoughts of Mike and her up-in-the-air life to the back of her mind. Time enough to worry when she was lying awake all night.

Mike almost called Jenny. Twice. And each time, he hung up before the call could connect. He was still on edge after having Sean ream him, so it probably wasn't the best time to talk to her anyway. But she was there. In his thoughts. In his soul.

She was off in the desert and hadn't bothered to tell him. Because when she told him about the baby, he'd turned on her.

That shamed him, but now, with Sean's temper still burning his ears, Mike admitted that it was past time to settle a few things that had been guiding him for years. He drove to his parents' house, determined to finally talk to his mother about what had happened so long ago. To figure out if that one day, that one secret, was worth steering his entire life by.

The house looked the same as it always had. No matter how successful he and his brother had become, Jack and Peggy Ryan hadn't allowed their sons to buy them a bigger place in a more upscale neighborhood. They preferred staying in the house where they'd raised their family, where they knew their neighbors and where every room held a memory. On this familiar street, houses were well cared for, yards were neat and nearly every driveway sported a basketball hoop.

Mike parked the car, then let himself in the front door, yelling to announce his presence. "Hey, Mom! It's me!"

The house was quiet but for the low murmur of the television, set to a 1960s music channel. He walked through the living room, past the neat kitchen and into the den, and still didn't find her. "Mom?"

"Mike, is that you?"

Relief shot through him as he turned to watch her approach. Her light brown hair was in a tangle and she was tugging at the hem of a pale pink shirt.

"You okay?" he asked, since she looked harried and a little nervous.

"Fine. You just caught me in the middle of something." Then his mother *blushed*.

Mike suddenly had the feeling that he'd walked in on something he'd rather not think about. "Look, I'll come back another time and—"

"Don't be silly," his mother said, already walking.

"Come into the kitchen. There's coffee and I made cookies this morning."

If she was willing to pretend she hadn't blushed, Mike could do it, too. "Sold."

"Good, good," she said, smiling now as she smoothed her hair. "Come and tell me why you stopped by. Is everything all right?"

"That's a good question."

"Sit down," she ordered when they were in the bright, sunny yellow kitchen. She poured coffee, set it in front of him, then brought a plate of cookies to the table, as well. Holding a cup of coffee, she sat down opposite him and said simply, "Tell me."

How many times over the years had he sat at this table with a plate of cookies in front of him and his mother listening to whatever problem he'd brought her? It was at this table where he'd found her crying. Where his life had taken that abrupt turn from innocence into suspicion. It was only fitting, he supposed, to be sitting at this table again while making the attempt to turn back.

So he told her about Jenny, about the baby, about Sean now knowing what happened all those years ago and how pissed his little brother was to find out he'd been lied to for years.

"What about Jenny?" his mother asked. "She's pregnant with your child. Do you love her?"

Mike shook his head. Of course she would zero in on that part of the story. "Another good question."

He pushed up from the table, walked to the counter, then turned around, bracing both hands on the granite countertop behind him. "But for right now, that doesn't even matter."

"Michael Patrick Ryan," his mother said, drawing a reflexive wince from her son, "love is *all* that matters."

"How can you say that, Mom, when—" He shook his head. "When you were cheated on. Lied to."

"That's it. I've had enough." Peggy stood up, pointed at the kitchen table and ordered, "Sit down. I'll be right back."

He did as instructed mainly because he was too tired to keep standing. If he didn't get some sleep soon, he'd go through life a zombie.

When his mother came back, she was dragging his father with her. Jack's hair was messy and he was trying to button his shirt as he was pulled in his wife's wake. And suddenly, Mike knew exactly what his parents had been doing when he dropped by. And yeah, he'd rather not think about that. Didn't matter how old you got, nobody wanted to imagine their parents having sex.

Mike stiffened and he noticed that Jack Ryan did the same. His father was an older version of himself, with sharp blue eyes, and a sprinkling of gray at his temples. The two of them were still so uncomfortable with each other over something that had happened twenty years before. But damned if Mike knew how to get past it, get over it.

"Both of you sit down right now," Peggy said and crossed her arms over her chest until her men complied. Then she looked from her husband to her son before saying softly, "Mike, I've tried to talk to you about this before, but you never wanted to listen. I could have *made* you hear me out, but your father wouldn't allow that." She spared Jack a glance and a smile. "He wanted you to come to us yourself when you were ready. Frankly, I thought it would never happen."

"Mom…"

"I never should have burdened you with what I felt that day," Peggy said. "But you came home early from practice and found me, crying, and somehow it all came out. And I hope you know that if I could wipe it from your mind, I would."

"I know all that, Mom—" He shot a look at his father, who looked every bit as uncomfortable as he felt. "We don't have to talk about it again."

"That's the problem," Peggy said, pulling out a chair and taking a cookie that she began to crumble between her fingers. "We've never talked about it." Her gaze softened as she looked at Mike. Then she took her husband's hand and threaded her fingers through his. "Mike, you were just a little boy, so you don't remember, but back then, your dad's business was in trouble."

Jack picked up the thread and Mike looked at his father as he spoke. "It's not an excuse but we were under a lot of pressure and instead of talking to each other about it—" he paused and smiled sadly at his wife "—we each closed down, shut each other out."

"We were wrong. We handled it all badly. But it takes two to make or break a marriage, Mike. So you were wrong to blame only your father all these years. We both made mistakes. We both nearly lost something most people never find."

Mike heard them, saw how together they were on this, but he couldn't let go. Turning to face his father, he said quietly, "You lied. You cheated."

"I did lie," Jack said. "I was hurt, worried about my family. Feeling like a damn failure and as if I were alone in the mess and missing your mother because we weren't talking to each other anymore."

"Oh, Jack…"

He squeezed her hand and then looked at Mike again. "I did lie, I give you that. And I cheated, too, I guess, but not the way you mean."

"What?"

Jack sighed. "The woman your mother heard about— I did take her to dinner. We talked. She listened to me, laughed at my jokes, made me feel important." He shook his head. "Stupid. It was stupid, but I didn't sleep with her, Mike." Jack's gaze met his son's squarely. "I never touched another woman from the day I married your mother."

Peggy spoke up then. "Instead of being there for each other, your dad and I pulled apart until we were each so far from the other, it was as if we were two strangers living in this house together."

Jack lifted their joined hands and kissed her knuckles. "What's important is that we found each other again before it was too late."

"I don't even know what to say," Mike muttered. For twenty years, he and his father had sidestepped each other, neither of them willing to talk about the thing that had put a wedge between them.

"Why didn't you tell me?" he asked.

"Because you wouldn't have believed me," Jack said.

"I guess that's true enough," Mike admitted. So much time being angry, letting old pains rule his life, believing that no one could be trusted because he had looked at a situation he didn't understand through the eyes of a wounded thirteen-year-old boy.

"The point is, honey," Peggy said, "you've been using your father as an excuse to keep everyone at a distance. You're protecting yourself from being hurt by not letting anything at all touch you." She shook her head. "That's no way to live, sweetie."

She was right, Mike thought. He had been using his father's betrayal as a way to keep everything and everyone else at a distance. And even with the walls he'd erected around his heart, Jenny had found a way in.

"You never should have been aware of that bump in our marriage," Peggy said. "And it breaks my heart to see the two of you so far apart."

Mike looked to his father and in the older man's eyes, he saw the same sorrow, the same sense of loss that Mike had felt for years. Now he was forced to do some serious thinking. Sean's words still echoed in his head as he thought back on all the years of sitting in a position of judgment, so sure he was right and everyone else was wrong. He had shut down emotionally. At the ripe old age of thirteen, not knowing anything at all about the world or what adults had to do to survive, he'd made a decision that had affected his entire life.

He had been a kid making a child's decisions, and he had allowed those decisions to rule him. If he'd once come down off his throne of righteousness and actually *talked* to the people around him, maybe this tightness around his heart could have been eased years ago.

"What happened wasn't your fault," his father said carefully. "You were a boy and you reacted how you had to at the time."

"Yeah," Mike said, rubbing his eyes to ease the throbbing headache settled behind them. "But I never let go of that decision. An angry, scared, thirteen-year-old boy chose that day to believe that no one could be trusted."

His father reached out and laid one hand on Mike's shoulder, and the heavy, solid strength of that touch seemed to ease away the last of that long-ago boy's resolve. He looked at his dad and said simply, "I'm sorry."

"You don't have to be," Jack told him. "Parents aren't supposed to give their kids burdens to carry. And I did that to you. I hurt you, your mother, all of us. It's something I'll never forgive myself for."

Peggy sniffled and swiped tears off her cheeks. "It's been long enough, hasn't it?" she asked. "Can we all let it go now and be the family we should be?"

Mike looked at his mother, still holding her husband's hand as she watched her oldest son with worry and hope at war in her eyes. The old hurts and fears and convictions dropped away, slipping into the past where they belonged, and Mike let them go. He felt as if a weight had been lifted from him and it surprised him to realize just how heavy that burden had been.

"Yeah," he said, smiling first at his mother and then at his father. "I'd like that."

Jack grinned, slapped Mike's shoulder again and then looked at his wife. Peggy gave him a watery smile in return then reached for her son's hand and held it tightly. "Good. This is good."

She was right about that. It was good, to get past pain and anger and betrayal. But his father wasn't the only one he'd judged. Mike thought back to that night in Phoenix when he'd spotted a beautiful blonde in a conference hotel bar. He remembered the rush, the pull toward her, and he remembered the next morning when he'd become judge, jury and executioner without once giving her a chance to explain.

Then those memories morphed into his last image of Jenny, at her house when he accused her of trying to trap him into marriage. He'd done the same damn thing to her all over again.

"Sean's right," he muttered. "I am an idiot."

"What's wrong, honey?"

He lifted his gaze to his mother's and sighed. "A lot. I've got some thinking to do. About Jenny. The baby." He stopped, smiled. "And you guys will have to get used to the idea of being grandparents."

"Oh, my goodness," Peggy exclaimed with a laugh. "With all the tumult I almost forgot that Jenny's pregnant!"

"Grandfather?" Jack asked.

"This is wonderful news!" Peggy jumped to her feet and wagged her finger at her son. "I'm making a fresh pot of coffee and you, mister, are going to tell us everything."

Jack picked up a cookie and handed it to him. "Congratulations. I hope you do a better job of it than I did."

Mike shook his head and took a bite of the cookie. He'd already made mistakes and his child wasn't even born yet. "You didn't do so badly, Dad. But for me, I swear I don't know what the hell I'm doing."

Jack laughed. "Welcome to parenthood. None of us know what we're doing, Mike. And even trying our very best, we all make mistakes. The trick is to keep trying to fix them."

Mike found Sean in his office the next morning. He'd thought about this all night, had worked out just what he wanted to say. But looking into his brother's unforgiving stare threw him for a second. The two of them had always been close, but now, there was a wedge between them that Mike himself had put there. So it was up to him to tear it out.

"You were right."

Surprised, Sean waved him to a chair. "Always a good start to a conversation. Continue."

Mike laughed and sat down. "I've been protecting you since we were kids," he said thoughtfully. He'd had all night to consider this situation from every angle. And no matter how he looked at it, he came off badly. That didn't sit well with him. "It got to be a habit."

"Okay," Sean said, acknowledging that with a nod.

"But it was wrong to lie to you all those years." Mike sighed, leaned forward and braced his forearms on his thighs. "Whenever you asked me what was wrong between me and Dad, I brushed it off. Covered it up, telling myself you were better off not knowing. So, yeah. I made that call and I shouldn't have. You've been grown-up a long time, Sean, so shutting you out was the wrong call, but you should understand why I did it."

"You're really not very good at apologies, are you?"

Grumbling, Mike admitted, "No."

"Well, points for effort anyway," Sean said.

"Thanks." Mike nodded and told him, "I stopped by the house yesterday. Saw Mom and Dad. We talked."

"And…?"

"And," Mike said with a rueful smile on his face, "I apparently interrupted an afternoon quickie."

"Oh, man!" Laughing, Sean covered his eyes with one hand. "I didn't need to know that."

"Hey, you're the one who doesn't want me lying to him."

"Discretion, man. There's a difference between lies and discretion. Look it up."

Glad things were smoothed out between his brother and him, Mike chuckled. "The point is, we finally straightened everything out. I think things will be all right now, between me and Dad."

"Good to hear." Sean sat forward, folded his hands on the desktop.

"They know you know," Mike said. "I told them that I talked to you about it."

"Great. When you decide to be honest, you go all out, don't you?" A half smile curved Sean's mouth. "Guess I'll be having a talk with them, too, now. But as long as they're good together, happy together, I'm fine with it. It's all their business, Mike. Not mine. Not yours."

"When did you get so rational?"

"When I grew up," his brother said. "You missed that, I think."

"Yeah, looks like." Mike frowned. "I think I missed a lot."

"Ah, now we get to the important part of the conversation. Jenny."

Shooting his brother a hard look, Mike said, "You'll butt out of what happens to our parents, but I'm fair game?"

"Hell, yes." Sean grinned. "So, have you talked to her?"

"No." He still hadn't called, because talking to her on the phone wouldn't be enough. He had to look into her eyes, read what she was thinking, feeling.

"Don't you think you should?" Sean asked. "She's pregnant with your baby."

"I don't need reminding," Mike said and hopped out of the chair. Walking to the wide window on the far wall, he looked out at the garden and didn't see a thing. How could he, when his mind was filled with images of Jenny.

"Maybe you do." Sean waited until his brother looked

at him again to continue. "You've been in charge of things so long, you've forgotten how to just be Mike."

"That's ridiculous."

"Is it? You talk to Jenny like she's your employee…"

"She is."

"She's more, too," Sean said. "And it's the *more* you're not getting. To get what you really want out of all of this, you're going to have to get humble."

Mike snorted. "And you think you know what I want?"

"Yep," Sean mused. "Don't you?"

Yeah, he did. He wanted Jenny. In his house. In his bed. He wanted to wake up in the morning reaching for her and have her curl up against him. But "humble" wasn't the way to get it.

"You can't just march up to Jenny and order her to forgive you," Sean said.

"It's the easiest way," Mike mumbled.

"Yeah, if you want to tick her off even more."

He might have a point, but Mike didn't want to think about it. "Can you handle things here at the office for a few days?"

"Sure," Sean said. "Why?"

"Because," Mike said, "I'm going to Laughlin."

"It's about time," Sean told him.

Early the next afternoon, Jenny stood back from the wall to take an objective look at the finished painting. It was just as she'd imagined it. Hints of danger hidden among the trees, moonlight filtering through the leaves to dapple on the overgrown ground. A river wound through the back of the painting like a silver snake, a moonlit, watery path that only the brave would dare follow. The painting was vaguely menacing and intriguing and set just the right mood for the River Haunt hotel.

The other artists were doing a great job on the murals and already the dining room motif was coming together. Another day or two and they could move upstairs. While the construction crew were mostly huddled in the kitchen finishing the cabinets and the new countertops, Jenny walked through the lobby into what used to be the lounge.

Here, the plan was to have clusters of furniture scattered throughout and several game-playing stations set up, with four-flat screen TVs that invited guests to dive into Celtic Knot games. There would be a bar on the far wall where a battered old piano now stood and one section of the room would be set up with wide tables so guests could also play the role-playing board games as well.

It was going to be a gamer's paradise, she told herself with a smile. And that wasn't even taking into account the midnight pontoon rides on the river, where animatronic banshees, ghouls and hunters would lunge from their hiding places onshore. It was all going to be amazing.

Jenny hated knowing that she'd have to quit her job at Celtic Knot. She enjoyed being a part of something so fresh and interesting and fun. But working with Mike now was just impossible. She couldn't see him every day and know she'd never have him. So she'd do her best on this project and then she'd walk away, head high. And one day, she promised herself, she'd come to the River Haunt hotel as a guest, just so she could see people enjoying what she'd helped to build.

Sighing, she stopped at the piano and idly stroked a few keys. She hadn't really played since she was a girl and Uncle Hank had paid for the lessons she'd wanted so badly. That phase had lasted more than a year, Jenny remembered, and then she had discovered art and playing the piano had taken a backseat.

For an old instrument, the piano had good tone and as her fingers moved over the keys in a familiar piece from her childhood, the music lifted into the stillness. She sat down on the bench, closed her eyes and let her troubled thoughts slide away as she listened only to the tune she created.

Mike found her there. A small woman with a halo of golden hair, sitting in a patch of sunlight, teasing beautiful music from a piano that looked as old as time.

His heart gave one quick jolt in his chest. Damn, he'd missed her. Everything in him was drawn to her. How had she become so important to him in so short a time? She was talented, brilliant, argumentative and beautiful, and he wanted her so badly he could hardly breathe. Now that he was here, with her, he wasn't about to wait another minute to touch her.

Wrapped up in the music that soared around her, she didn't hear him approach. When Mike laid both hands on her shoulders, she jumped, spinning around on the bench, eyes wide.

"You *scared* me."

He grinned at the glint in her eyes. He'd even missed her temper. "I didn't mean to sneak up on you, but with the music, you couldn't hear me. I didn't know you played piano."

"I told you before, there's a lot you don't know about me."

"Yeah, I guess you're right," he said, and pulled her

up from the scarred wooden bench. "But there's plenty I do know."

"Like what?" she asked, taking one short step backward.

"Like," he said, closing the gap between them, "you're so stubborn you're probably getting ready to quit your job at Celtic Knot."

Clearly surprised, she asked, "How did you know that?"

"Wasn't hard to figure out, Jenny. You think it'll be too hard for us to work together now."

"I'm right and you know it, Mike."

"No. You're not," he said, and watched hope bloom in her eyes. Sean had been wrong. All Mike had to do was lay out his plan and she'd see that it was the best thing for everyone. "I think we should work together and more. We both want our baby. We have great chemistry. Passion."

His hands came down on her shoulders and he drew her closer. Looking down into those blue eyes of hers, he said, "We forget about the past. Let it all go and just move on from here. We're going to get married, Jenny. It's the right thing to do. For all of us."

He waited, for her to smile at him, go up on her toes and kiss him. He wanted the taste of her in his mouth again. It had been days and he felt as if it had been years. All she had to do was say yes.

"No."

She was screwing up a perfectly good plan. Staring down at her, he blurted, "Why the hell not? You're pregnant, remember?"

She laughed shortly. "Yes, I remember. And I won't marry you because you don't love me. You don't trust me. Passion isn't enough to build a marriage on, Mike.

And I won't risk my baby's happiness on a marriage doomed to failure."

"It's not doomed."

"Without love it is," she said, shaking her head. Laying one hand on his forearm, Jenny continued. "It's *our* baby, Mike. I would never try to keep you from him. Or her. But I won't marry a man who doesn't trust me."

Then she kissed him.

And left.

Ten

Jenny had a stalker.

For the next few days, every time she turned around, Mike was there. He carried her paints and insisted on getting her a chair if she so much as yawned. Only that morning, when she climbed a step ladder to add a few silvery cobwebs to a naked tree on an elevator door, he'd snatched her off the darn thing and carried her to her room. In spite of her loud protests. The man had appointed himself her caretaker whether she wanted one or not. It was annoying and endearing at the same time.

She didn't want to get used to this kind of treatment, though. Firstly because she was perfectly healthy and able to take care of herself. But mainly because she knew it was all for show. He was trying to schmooze her into marrying him on his terms.

But she couldn't do it. Couldn't give up her fantasies of a loving husband and settle for a man who didn't trust her, didn't love her. Passion was a poor substitute for real love.

"Jen, what do you think of this?"

Jenny popped out of her thoughts and focused instead on the job at hand. "What've you got, Christa?"

The other artist was tall and thin, with black hair cut close to her scalp and a penchant for wearing eye-searing colors. She was also fast, talented and eager to please.

"I was thinking about adding in a few of the Death Flowers among the vines here at the windows."

"Death Flowers?" Jenny repeated with a smile.

Christa shrugged. "I admit, I love the 'River Haunt' game. I play it with my fiancé all the time."

"Do you win?"

"Not so far," she admitted, "but I keep trying. Anyway, you know the bloodred flowers that have fangs? I thought if it's okay with you, I'd add a few of them here on these vines. I mean, they're not on the original design so I wanted to run it by you before I did anything."

The dining room was nearly finished. The far wall was complete and the forest scene was spectacular. Though she'd had a few problems with one of the artists, she couldn't fault the work. Jenny looked up at what Christa had done so far. The vines were thick and lush, wrapped around the edges of the windows and down to the bottom of the wall where a few of them even pooled on the floor. "You've done a great job here, Christa."

"Thanks," she said, stepping back to check out her own work. "I'm really grateful for the opportunity."

Jenny looked up at her. As short as she was, she pretty much looked up at *everyone*. "The flowers are a fabulous idea. I love it."

Christa grinned.

"Use your own eye for placement. Seeing your work, I trust your judgment."

"That is so cool. Thank you, Jenny." Christa's features lit up in pleasure.

"You know, when this project's finished, if you're interested, I'll talk to Dave Cooper, he's the head of the graphic arts department for Celtic Knot. I'm sure he could use an artist like you." She paused. "If you're interested."

"Seriously? Interested?" Christa laughed, then scooped Jenny up for a tight hug. "That would be like my dream job."

When she was on her feet again, Jenny grinned at the other woman's enthusiasm. "You could probably work from here, but Dave might ask you to move to California."

"Not a problem," Christa swore, lifting one hand as if taking an oath.

"What about your fiancé? Would he be willing to move for your job?"

Christa smiled. "He loves me, so sure. Of course. Plus, he's a writer, so he can work anywhere."

"Then I'll talk to Dave and let you know what he says."

"Thank you, Jenny. I mean it. This is just the ultimate thing that could have happened."

"You're welcome. But for right now, concentrate on the Death Flowers."

"They'll be the most bloodthirsty blossoms in the universe when I'm done with them," Christa vowed, and immediately bent to her paint palette.

Sure what she was feeling was etched on her features, Jenny was grateful that the other woman had turned away. She heard Christa's words echoing in her mind. *He loves me. So sure. Of course.* Envy whipped through her like a lash, leaving a stinging pain behind. Christa was so certain of her fiancé. So confident in his love and support. And Jenny yearned to know what that feeling was like.

Sighing, she watched for a few minutes as Christa laid out quick sketches for placement of the flowers. It was nice to be able to help someone so talented. Someone who'd already proven herself to be a team player. Jenny was sure that Dave would jump at the chance to bring aboard such a skilled artist. Especially since he'd be needing someone to take Jenny's place once she turned in her resignation. Oh, that thought hurt. She loved her job. Loved being a part of the magic of imagination. But she had to give it up. For the sake of her own sanity.

Jenny left the main floor and took the stairs to the third. She couldn't take the elevators, since they were shut down temporarily so the paintings on the doors could be completed. Wanting to take a quick look at the hallway up here, Jenny walked slowly, checking the progress of the artwork.

On the third floor, there were werewolves sprinting along the wall, muscled bodies ripping through ribbons of fog as they gazed out at the hall as if staring at those who walked past. Jenny admired the art even as she shivered at the images. Not exactly the kind of thing designed to promote an easy night's sleep. But then again, the gamers who would flock to this hotel would love the imagery. Then they would slip into their hotel rooms and play the games on the top-of-the-line gaming systems.

She smiled to herself, then gave a quick glance to the antiqued brass wall sconces, shaped to give the illusion of torches. A dark blue carpet runner stretched the length of the hallway, covering the center of the wood-grain ceramic tiles. It was a good idea, she thought, for the flooring. Giving the feel of wood while offering the much-easier-to-care-for tile.

She headed back to the staircase and then walked down to the second floor to peek at what the other two artists were doing with the banshee/ghost halls. When she found them, the artists were in a heated discussion and didn't even notice her approach.

"The banshees all have white hair," Lena shouted. "Have you ever played the game?"

"I'm an artist, I don't waste my time playing video games," Tony argued. "And what difference does it make if a banshee has black hair? They're not *real*, you know."

"No," Jenny said loudly enough to interrupt their argument. "Banshees aren't real, but they are integral to the game you're supposed to be replicating here."

He sighed heavily, dramatically, as if to let her know how put-upon he was to be questioned by anyone about his artistic decisions. Jenny had known when she hired the man that he was going to be difficult. But the sad truth was, his talent had won him the job. She'd run out of names of local artists and had had to take a chance on him being willing to play by the rules stated. It looked as though she'd made a bad call.

"Artistically speaking, a black-haired banshee will pop more from the cream colored walls," he argued.

"You jerk," the other artist countered. "If you knew anything about shadows and highlighting, you'd know how to make that white hair stand out. It's supposed to be otherworldly, not like a photo shoot for a fashion magazine."

"What you know about art," he shouted, "could be printed on a business card with room left over for a Chinese menu."

"I know enough to do what I've been contracted to do," she said.

Jenny's head ached. They'd had the same problems with Tony while finishing the mural in the dining room. He wanted things done his way—too bad for him, he wasn't in charge. Holding her hands up for quiet, Jenny felt as if she were refereeing a fight between second-graders. "That's it. Lena, thanks, you're doing a great job. Just get back to it, okay?"

With muttered agreement, the woman did go back to work, throwing one last fulminating glare at the man smirking at her.

Jenny lowered her voice when she spoke again. There was no need to humiliate the man, but she wasn't going to be ignored, either. "Tony, you agreed when you signed on to this project to follow the planned art designs."

"Yes, but—"

"And," Jenny said, a little more loudly, "whatever you think of video games, the guests who will be coming to this hotel know these games like the backs of their hands."

Tony sighed heavily again. "If you'll only let me show you what I mean—"

"So," she said, overriding him again, "you will either do what you agreed to do, or you can pack up your paints and leave."

Insulted, he jerked his head back and glared at her. "You can't fire me."

"Oh, yes," a deep voice sounded from behind her. "She can."

Jenny looked over her shoulder, unsurprised to see Mike coming up behind her. The man was always close at hand these days.

"Mr. Ryan…"

Mike shook his head and continued speaking to the artist. "But allow me to repeat it so you'll understand. Either follow the planned design, or leave and we'll send you your last check."

"I'm an artist," Tony said hotly, lifting his chin with its wispy goatee. "If all you want is someone to fill in the lines with color, you don't need an artist. You need a child with a box of crayons."

"Your choice," Mike said. "Thanks for your time."

Clearly outraged, the man flushed darkly, then spun around to pack up his supplies, muttering all the while. From the corner of her eye, Jenny saw Lena do a little hip-shaking happy dance at the other artist's exit and she smiled.

"Well, that was fun." Jenny looked up at Mike. "I was handling it, you know."

"I saw and you were doing a great job." He smiled at her and Jenny's foolish heart gave a hard thump in response. "Any reason why I shouldn't help out when I can?"

"I suppose not," she said, but inside, she whispered that it wasn't a good idea for her to learn to depend on his help. Because it wouldn't always be there.

"Lena, are you all right here on your own?" Jenny asked.

"Are you kidding?" She laughed. "With Tony gone, it'll be like a vacation."

"Great. I'll send Christa up to help you when she finishes in the dining room."

"Fab, thanks. Oh, boss?"

Jenny and Mike both answered, "Yes?" Then Mike waved one hand as if telling Jenny to take it.

"I had an idea I wanted to run by you."

"Shoot."

Another grin from Lena. "I was thinking, what if I drew out one or two of the banshees so that their arms are stretched across the door—you know, so their clawed hands look like they're reaching for the guest opening their door…" She bit her lip and waited for a decision. She didn't have to wait long.

"That's a great idea," Jenny said and glanced at Mike. "What do you think?"

Nodding, he said, "I love it. Good thinking, Lena."

"Thanks."

"And your banshees look like they stepped right out of the game, I appreciate that," Mike added.

"Hey," Lena said, "I love that game!" When she turned to go back to work, humming to herself, Jenny and Mike headed back down the hall.

"The elevators are turned off, so we have to take the stairs."

"Yeah," Mike said, "I know. But I don't like you climbing up and down those stairs every day. What if you tripped and fell?"

"What am I, ninety?" Jenny shook her head and laughed to herself. "You're being ridiculous, Mike."

"I'm being concerned, Jenny," he said, pulling her to a stop just inside the stairwell. "I care about you. About our baby."

Care was such a pale word. It was pastel when what she wanted was bold, primary colors.

"I appreciate it, but we're both fine and I've got to

get downstairs to finish the main-floor elevator doors. We're one artist short now." She started for the stairs, but Mike was too quick for her. He scooped her up into his arms and Jenny huffed out a breath of exasperation.

He was smiling at her, holding her, and though she wanted nothing more than to hook her arms around his neck and hold on, she knew she couldn't. "You're not playing fair, Mike."

"Damn right, I'm not," he agreed, walking down the stairs with her held close to his chest. "I've told you how it's going to be between us, Jenny. I'm just giving you time to get used to the idea."

Later that night, the construction crew was gone for the day and most everyone else had headed into Laughlin for dinner and some fun. In the quiet darkness, Jenny went out onto the pool deck by herself, eager for a little solitude. It had been days now since Mike showed up at the hotel and it looked as though he had no intention of leaving anytime soon. Didn't he know that by staying, he was making this whole situation so much harder on her?

"Of course he does," she whispered wryly. "That's his plan, Jenny. He's trying to make you crazy enough that you'll agree to marry him, even though you know it would be a mistake."

Oh, God, she was so tempted to make that mistake.

Shaking her head at her own foolishness, Jenny sat down on the edge of the pool, took off her shoes and dangled her feet in the warm water. It was still cool in the desert at night, so she enjoyed the mix of a cold wind brushing over her arms and the warm water lapping at her legs. Lazily kicking her feet through the water, she leaned back on her hands and stared up at the night sky.

"Beautiful," she said to no one. With no light pollution here, the stars were brilliant and there were so many of them. It was like a painting, she thought and instantly, her mind drifted to just how she would capture that scene on canvas, though she knew she would never be able to do it justice.

"It is, isn't it?"

Jenny sighed and tipped her head down to watch Mike come toward her. Her time alone was over and though she knew that spending time with Mike was only prolonging the inevitable, she relished the hard thump of her heart at the sight of him. She'd thought he went into town with the others, but she should have known better, she told herself now.

He took a seat beside her, dropped his bare feet into the water and looked up at the sky. "Being in the city, you never see this many stars," he said, voice low, deep, intimate. "You forget how big the sky really is."

Jenny knew he hadn't come out here to talk about the stars. "Mike…"

He looked at her and in the shadowy moon and starlight, his blue eyes looked dark, mysterious. "I talked to Dave today," he said, surprising her. "He says you quit your job as of this project's completion."

Jenny had hoped he wouldn't find out so quickly. Turning in her resignation had cut at her. She loved her job and would miss everyone there, but she'd felt obligated to give Dave as much time as he might need to cover her absence. "I had to."

"No, you didn't," he mused quietly, sliding his bare foot along her leg, giving her chills that had nothing to do with the cool night air. "Dave also said you recommended he hire Christa full-time."

She shrugged. "He'll need someone to fill in for me when I'm gone. Christa's good. Talented, but willing to take direction."

"If you think she'll work out, that's good enough for me."

Pleased that he thought so highly of her suggestion, she smiled briefly. "Thanks for that."

"You could have stayed with the company, you know." He tossed a quick glance at the sky, then shifted his gaze to hers again. "Could have pulled the the-boss-is-my-baby's-father card."

She stared at him, shocked. "I would never do that."

His gaze moved over her face as he slowly nodded. "Yeah, I'm getting that. I'm beginning to get a lot of things."

"Mike," she said, hoping to make the situation perfectly clear between them. "Quitting my job was the right thing to do. For both of us. Working together every day would just be too hard. Besides, I don't need your money to take care of my baby. I don't need the Ryan name to make sure my future's secure—"

"What *do* you need, Jenny?"

Oh, wow, that question had too many answers. Too many pitfalls should she even try to tell him what was in her heart, her mind. So she smiled and said softly, "Doesn't matter."

"It does to me," he said.

Tipping her head to one side, she looked at him and asked, "Since when, Mike?"

"Since I woke up and started paying closer attention." He took her hand and smoothed his thumb across the back, sliding across her knuckles until she shivered at the contact. "I want you, Jenny. More than anything else in my life, I want you with me."

Her breath caught in her chest and her heartbeat quickened until it fluttered like a deranged butterfly. To be wanted. It had been the driving force in her life since she was a child. But now, she knew it wasn't enough. *Want* wasn't *love*.

"You do for now, Mike," she said quietly. "But what about in five years? Ten?" Shaking her head, she continued, "Want, need, passion, they're all good things. But without love to anchor them, they fade and drift away."

"They don't have to." He gripped her hand even tighter. "Love is something I've avoided, Jenny. Too big a risk."

She could see what it cost him to admit that, but with her heart hurting so badly, she couldn't tell him that she was all right and that she understood. "It's worth the risk, Mike. Because without love, there's nothing."

"Need is something. Want is something."

"But not enough." Sadly, she pulled her hand free of his, swung her legs out of the water and stood up. Looking down at him, she took a breath and braced herself to give him the hard truth she was only just accepting. "We have a child together, Mike. But that's all we have."

She walked back to the hotel and stopped in the doorway to look back at him. He was alone in the starlight, watching her, and it took everything Jenny had to keep walking.

Two days later, things were still tense between Mike and her. She had hoped that after their last conversation at the pool, he would give up and go home. He had to know that nothing was going to come of this. They each needed something from the other that they couldn't have. Jenny needed Mike to love her. To trust her. Mike needed her to settle for less than she craved.

Her time here at the hotel was almost done. Most of the paintings were completed now and what was left, Christa and Lena could finish on their own. Jenny couldn't stay much longer. Because Mike refused to leave her side, she had to be the one to leave. She had to get some distance from him before she did something stupid like rush into his arms and accept whatever crumbs he was willing to offer.

The cacophony of sound at the hotel was familiar now and Jenny half wondered if the silence of her apartment once she was home again would feel stifling. Between the men talking, the tools buzzing and crashing, and the roar of Jet Skis on the river, it was hard to hear yourself think. But in her case lately, maybe that was a blessing.

"Jenny! Jenny, where are you?"

Up on the second-story landing, Jenny was just adding a few finishing touches to the naked tree sprawled across the elevator doors when she heard that familiar voice booming out over the racket.

"Uncle Hank?" she asked aloud. Setting her paintbrush aside, she quickly went down the stairs and spotted her uncle, Betty right beside him, taking a good look around the front lobby.

"There she is," Betty shouted over the construction noise and used her elbow to give Hank a nudge in the ribs for good measure.

The older man's face brightened as he grinned and came toward her.

"Uncle Hank, what're you doing here?"

To her surprise, the usually stoic man gave her one hard hug, then let her go and beamed at her. "Well, Betty and I wanted to see what you were doing out here. Take a look around and see what's what."

"Darn fool, we could have caught a plane," Betty said, scraping her hands across her tangled hair. "But no, he insisted on driving so he could try out his new toy."

"No point in having a new car if you're not going to drive it," Hank pointed out.

"New car?" Jenny looked out the front window and saw a shiny red convertible. She couldn't have been more surprised. Though he was a wealthy man, Hank had been driving his classic Mercedes sedan for twenty years, insisting he didn't need anything new when that one ran just fine. Shifting her gaze back to her uncle, she asked, "That's yours?"

"It is," he said proudly.

"Like to froze me to death, driving out here with the top down the whole way," Betty muttered.

"No point in having a convertible if you keep the top up," Hank argued.

Jenny just laughed. It was so good to see them; she was enjoying their usual banter. But she had to ask, "You didn't drive all the way out here just to look at my paintings, did you?"

"Well," Hank hedged, "that's part of it, sure." His eyes narrowed on something behind her and without even looking, Jenny knew who was coming up beside her. Her uncle's features went cold and hard as Mike stopped alongside Jenny.

"Mr. Snyder," Mike said with a nod.

"Ryan." Hank gave him another narrow-eyed stare, then shifted his gaze to Jenny, ignoring the man beside her completely. "Jenny, I came to tell you I've sold Snyder Arts."

"What?" Stunned and in shock, Jenny stared at the man who'd raised her. First a convertible, now *this*? His company had been Uncle Hank's life. He lived and breathed the business, dedicating himself to building Snyder Arts into a well-respected, multimillion-dollar firm. She couldn't imagine him without it. "Why would you do that? You loved that business."

Still ignoring Mike, Hank moved in on her and dropped both hands on her shoulders. "I love *you* more," he said and Jenny received her second shock of the day.

He'd never said those words to her before and until that moment, she hadn't been aware of how much she'd wanted to hear them.

"Uncle Hank..."

"I see tears," he blurted and warned, "don't do that."

She laughed and shook her head. "I'll try. But tell me why."

"Main reason?" he said, sliding an icy glance toward Mike. "So no one could accuse you of being a damn spy for me."

"Damn it," Mike muttered from beside her.

Jenny hardly heard him as she stared into her uncle's sharp blue eyes. Oh, God. Guilt reared up and took a bite of her heart. He'd given up what he loved to prove something to Mike and it was all for her sake. "You shouldn't have done that," she whispered.

"It was time," Hank said, pausing long enough to glare at Mike.

"There's more to it than that," Betty interrupted, her

clipped tone cutting through the sentiment that was suddenly thick in the air.

Stepping in front of Hank, Betty looked at Jenny and said simply, "It was long past time he sold that business. Haven't I been trying to get him to live a little before he dies?"

"Who said anything about dying?" Hank wanted to know.

"Nobody lives forever," Betty snapped, then focused on Jenny again. "With the company gone, we'll both have time to help out when the baby comes. We can both be there for you, Jenny. And that's the important thing. Family stands for family. You understand?"

"I do," Jenny said and reached out to hug the woman who had always been a constant in her life. Heart full, she looked at the older couple and realized that she'd always had family—she'd just been too insecure to notice. Now, she couldn't understand how she had ever doubted what these two amazing people felt for her.

"Now, you just show us around," Hank said, letting his gaze slide around the lobby and briefly rest on her entry wall painting. "Let us see what all you've done here, then you can quit this job and come home with us where you belong."

She opened her mouth to speak, but Mike cut her off.

Speaking directly to Hank, he said, "I know you've got no reason to trust me, but I need a minute with Jenny."

"Mike—" She didn't want more time alone with him. Didn't think she could take much more.

"I think you've said plenty already," Hank told him.

"I agree with Hank," Betty said, lifting her chin imperiously.

"Please," Mike said, looking at Jenny directly, catching her off guard with the quietly voiced plea.

In all the time she'd known him, Jenny had never heard him say *please* to anyone. And that one simple word decided it for her.

To her uncle, she said, "I'll be back in a minute." Then she turned, walked into the game room, which was currently unoccupied, and waited for Mike to join her.

With so much happening, Jenny's heartbeat was fast, her mind spinning. She hardly knew what to think. Her uncle selling the company, her quitting her job, having a baby. And now Mike, wanting to talk again when they'd already said both too much and too little to each other.

She tried to calm the jumping nerves inside her by focusing on the view out the window. The desert landscape was softened by the trees swaying in a soft wind. Jenny focused her gaze on the purple smudge of mountains in the distance and tried to steady her breathing.

"Jenny?"

She turned to face him and her heart raced. He looked—unsure of himself. Something she'd never seen in Mike Ryan. That realization shook her. She wouldn't be persuaded, in spite of her instinctive urge to go to him and hold on until she eased whatever was bothering him.

"I feel like an idiot," he muttered, scraping one hand through his hair.

"Not what I expected to hear," she admitted.

"Oh." He laughed, but there was no humor in the sound. "There's more." He took a step closer, then stopped, as if not trusting himself to get within reach. "I can't believe your uncle showed up out of nowhere," he muttered.

"You're upset about Uncle Hank coming to see me?"

"Not the act," he said, "just the timing."

Now she was really confused.

"You should know that I was wrong about you. Right from the beginning, I was wrong and I think somehow I knew that, I just couldn't admit it," he grumbled in irritation. "Just like I know I've loved you from the first moment I saw you in that bar in Phoenix."

Suddenly unsteady, Jenny reached down and grabbed the back of a chair for support. *He loved her.* She hadn't thought to ever hear those words from him. Only yesterday, that confession would have had her glowing in happiness. Now, though, it was too late. "Mike—"

"Just hear me out," he said, moving in close enough to touch her. To hold her. Hands at her waist, he spoke more quickly now, as if afraid she'd stop listening. "I'm asking you to marry me, Jenny. Not *telling* you, *asking* you. It's not for the baby's sake, or convenience or any other damn reason except that I love you. I want to go to bed with you every night and wake up beside you every morning." His eyes locked with hers and she read the truth there and wished, so wished he had said all of this sooner.

"You're it for me, Jenny," he confessed. "Maybe that's why I fought it so hard. Seeing your future spilling out in front of you can be…overwhelming. But the thing is, no matter how I looked at the future, you were there." His hands tightened on her waist and the heat of his touch slipped inside her. "There is no future without you, Jenny. There is no *me* without you."

Her mouth worked, but anything she might have said was choked off by the river of tears crowding her throat.

"I need you to believe me, Jenny," he said urgently. "I love you. I trust you. Please marry me."

Oh, God, it was everything she'd ever wanted. The

man she loved was giving her the words she'd yearned to hear and it was too late. How could she ever believe in him when it had taken her uncle selling his company to make him believe in her? What kind of irony was it that she was given exactly what she longed for and couldn't have it?

Disappointment rose up inside her and she couldn't keep it from spilling out. "No, Mike, I won't marry you. I can't. You're only saying this now because Uncle Hank gave you proof your suspicions about me were wrong."

"No, that's not true."

She shook her head wildly. "I wish you had said all of this before Uncle Hank arrived. It would have meant everything to me."

"This is what I meant about Hank's timing. I was going to talk to you tonight." He shook his head and laughed ruefully. "I had it planned. Moonlight, seduction, romance…"

"Mike, you're just saying this now, to try to make it better."

"No, damn it." He scowled. "You're wrong. I believed before today. It was that talk the other night, out at the pool?" He pulled her tight as if expecting her to make a bolt for escape. "It was then reality crashed down on me. When you said you didn't need me. Didn't want my money. When you made me see that you're not the kind of woman who has to *trap* a man into anything.

"You're one of the strongest women I've ever known. You're beautiful, talented. You're kind and funny and you don't take any of my crap."

She laughed, but it hurt her throat, so she stopped short.

"You're everything to me, Jenny. You have to believe me."

"I want to," she admitted. "So much."

He smiled, just one brief curve of his mouth. "Then let this convince you." Digging into his pants pocket, he pulled out a small deep blue velvet box.

Jenny's eyes went wide and she sucked in a gulp of air and held it. He was telling the truth, she thought wildly. He'd already had a ring for her when Hank showed up. It was real. It was staggering.

Mike flipped the top of the box open, and showed her a canary yellow diamond, glittering in an old-fashioned setting that seemed to Jenny as if it were made especially for her. "When did you—"

"Yesterday," he said. "After our talk the night before last, I drove into Vegas, found the best jeweler in the city and got this ring for you." He lifted her chin with the tips of his fingers until her teary eyes met his. "I knew, before your uncle showed up, that I love you. I trust you. I need you, Jenny. I always will."

"Mike…" Her bottom lip trembled.

Taking her left hand in his, he slid the ring onto her finger and sealed it there with a kiss. "Say you'll take the ring, Jenny. And me."

It was a gift, Jenny told herself. A gift from the universe, because suddenly she had everything she'd ever wanted most in her life. She looked up into his beautiful eyes and saw her own love shining back at her.

"Jenny?" he asked, a half laugh in his voice, "you're starting to worry me…"

"There's no need, Mike. I love you. I have since that first night in Phoenix." She went up on her toes and kissed him lightly. "I'll take the ring. And you. And I promise I will love you forever."

"Thank God," he whispered and pulled her in close.

His arms wrapped around her, her head nestled on his chest, she heard him say, "You are the best thing that has ever happened to me, Jenny Marshall, and I swear I will never let you go."

Epilogue

A few months later, the wedding was held at the Balboa Pavilion. Built in 1905, the Victorian-style building was on the National Register of Historic Places, and a California landmark. The grand ballroom boasted dramatic floor-to-ceiling windows that provided a spectacular view of one of the largest small-yacht harbors in the world.

Candles flickered on the linen-draped tables scattered around the wide room. Yellow and white flowers decorated every surface and cascaded over the front of the bride-and-groom table. And tiny white fairy lights sparkled and shone on every window as the day wore down and night rushed in.

"It was all perfect," Jenny mused, leaning back against her brand-new husband.

Mike's arms wrapped around her middle, his hands

tenderly cupping the bump of their child, and he dipped his head to kiss the curve of her throat. "It was, and you are the most beautiful bride ever."

Jenny did feel pretty in her white off-the-shoulder dress that clung to her bosom and waist, then fell in a soft swirl of skirt to the floor. Mike, of course, was gorgeous: tall, handsome and looking as though he'd been born to wear a tux.

"I love you," she whispered, tipping her head back to look at him.

"Never get tired of hearing that." He grinned, kissed her and swore, "I love you, too. And I'm going to show you how much every day of our honeymoon."

A slow, knowing smile curved her lips. "You haven't had a vacation in years. I can hardly believe we're taking a week in Ireland *and* a week in London."

"And," he teased, "another week in Tuscany."

"Really?" Jenny turned in his arms and hugged him. "You didn't tell me!"

"Surprise!" He grinned down at her and said, "An artist really should tour Italy, don't you think?"

"Absolutely." Jenny couldn't possibly be happier, she thought. A man who loved her, a baby on the way, a job she loved and so many friends who had come to wish them well.

"Maybe we'll look around, see if we can find a spot we like, buy a place of our own there."

"Seriously?" He shrugged. "Why not? We can take the kids there every summer."

"Kids?" she repeated, still grinning.

"Well, we're not gonna stop at one, are we?" He patted her belly and she caught his hand and held it in place, linking the three of them.

"No, we're not," she agreed, then leaned back against him and watched their guests dance on the wide wooden floor beneath thousands of tiny white lights.

"Your uncle and Betty look like they're having fun," he said, giving a nod toward the dance floor.

Jenny smiled to see Hank and Betty dancing together, alongside Mike's parents. The four of them had hit it off well enough that they were all planning a trip to wine country together. Their family was big and growing, Jenny thought, and she couldn't be happier.

"You two should be dancing," Brady said as he and Aine approached. Their infant son had stayed home in Ireland with Aine's mother, and though of course they were worried about leaving him, they were also enjoying the little break from parenthood.

"Why aren't you?" Mike asked with a laugh.

"We're about to," Brady assured him with a slap on the shoulder. "But first, we wanted to say happy wedding, happy life and good luck with the baby."

"Thanks," Mike said and pulled his oldest friend into a hard, one-armed hug.

"What's all this?" Sean asked as he walked up to join them. "People partying without me?"

"Where've you been?" Mike demanded. "You disappeared like an hour ago."

"On the phone with the contractor from hell," Sean muttered, glaring down at the phone so he didn't see the amused glances Mike and Brady shared.

"How is the very efficient Kate?" Brady asked.

"Driving him crazy," Mike offered.

"Hey, you try dealing with a know-it-all," Sean quipped.

"We do it all the time," Aine said, with a grin for Jenny.

"She's right," the new bride agreed.

"All right, enough of the insults." Brady pulled his wife onto the dance floor and her delighted laughter spilled out in her wake.

"Can I dance with the bride now?" Sean asked.

Mike strong-armed him out of the way. "Get your own girl.

"You owe me a dance, Mrs. Ryan," Mike said and spun Jenny into his arms and then around in a tight, fast circle.

"Sweep me away, Mr. Ryan," Jenny said and laughing, she wrapped her arms around his neck and held on tight. While the music played and the night wore on, joy shone as brightly as the fairy lights in the darkness.

* * * * *

Jacob suspected the game had changed the instant Anna walked into that bar.

She was no longer a naive coed. She was a powerful businesswoman—confident, cool, in control. Formidable for her business pedigree, she came from one of the most successful entrepreneurial families in history. Other men in the bar had taken notice, too. Her beauty only upped the intimidation factor, with thick brown hair falling around her shoulders, a dancer's grace and posture, and lips that suggested sweetness and hinted of a storm.

Anna's lips had fallen on his once—a few scorching heartbeats still emblazoned in his memory. The way she pressed against him had resonated to his core. She'd been so eager to surrender her body, so ready to explore his. Turning her down, saying he'd betray his brotherly friendship with Adam if things went further, had been the upstanding thing to do.

He'd been raised as a gentleman and no gentleman made a move on his best friend's sister, however tempting she might be. Anna had been astoundingly tempting.

Did he want to meet with gorgeous Anna Langford? The prospect, although ill-advised, was intriguing.

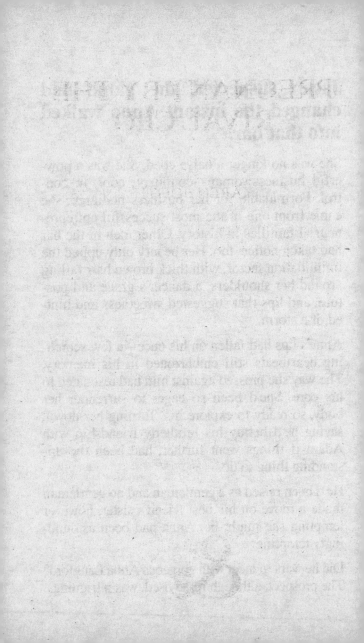

PREGNANT BY THE RIVAL CEO

BY
KAREN BOOTH

First Published in Great Britain 2016
By Mills & Boon, an imprint of HarperCollins*Publishers*
1 London Bridge Street, London, SE1 9GF

© 2016 Karen Booth

ISBN: 978-0-263-91844-1

51-0116

Our policy is to use papers that are natural, renewable and recyclable products and made from wood grown in sustainable forests.The logging and manufacturing processes conform to the legal environmental regulations of the country of origin.

Printed and bound in Spain
by CPI, Barcelona

Karen Booth is a Midwestern girl transplanted in the South, raised on '80s music, Judy Blume and the films of John Hughes. She loves to write big-city love stories. When she takes a break from the art of romance, she's teaching her kids about good music, honing her Southern cooking skills or sweet-talking her super-supportive husband into mixing up a cocktail. You can learn more about Karen at www.karenbooth.net.

In memory of Holly Gilliatt, brilliant author
and fabulous friend. You taught me the
importance of embracing the good
and the sheer power of defying the bad.

One

"Strangle me? Isn't that a little harsh?" Anna Langford gaped at her friend and coworker, Holly Louis.

The pair stood in the luxe lobby of The Miami Palm Hotel, just outside the bar. Anna was preparing to see her bold business plan to fruition. If only Holly could find it in her heart to say something encouraging.

"I've only been in a few meetings with your brother, but he's going to hit the roof when he finds out you want to cut a deal with Jacob Lin."

Anna glanced back over her shoulder. The bar was humming with people, all fellow attendees of the two-day Execu-Tech conference. As Senior Director of Technology Acquisitions for LangTel, the telecom her father had started before she was born, Anna had the job of scouting out the next big thing. Her brother Adam, current LangTel CEO, had been crystal clear—he expected to be dazzled.

The company had been floundering in the months since their father's death, and Anna had a bead on a game-changing cellphone technology, only Adam didn't know it. She was fairly sure that LangTel's competitors hadn't figured it out either. Unfortunately, getting to the next big thing meant going through Jacob Lin, and he absolutely hated her brother. Adam, without a doubt, despised him right back.

"That's him, isn't it?" Holly asked in a whisper, nodding in Jacob's direction. "Damn. I've never seen him in person before. He's fifty times hotter than in pictures."

Tell me about it. Anna was well acquainted with Jacob Lin and his hotness. She'd been rebuffed by him and his hotness. Six years later and it still stung.

"Does he always have that aura?" Holly swirled her hand in the air. "The one that says he's genetically superior to every man within a fifty-mile radius?"

Anna didn't even need to look. "Yes, and he comes by it honestly. It's not an act."

"Wow." Holly patted Anna's shoulder. "Well, good luck. I'd say you'll need it."

"What?" Any confidence Anna had mustered was evaporating. "Do you really think it's going to be that bad?"

"You're a Langford. He hates your family. So, yes. I do think it's going to be that bad."

"Technically, I could order you to come with me. You're a member of my team."

Holly shook her head so fast it made her curly hair frizz. "My job description does not include suicide missions."

Another wave of doubt hit Anna, but she did her best to brush it off. She had to do this. If she was ever going to convince her brother that it was okay to step aside and allow her to take over as CEO, just as he'd promised her before their father died, she had to make tough decisions and dangerous moves.

Holly wasn't wrong, though. There was no telling how Jacob would react given his history with the Langford family. "I'm telling you right now, it's going to be great." Anna feigned conviction. "Jacob is a money guy and I can offer him a big pile of money. And once Adam sees how huge this could be for LangTel, he'll get past the personal stuff, too. It's business. Nothing else."

"So what's your plan to approach Mr. Hottie?"

"I'm going to ask the bartender to give him a note."

Holly squinted one eye as if she had a migraine. "Oh, because that won't seem weird?"

"I can't call him," Anna pled. "I don't have his cell number." The only number she had for Jacob was six years old, acquired during the week he spent with her family at Christmas, the year she fell for him, the year she'd kissed him. The year he'd told her "no." That old cell number was no longer his. She'd tried it, and no dice.

"You can't exactly go up to him and start talking either. You won't just get the rumor mill going, you'll set it on fire."

"No. I can't just walk up to him." However ridiculous it sounded, if ever there was an understatement, that was it. Everyone in the tech world was aware of the feud between Adam Langford and Jacob Lin. The backstabbing had been ruthless and very public.

"If anyone can make the impossible happen, it's you," Holly said. "Text me later and let me know what happened. Good luck."

"Thanks," Anna muttered. She straightened her

blouse and strode into the room with her head held high, then sidled up to the only available seat at the bar. She discreetly took a piece of paper and pen from her purse. It was time to conjure her steeliest tendencies. No looking back now.

> *Jacob,*
> *I'm sitting at the far end of the bar. I need to*
> *meet with you to discuss a business proposition.*
> *I thought it best not to approach you in the open*
> *considering the state of things between you and*
> *Adam. Text me if you're interested.*
> *Anna*

She added her cell phone number and signaled to the bartender. She leaned forward, hoping the men sitting on either side of her wouldn't hear. "I need you to give this to the gentleman seated in the corner. The tall one in the gray suit. Black hair." She skipped the part about his ridiculously square jaw and sublime five o'clock shadow. She also left out his superhuman sexiness and his perfect, tawny complexion, the product of his Taiwanese and American background.

The bartender raised an eyebrow, looking down at the note.

Give me a break. Anna slid a ten-dollar bill across the bar.

The bartender swiped the money away. "Sure thing."

"And a dirty martini when you get a chance. Three olives." Liquid courage would be right on time. She scratched her head, striving to remain inconspicuous while studying Jacob. He ran his hand through his hair when he took the note from the bartender. She caught a glimpse of his deep brown eyes. It wasn't hard to remember the way they lit up when he smiled, but she doubted her message would prompt such a response.

His forehead crinkled as he read. What was he thinking? That she was crazy? Now that he had personal wealth north of one billion, was incredibly accomplished in the field of venture capitalism, and at the top of his game, it seemed a little childish to have sent a note. And to think she'd once hoped it would end well when she kissed him.

Jacob shook his head and folded the paper. He tapped away at his phone. How had she forgotten how bewitching his hands were? Like the rest of him, they were big and manly. They seemed so…capable. Sadly, her bodily familiarity with his hands didn't go beyond one of them on the small of her back and the other on her shoulder when he'd delivered the stinger that had stuck with her for years. *I can't, Anna. My friendship with Adam means too much.*

It had taken buckets of self-analysis to get over him, and just being in the same room was bringing it all back—in a deluge, where there was no dodging a drop of water. With all of the serious business-related thoughts rolling in her head, her mind kept drifting to their past—every smile, laugh, and flirtatious look they'd ever shared still haunted her. Dammit. She'd been so sure she was beyond this.

Jacob tucked his phone inside his suit coat pocket and finished his drink.

The screen on Anna's phone lit up. Her pulse throbbed in her throat. What would he say? That he wanted nothing to do with her or her family? That she was lucky he didn't call her out in the crowded bar?

She swallowed hard and read the text.

Penthouse suite. 15 minutes.

Anna forgot how to breathe. The message was so like Jacob. Direct. To the point. Just intimidating enough to make her doubt herself even more. She wasn't put off by powerful men. She worked alongside them every day, could hold her own in any tense business situation. But those men didn't have the pull on her that Jacob had once had. Those men hadn't once held her heart in their hands, and she sure hadn't spent years pining for any of them, writing dozens of heartfelt letters that she would ultimately never send.

Jacob stood and bid a farewell to a man he'd been talking to. With the grace of a cat, he wound his way through the jam-packed bar, towering above nearly everyone at six-foot and several more inches, acknowledging the few who had the guts to greet the most formidable and successful technology venture capitalist quite possibly ever.

A shiver crawled along Anna's spine as he came closer. He brushed past her, not saying a word, leaving behind his heady scent—sandalwood and citrus. Fifteen minutes. She had to pull herself together and prepare to be alone with the one man she would've once done anything for.

Anna Langford. I'll be damned. Jacob pressed the button for the private elevator to his suite. He'd spent the last six years convinced that the entire Langford family despised him, a feeling he'd had no choice but to return.

After the note from Anna, he didn't know what to think, which was unsettling. He always knew what to think.

Did he want to meet with gorgeous Anna Langford, youngest of the three Langford siblings, the woman stuck with an untrustworthy jerk for an older brother? The prospect, although ill-advised, was intriguing. He and Anna had once been friends. On one memorable night they'd been a little more. But did he want to speak to Anna Langford, a member of the LangTel executive board? On that count, it depended on what she wanted to discuss.

His plan to engineer a takeover of LangTel wouldn't simply backfire if Anna discovered it—he'd be sunk. The War Chest, a secret high-roller investment group led by Jacob, had watched the decline of LangTel stock after the death of Anna and Adam's father, Roger. The company was vulnerable with Adam in charge—he didn't have the confidence of the board of directors the way his dad had. LangTel was ripe for the picking.

The War Chest's plan had been born over cards and too much bourbon one night in Madrid, at a retreat for key players. Jacob had put it out there—*What about LangTel? Could a company that large be taken over?* It would be a daunting challenge, requiring a massive money pool and meticulous planning, but this was precisely the kind of project the War Chest loved. Without risk came no reward. There was money to be made, and a lot of it, because a company that well established would eventually rebound. Carving out a slice of revenge against Adam by ousting him as CEO would merely be giving Adam exactly what he deserved.

Jacob rode the elevator upstairs. The game had changed the instant Anna walked into that bar. She was no longer a wide-eyed coed. She was a powerful businesswoman—confident, cool, in control. Other men in the bar had taken notice, too—she was formidable for her business pedigree, coming from one of the most successful entrepreneurial families in US history. Her beauty only upped the intimidation factor, with thick brown hair falling around her shoulders, a dancer's grace and posture, and lips that suggested sweetness and hinted of a storm.

Anna's lips had fallen on his once—a few scorching heartbeats still emblazoned in his memory. The way she pressed against him had resonated to his core. She'd been so eager to surrender her body, so ready to explore his. Turning her down, saying he'd destroy his brotherly friendship with Adam if things went further, had been the upstanding thing to do.

He had no way of knowing that Adam would betray him months later by ending their business partnership, making millions from the sale of the company they'd started together and publicly bashing Jacob's contribution to the project. The words Adam had said could never be erased from Jacob's memory. *It's your fault you never asked for a partnership agreement.* And to think he'd trusted Adam...that had been his first mistake.

He keyed into his suite—quiet, sprawling luxury, echoing his private existence at home in New York. Outside of a maid or a cook or an assistant, there was never anyone waiting when he walked through the door at the end of the day, and that was how he preferred it. Most people were nothing but a disappointment—Exhibit A, Adam Langford.

A business proposition. What was Anna's angle? It'd be brave of her if it involved peacemaking. The feud between himself and Adam only continued to get worse.

It seemed as if the more successful Jacob became, the more Adam said crude things about him at cocktail parties and in business magazines. *Jacob Lin doesn't have an entrepreneurial mind. He's good with money and nothing else.* Jacob had given into it, too. *Adam Langford will coast on his family name for as long as the world lets him.* It was impossible not to engage, but it had also occurred to Jacob after the last barbs were exchanged in the newspapers, that words were no way to go. Actions spoke louder. He'd no longer tell the world what he thought of Adam. He'd show them.

Jacob picked up the direct line to the twenty-four-hour concierge.

"Good evening, Mr. Lin. How may I assist you?"

"Yes. Can you please send up a bottle of wine?" He flipped through the room service menu. "The Montrachet, Domaine Marquis de Laguiche?" He rattled off the French with no problem. Years of shuttling between boarding schools in Europe and Asia had left him fluent in four languages—French, English, Japanese and Mandarin, the language his father had grown up speaking in Taiwan.

"Yes, Mr. Lin. We have the 2012 vintage for fifteen-hundred dollars. I trust that is acceptable?"

"Of course. Send it up right away." *Life is too short for cheap wine.*

Actually, he and Anna had consumed more than their fair share of cheap wine during their marathon late-night talks at the Langford family home in Manhattan. That felt like a lifetime ago.

His friendship with Adam had meant the world then. They told each other everything, commiserated over growing up with powerful, yet emotionally reclusive, fathers. They bonded over career aspirations, came up with ideas effortlessly. Jacob had hit it off with Anna equally well, except that he'd only had a sliver of time with her—ten days during which they drank, played cards and joked, while attraction pinged back and forth between them. He'd thought about acting on it many times, but never did.

He'd been raised as a gentleman and no gentleman made a move on his best friend's sister, however tempting she might be. Anna had been supremely tempting. It physically hurt to say "no" to her when she'd kissed him and it wasn't only because she'd given him a mind-numbing erection. He'd sensed that night that he was turning down more than sex. It was difficult not to harbor regrets.

After room service delivered the wine, Jacob removed his suit coat and tie. He was essentially shedding his armor, but it would make things more informal. If the Langfords were aware that a takeover was in the mix and Adam had sent her to spy on him, this would make him seem less threatening. The War Chest investors had been careful, but some tracks were impossible to cover.

The suite doorbell rang. Jacob had given his personal assistant the night off, so he strode through the marble-floored foyer to answer it. When he opened the door, he couldn't help himself—he had to drink in the vision of Anna. A stolen glimpse of her in the hotel bar had nothing on her up close. Her sweet smell, her chest rising and falling with each breath, sent reverberations through his body for which he was ill prepared.

"May I come in?" she asked. "Or did you answer just so you could slam the door in my face?" The look in her eyes said that she was only half kidding. He had to give her credit. It couldn't have been easy to break the silence between himself and the Langfords.

"Only your brother deserves that treatment. Not you." Jacob stepped aside. He'd forgotten about the sultry nature of her voice, the way it made parts of him rumble and quake.

"I won't take up your time. I'm sure you're busy." She came to a halt in the foyer, folded her hands in front of her, playing the role of steely vixen all too well.

"Anna, it's eight o'clock at night. Even I don't schedule my day nonstop. The evening is yours. Whatever you want." The more time he spent with her, the more sure he could be of her motives.

She straightened her fitted black suit jacket. The long lines of her trousers showed off her lithe frame. "You sure?"

"Please. Come in. Sit."

Anna made her way into the living area and perched on the edge of the sofa. Palm trees fluttered in the wind outside. Miami moonlight filtered through the tall windows. "I came to talk about Sunny Side."

Of the things Jacob thought Anna might come to discuss, he hadn't considered this. "I'm impressed. I thought I'd managed to keep my investment role at Sunny Side quiet. Very quiet. Silent, in fact." Exactly as he hoped he'd kept his LangTel investments. Was he losing his touch? Or was Anna that good?

"I read about them on a tech blog. It took some digging to figure out where their money was coming from, but I eventually decided it had to be you, although that was just a hunch. Thank you for confirming my suspicions." She smiled and cocked an eyebrow, showing the same satisfied smirk her brother sometimes brandished.

The times Jacob had wanted to knock that look off Adam's face was countless, but on Anna? Coming from her, delivered via her smoky brown eyes, it was almost too hot to bear. He was intrigued by this sly side of her, more self-assured than the coltish twenty-year-old he'd first met. "Well done. Would you like a glass of wine? I have a bottle on ice."

Anna hesitated. "It's probably best if we keep our conversation strictly business."

"There's no business between you and me without the personal creeping in. Your family and I are forever enmeshed." She could turn this point on him later if she learned of the War Chest's plans, not that he cared to change a thing about it. The ball was rolling.

Anna nodded in agreement. "How about this? Talk to me about Sunny Side and I'll stay for a glass of wine."

Was it really as innocent as that? His skeptical side wanted to think that it wasn't, but it'd been a long day. At least he could enjoy a glass of good wine and derive deep satisfaction from admiring his nemesis's little sister. "I'll open it right now."

"So, Sunny Side," Anna said. "They could be an amazing acquisition for LangTel."

Jacob opened the bottle at the wet bar, filled two glasses and brought them to the lacquered cocktail table. He sat near Anna and clinked his glass with hers. "Cheers." Taking a long sip, he studied her lovely face, especially her mouth. He'd only had her lips on his for a few moments, but he knew the spark beneath her composed exterior. She could so easily be his undoing. He hadn't anticipated this beguiling creature resurfacing in his life. Or that she might disrupt the riskiest investment venture of his career.

"Well?" she asked. "Sunny Side?"

"Yes. Sorry. It's been a long day." He shook his head, trying to make sense of the situation. "Is there a point in discussing it? Sunny Side might consider an offer from LangTel, but the problem is Adam. I don't see him wanting to acquire a company I'm so deeply entrenched with and frankly, I'm never getting into bed with him either." Getting into bed with Adam's sister might be another matter. Loyalty was no longer standing in the way.

She nodded, intently focused. "I'll take care of Adam. I just want to know if you can put me in the room with Sunny Side."

"Just so you know, it's about more than money. The founder is very leery of big business. It took months for me to earn his trust."

Her eyes flashed. She was undaunted by obstacles. If anything, it brought out her enthusiasm. "Of course. The technology has limitless applications."

"It will revolutionize the entire cell phone industry." One thing dawned on him—the War Chest's interest in LangTel was with the mind of turning the corporation into a bigger moneymaker once Adam was gone. Sunny Side would be a major player in the industry, so why *not* put the two together? It could have an enormous upside.

"So, can we make this happen?"

Jacob admired her persistence. Among other things. "Only if Adam stays out of it."

"Tech acquisitions is my department. Think of it as doing business with me."

"How long do you think you'll stay in that job?" He'd been surprised she'd taken a job with LangTel at all. She always seemed to hate being in her brother's shadow.

"Not forever, hopefully."

"Setting your sights on bigger and better things?"

She smiled politely. "Yes."

He was relieved that she saw herself eventually leaving LangTel. She'd still make a boatload of money from her personal stock if he was successful with a takeover, and her career wouldn't be derailed. Adam was his target, not Anna. "Okay, well, if we're going to talk about Sunny Side, Adam has to stay out of it. A negotiation requires compromise and he is incapable of that. He hates it when you disagree with him."

"I'm familiar with that aspect of his personality." She ran her finger around the edge of the wine glass, her eyes connecting with his and sending a splendid shock right through him. "I could never get Adam to tell me exactly what happened. Between the two of you."

Although Jacob wasn't certain what made Adam react the way he had, he suspected Roger Langford was at the root of it all. It started when Jacob spotted problems with Adam's central idea for Chatterback, the social media website they were starting. They needed to rethink everything. Adam vehemently disagreed. He brooded, they argued for days on end. Jacob suggested Adam consult with his dad—maybe he could talk some sense into him. The next day, Jacob had been cut out entirely. "I find that surprising. I assumed he bad-mouthed me to anyone who would listen."

"He did some of that, but he mostly just never wanted to talk about it." Anna wound her arms around her waist.

Did he care to venture down this road tonight? Absolutely not. The details were too infuriating—money lost, countless hours, passion and hard work unfairly yanked away. Plus, he couldn't tell Anna that he suspected her father had been the problem. She was likely still grieving him. "I don't want to be accused of trying to taint your opinion of Adam. He is your brother, after all."

"Okay, then at least tell me that you'll put me in the room with Sunny Side."

His mind went to work, calculating. There were myriad ways in which this could all go wrong. Of course, if it went right, that could be a real coup. "I'll make it happen, but this is only because of you. I don't want Adam interfering."

"Believe me, I won't let him get in the middle." Anna took a sip of her wine. When she set down the glass, she laughed quietly and shook her head. "It was bad enough when he was the reason you didn't want me to kiss you."

Two

Adam's fiancée, Melanie, pointed to the dog-eared pages of bridal magazines spread out on the dining table in Adam's penthouse apartment. "Anna? What do you think? Black or eggplant?"

Bridesmaid's dresses. Talking about the dress she'd have to wear for Adam and Melanie's January wedding felt like a speed bump. Anna'd been trying to broach the subject of Jacob and Miami for nearly the entire week, but Adam kept putting her off.

"Do you have a preference?" Melanie asked.

Anna shook her head, setting down her dessert spoon. The chocolate mousse Melanie had served with dinner was delicious, and perfect, just like Adam and Melanie's life—a well-matched couple giddily in love, wedding a few months down the road. "I'm sorry. What were you saying?"

"Classic black A-line or strapless dark purple?"

Anna choked back a sigh. She was happy for Adam and Melanie, really she was, but their wedding had taken over Langford family life. It was the only thing their mother, Evelyn, wanted to talk about. Just to make things especially fun for Anna, her mother usually added a comment about how her first project after the wedding was helping Anna find the right guy. January couldn't come—and go—soon enough.

She loved her brother dearly. Melanie had become a close friend. It was just that it was painful to watch them reach a milestone Anna was skeptical she'd ever reach. At twenty-eight, being hopelessly single in a city full of men who didn't have eyes for women with lofty aspirations, there wasn't much else to think. Most men were intimidated by her family and the job she'd already ascended to at LangTel. It wasn't going to get any less daunting for them if and when she took over as CEO.

"The black, I guess," Anna said. "But you should pick what you want. Don't worry about me. It's your big day, not mine."

"No, I want you to be happy. I think we'll go with the black." Melanie smiled warmly.

Anna really did adore her future sister-in-law. These days, Melanie was the only thing that made being around Adam tolerable, which was so sad. Adam had once been her ally. Now it was as if she had a grizzly bear for a brother and a boss—she never knew what would set him off, and most days, it seemed as if everything did.

She'd assumed she and Adam would lean on each other after their father passed away, but instead, Adam had withdrawn. He'd holed up in Dad's big corner office and become distant. The tougher things got, the more

Adam shut her out. She'd been exercising patience. Everyone dealt with death differently. If only he'd trust her with more responsibility, she could lighten his workload and remind him that she was well equipped to take over.

Melanie took Adam's hand across the sleek ebony table, her stunning Harry Winston engagement ring glinting. "I still can't believe we're getting married. I pinch myself every morning."

"Just wait until we have kids," Adam quipped. "Then things will really get surreal."

"You're already talking about children?" Anna tried to squelch the extreme surprise in her voice.

"We are," Melanie answered. "Two of my sisters had trouble getting pregnant. If we're going to have kids, I don't want to risk waiting too long."

Anna nodded. She'd worried about how long she would have to wait. Her friends from college were having kids, some their second or third. On an intellectual level, she knew she had time, but after her dad had died, emotion had taken over reasoning, and she panicked.

Feeling alone while watching Adam move forward with his life, Anna decided she wasn't about to wait for a man to show up in hers. She'd looked into artificial insemination. It was a just-in-case sort of thing—a fact-finding mission. Hopefully, she'd find love and a partner and none of it would be necessary, but at that moment when she'd felt powerless, taking action was the only comfort she could get.

Unfortunately, the visit to the clinic brought a devastating problem to light—a tangle of scar tissue from her appendectomy, literally choking off her chances of conception unless she had surgery. If she didn't fix the problem and she did become pregnant, carrying a baby to term was unlikely. With things crazy at work, Anna hadn't done a thing about it, although she planned to. Some day.

"We aren't going to have to try, Mel." Adam leaned back in his chair, folding his hands behind his head. "If I have my way, you'll be pregnant by the end of the honeymoon."

Melanie laughed quietly. "Did Adam tell you about Fiji?" she asked Anna. "Two weeks in a private villa on the beach with a chef and an on-call masseuse, all while the rest of New York is dealing with gray snow and cold. I can't wait."

Fiji. In January. Anna took a cleansing breath. She hated these feelings of envy. She wanted to squash them like a bug.

"We need to talk about that, because we're going to be away for a full two weeks," Adam said to Anna. "If you think that's too long a stretch for you to be in charge at LangTel, you need to tell me now."

Anna blew out an exasperated breath. "I can't believe you think there's a chance I can't handle it."

Adam fetched a bottle of beer from the fridge and returned to the table. "What about Australia? What if something like that happens when I'm gone? We're still sorting out that mess."

"First off, *we're* not sorting out that mess, I am. And you asked me to make those changes. I was following orders."

"If you're going to be CEO, you have to think for yourself." He took a sip of his beer and pointed at her with the neck of the bottle. "There will be no orders to follow."

How she hated it when he talked down to her like that,

as if she didn't know as much about business, when she absolutely did. "And I will do that once you finally hand over the reins." Anna tightened her hands into balls. She was so tired of her dynamic with Adam, constantly at war.

Melanie buried her nose in a bridal magazine. Surely this wasn't a comfortable conversation to sit in on.

"When you're ready and not a day sooner," Adam barked. "You know we're in a delicate position. The company stock is fluctuating like crazy. I keep hearing rumblings about somebody, somewhere, wanting to take over the company."

She'd heard those same rumors, but had ignored them, hoping they were conjecture and nothing more. "Adam, change brings instability. I think you're making excuses, when the truth is that you suddenly have zero confidence in me."

"You don't make it easy when you make mistakes. Half of the board members are old guard. They do not want to see a woman take over the company, no matter what they might say to your face. We have to find the right time."

Anna felt as though she was listening to her father speak. Was there something about working out of that office that made a person completely unreasonable? "You mean I have to wait until you decide it's the right time."

"You have no idea the amount of pressure I'm under. People expect huge things from me and from LangTel. I can't let what Dad started be anything less than amazing."

Anna kept her thoughts to herself. Adam was struggling with their father's death even more than she was. He might not realize it, but she was sure his iron grip on LangTel had more to do with holding on to the memory of their dad than anything else. Tears stung Anna's eyes just thinking about her father, but she wouldn't cry. Not now.

"I can do this. I thought you believed in me."

"I do, but frankly, you haven't dazzled me like I thought you would."

"Then let me dazzle you. I have an idea for an acquisition after the conference in Miami. That's what I've been trying to talk to you all week about."

"I don't want to spend our entire evening talking shop. Send me the details in an email and we'll talk about it tomorrow."

"No. You keep blowing me off. Plus, I'm starting to think this isn't a discussion for the office."

"Why not?"

You might get mad enough to set off the sprinkler system. "Because it has to do with Jacob Lin. I'm interested in a company called Sunny Side, and he's the majority investor."

Adam's jaw dropped and quickly froze in place. "I don't care if Jacob Lin is selling the Empire State Building for a dollar. We're not doing business with him. End of discussion."

That last bit was so like her dad, and such a guy thing to do, attempting to do away with an uncomfortable subject with male posturing. It insulted every brain cell in her head, which meant it was time to forge ahead. She wasn't about to wait for another time. It might never come. "The company makes micro solar panels for cell phones, phones that will never, ever need an electrical charge."

"Sounds amazing," Melanie chimed in from behind the shield of her magazine.

Adam shook his head, just as stubborn as Anna had imagined he'd be. "No, it doesn't."

"Yes, it does," Anna said. "We're talking about a revolution in our industry. Imagine the possibilities. Every person who ever wandered around an airport looking for an outlet will never see a reason to buy a phone other than ours."

"Think of the safety aspects. Or the possibilities for remote places," Melanie added. "The public relations upside could be huge."

"Not to mention the financial upside," Anna said.

Adam kneaded his forehead. "Are you two in cahoots or something? I don't care if Jacob has invested in a cell phone that will make dinner and do your taxes. He and I tried to work together once and it was impossible. The man doesn't know how to work with other people."

Her conversation with Jacob was fresh in her mind, what he'd said about the end of his friendship with Adam. What if things had been different and they had remained friends? "Funny, but he says the same thing about you."

Adam turned and narrowed his focus, his eyes launching daggers at Anna. "You spoke to him about this?"

"Actually, I met with him. I told him that LangTel is interested in Sunny Side."

"I can't believe you would do that."

"Come on, Adam." Anna leaned forward, hoping to plead with her eyes. "We would be passing up a huge opportunity. Just take a minute and look past your history with Jacob for the good of LangTel. You'll see that I'm right."

Adam stood up from the table. "I can't listen to this anymore. I'm going to answer emails and take a shower." He leaned down and kissed the top of Melanie's head. "Good night."

"That's it?" Anna asked, bolting out of her seat, her chair scraping loudly on the hardwood floors. "The almighty Adam passes down his decree and I'm supposed to live with it, even when my idea could make billions for the company he won't hand over because he's so concerned with its success?"

"Look, I call the shots. I'm CEO."

Anna felt as if she'd been punched in the stomach. "You've reminded me of that every day since you took over."

"Good. Because I don't want to talk about this ever again. And I don't want you to speak to Jacob Lin ever again, either." He started down the hall, but turned and doubled back, raising a finger in the air as if he'd just had the greatest idea. "In fact, I forbid it."

"Excuse me?" She remained frozen, beyond stunned. "You forbid it?"

"Yes, Anna. I forbid it. You are my employee and I am forbidding you to talk to him. He's dangerous and I don't trust him. At all."

Three

Jacob ended his first conversation with Adam Langford in six years with a growl of disgust, dropping his cell phone onto the weight bench in his home gym. Where exactly did Adam get off calling him? And issuing orders? Stay away from his sister? Keep your little cell phone company to yourself? Jacob had a good mind to get in his car, storm through the lobby of LangTel up to Adam's office and finally have it out, once and for all. Lock the door. Two guys. Fists. Go time.

Jacob leaped up onto the treadmill, upping his pre-set speed of six miles per hour to seven. Rain streaked the windows. Morning sunlight fought to break through gray September clouds looming over the Manhattan skyline. His long legs carried him across the conveyor belt, his breaths coming quicker, but it wasn't enough. It wasn't hard. It wasn't painful. He upped his speed again. He craved every bit of release he could get—no sex in two months, a powder keg of a job and an infuriating phone conversation with his biggest adversary made him feel as if he might explode.

It was more than what Adam had said, it was the way he'd said it, so smug and assuming. Adam wasn't all-powerful. He never had been, although he loved to act as though he was. Adam did not control him. The suggestion, even the slightest hint that he did, made his blood boil. He'd show Adam. He'd do whatever the hell he wanted. He would get as close to Anna as humanly possible, in any way she wanted to be close to him. If she wanted to do business, they would. If she wanted a replay of that kiss, they'd do that, too.

Jacob quickly finished five miles, every stride only steeling his conviction that Adam needed to be humbled, big time. He'd felt that way before Anna had come into the picture, and although she had no idea, she'd set off a chain of events that left him fixated on his goal. Adam needed to know what it felt like when someone destroyed everything you'd worked so hard for.

That was merely the business side. There were other unpaid debts. When Adam had betrayed him, he'd thrown away their friendship as if it meant nothing. That left a familiar void—Jacob found himself without a close friend, exactly as he'd lived out much of his childhood and adolescence, shuttled from one private school in Europe to another, never having enough time to fit in.

He'd been a straight-A student, but hardly had to try at all—that annoyed the hell out of the smart kids. He came from unspeakable wealth, but it was new money. He'd had to learn the hard way that there was a difference. He didn't have a notable lineage behind his family name. His father was immensely powerful, but that was in the Asian banking world, not the entrenched circles of old-world high society in England and France. Jacob was left in a no-man's-land, with plenty of money for the highest tuitions, the grades to get into the best schools and nothing to focus on but studies that didn't challenge him in the slightest.

The real shame was that his friendship with Anna became collateral damage when things went south with Adam. Their immediate rapport had shown so much promise. He felt truly at ease with her. He could talk to her about anything, especially his upbringing, something he did not share easily. She always listened. If she hadn't had the same experiences, she still empathized, and she found a bright spot in everything.

The night she'd kissed him, he'd been equal parts shocked and thrilled. He'd been pushing aside thoughts of his lips on hers from the moment he met her. She was off-limits, his friendship with Adam too precious. So he'd had to tell her "no." He'd been sure his bond with Adam would be stronger because of it. But that had been a mistake. Every mistake he'd made because of Adam was an open wound, refusing to heal.

What if he and Anna brought things full circle? For just one night? They could start where they left off with that kiss six years ago, this time without Adam in the way. It would be more than physical gratification. A tryst with Anna would be another instance in which Jacob showed Adam just how little control he had.

Jacob muted the bank of televisions airing global financial news in front of him. He sat back down on the weight bench, picked up his phone and called the founder of Sunny Side. He was open to meeting with Anna, but could they do it upstate? Mark and Jacob had homes thirty minutes from each other. Perfect. Out from under the meddlesome reach of Adam.

He ended the call and scrolled through the contacts until he found Anna. Rational thought and urges warred inside his head. Could he cross that line? He would never hurt her. Business or pleasure—Sunny Side or sex, he'd follow her lead, but they could get nowhere until he set them on the right path.

"Jacob. Hello," she quickly answered, hushing her voice.

Her softly spoken words were much like early-morning pillow talk, bringing a pleasant sensation, a rush of warmth. Perhaps it was the knowledge that his actions would enrage Adam. "Anna. How are you today?"

"Good. You?"

She had to be covering. Adam must've been hard on her when she'd brought up the notion of doing business with Jacob. Too bad for Adam—this call was about Anna and Jacob putting together a deal. No more letting Adam get in the way. "I'm good. I wanted to talk to you about Sunny Side. I spoke to Mark, the founder, and he's amenable to the three of us meeting this weekend."

"Really? That would be fabulous."

Jacob was surprised by Anna's lack of hesitation. She'd spoken to Adam about this—Adam had said as much, and yet she seemed undaunted, unwilling to conform to Adam's wishes. A woman after his own heart. "We'll see how things go. If you two talk and it's not a good match, that's the end of that. But I can't imagine you not hitting it off with Mark. I doubt he'll have a defense for the Anna Langford charm."

That last part was the truth, not necessarily meant as flirtation, although he knew very well it came out that way.

"I could always wave a fat stack of cash in his face," she quipped.

"Coming from you, I'd say that sounds incredibly sexy." Visions of Anna seductively thumbing through a bundle of hundreds materialized. That *would* be sexy. Insanely sexy.

"I'll be sure to run by the bank."

A protracted silence played out over the line. It was partly his fault. He'd really tripped himself up with "sexy." He cleared his throat. "So you're up for the meeting?"

"Absolutely."

How he loved her decisiveness, her fire. It made him want to kick himself for ever saying "no" to her. "We're meeting at my place in Upstate New York if you can make that work. Mark bought a house about a half hour from mine. I don't know about you, but I could really use the getaway."

"Getaway? You and me?"

"Just for a night. It's too far to go for just a few hours. Or at least that's what I say to force myself to take a break from work."

"Oh. I see."

Why was going away with him the one point of hesitation? Was she thinking he was making a pass? He didn't want her to think so. "It'll be like old times. If you're lucky, I might even beat your butt at cards."

"We have to have this meeting and talk hard numbers. That's really important."

He blew out a breath. Maybe it was for the best that

she was determined to focus on business. That would make it more difficult for his mind to stray to other thoughts of Anna. It would be trial enough to be alone in the same house. "Of course. Everything you need."

She hummed on the other line, as if mulling over her decision. "Yes. I'll be there. Should I hire a car or is there a flight I can catch?"

"We can ride up together. Text me your address and I'll pick you up early tomorrow morning."

"Oh, okay. Great. Is there anything special I need to bring?"

"Maybe your bikini?" The instant it came out of his mouth, he realized it sounded like a bad pick-up line.

"Not really my go-to for a meeting."

Find a save. Find a save. "And there's nothing like a soak in the hot tub after a tough negotiation."

A getaway. With Jacob. Anna pressed the button to take the elevator down to the lobby of her building. She sucked in a deep breath. Her skin noticeably prickled when she thought about what she was doing and with whom she would be doing it. This was about as wrong as wrong could be—going away to discuss a business venture that was supposed to be a dead issue. Going away with the man her brother despised, the man she'd been warned to stay away from.

But Anna spent every day doing what everyone expected of her and where had that gotten her? Frustrated and running in circles. There was no reward in playing it safe. Of that, she was absolutely sure.

Could she have devised a more tempting plan to make Adam regret ever selling her short? Not likely. So, she'd be spending it in close proximity to the man she had a certifiable weakness for, a man who'd been sure to remind her to pack a bikini. She was strong, or so she hoped.

After she and Jacob had gotten off the phone the day before, the bathing suit talk had sent her rushing to the salon to get everything imaginable waxed as well as getting her nails done. Sure, it was girlish and vain, but if she was going to let Jacob see her climbing into his hot tub, he was at least going to second-guess the wisdom of ever turning her down.

Anna stepped off the elevator. As she made her way to the glass doors, a sleek, black SUV pulled up to the curb. She wasn't sure exactly what make it was, only that several guys eyed it as they walked by, as if it was a supermodel bending over in a short skirt. Jacob rounded the front of the vehicle in a black sweater, jeans and dark sunglasses. Had he managed to get hotter since she'd seen him in Miami? He was as tempting as ever, square-shouldered, as if he was bulletproof. *Damn.*

She ducked into the revolving door with her overnight bag just as Jacob caught sight of her. He came to a halt on the sidewalk, grinning. His magnetism was so effortless. It was in his DNA. He ran his hand through his shiny, black hair and pushed his sunglasses up on his nose. That seemingly harmless sequence of motions left her dizzy. Hopefully she'd get reacclimated to Jacob quickly, desensitized to the ways he could make the most benign action enticing. She had more than a few recollections of staring at his hands while he shuffled playing cards.

"Ready?" His impossibly deep voice stood out amidst the sounds of the city.

"Yes," she answered with a squeak.

He reached for her bag, grasping the handle. Their

fingers brushed and her body read it as an invitation, even though her brain insisted it was nothing. Meaningless. Still, if he touched any more of her than that, she was a goner. He opened the passenger door. Something about him standing there, waiting for her to climb in, gave this the distinct feel of a date, even when she was sure it was only because Jacob was a perfect gentleman.

"I'm a little surprised you're driving. I figured you and your driver would pick me up," she said after he'd tossed her bag into the backseat and gotten in on the driver's side.

Jacob shook his head and started the car. The engine roared, quickly calming to a low and even hum. "I figured this made for more quality time to catch up. No prying eyes."

Anna swallowed hard as Jacob expertly zipped into the confusion of cars whizzing by. "Oh. Sure."

"I trust my driver, but he's only been with me a few months and you never know. I've been burned before by people who talk behind my back. This way, it's one less person who knows what we're doing."

She nodded. *What we're doing.* What in the heck were they doing? Tempting fate? Undoubtedly. If Adam found out about this, especially before she had a chance to be out in front of it, he wouldn't merely go ballistic. He would explode into millions of pieces, only after he was certain she and Jacob were in the bull's-eye of the blast zone. "Thank you. I appreciate that."

"Look, the last thing I want is for you to end up in the doghouse with your brother. We have legitimate reasons to explore this business venture, but we need to put some real numbers together before you can entertain it seriously. If this meeting doesn't go well, no harm, no foul. Adam never needs to know it happened."

"Sounds reasonable to me." The covert nature of their trip was appealing for practical reasons, but misbehaving was its own temptation. She was always the good girl, always did what was expected of her. For once she could deviate from plan, even if her confidence about it wavered. She didn't like deceiving anyone, especially not her family.

That didn't change the fact that she had to get Adam's attention and shake him out of the mindset that she wasn't ready to take over as CEO. Jacob had become her very unlikely ticket to doing that. She had to wonder if money was Jacob's only motivation, or if he thought this deal might show Adam that he'd made a mistake by ending their working relationship. He certainly seemed focused on the business aspect. Telling her to bring her bathing suit was probably a slip or Jacob being a good host. It was hard to imagine it was anything else.

There was a big part of her, however, that wished there was something else. She never did well with the idea of possibilities left unexplored. The night she kissed Jacob, she'd already spent many nights imagining what came next, of what it would be like to have his hands all over her, to share the same bed with him. When he'd cut it short, she couldn't help but feel as though she'd been robbed of something. That was difficult to let go.

She glanced over at Jacob as he fiddled with the satellite radio while navigating the snarl of traffic leaving the city. His profile was endlessly enthralling. She could've sat there and studied his strong, dark brows or his uncannily straight nose for hours. That would only lead to the examination of his perfect lips, the way his angular jaw was accentuated by his well-groomed scruff. It would be so nice to trail her finger along the line from his ear to his chin, kiss him again and see if he wanted to explore their unfinished business.

But what if he'd only used Adam as an excuse, a means of covering up the fact that he hadn't wanted to kiss her at all? If she tried anything a second time, he might be honest with her. That would be brutal.

He turned and narrowed his focus on her for an instant, making her heart leap into her throat. "Everything okay?"

She nodded, swallowing back a sigh. "Oh, sure. I was just wondering how long the drive is."

He looked back over his shoulder and sped up, changing lanes like a man who wasn't about to let anyone get in his way. The scent of his cologne wafted to her nose, making her lose her bearings. "Five hours. Four and a half if I can get out of traffic." He reached across and patted her on the leg, the width of his palm and fingers spanning her thigh. "Sit back and enjoy the ride."

She stared down at her lap, the place where he'd left an invisible scorching-hot handprint. Five hours? Alone in a car with Jacob? She'd be on fire by the time they got there.

Four

In the years since he'd graduated from Harvard Business School, the only time Jacob had mixed business and pleasure was right now—taking Anna away for the weekend. Time alone in the car with her had quickly illustrated that being with her made things muddy, messy. Nothing was clear-cut and that made him nervous. Considering the game he was playing with LangTel stock, getting close to Anna was dangerous. It wasn't just playing with fire. It was tantamount to walking a tightrope over an active volcano.

But the fire was so tempting—her sweet smell, the way she pulled out her ponytail and redid it when she was thinking about something. He'd struggled to keep his eyes on the road. The deep blue turtleneck she wore was maddening. His brain wouldn't stop fixating on trying to remember the exact arrangement of freckles on her chest. And then there were the jeans. Sure, he'd held the car door to be a gentleman, but he'd committed every curve to memory, frame by frame, as she'd climbed inside his car.

Finally at their destination, he turned from the main road and stopped between the pair of towering stone pillars flanking the entrance to his estate. Cool autumn air rushed in when he rolled down the window to punch in the security code. Silently, the wrought iron gate rolled aside, granting entry into his retreat, a world that intentionally bore no resemblance to the one they'd left behind in Manhattan. The fall leaves blazed with a riot of brilliant orange and rust and gold. The trees rustled with a stiff breeze, leaves breaking free from their branches, some landing on the hood and windshield, the rest drifting until they came to rest on the white crushed-stone driveway.

The massive house stood sentry at the head of a circular parking area.

"Wow," she muttered, leaning to the side and peering out her window as he parked the car. "It's so gorgeous, Jacob. And huge."

Surely Anna had been to impressive estates, but she seemed quite taken with what he had to offer her for the weekend—pristine grounds, crisp, white clapboards wrapping the spires at each corner of the house, a wide sweep of stone stairs leading to the front door, flanked by hand-leaded windows. His pride swelled. He couldn't help it. He'd impressed her and he was glad that he had.

"The house was built in the twenties. I had it completely remodeled when I bought it three years ago." As much as he loved his job, it was a pressure cooker, and being in Manhattan only exacerbated it. "I figured it was a good investment and I wanted a getaway that would always be here. Something I could depend on. Something comfortable."

Jacob snatched up the keys in his hand and climbed out of the car. He didn't make it around in time to open Anna's door for her, but he was able to grab her overnight bag before she had the chance to do so. He wanted to at least do some things for her. In fact, he'd purposely called the house's caretaker and asked him to give them a wide berth this weekend. There would already be his cook and housekeeper around.

"Seems like a lot of space for one person," Anna said, as they made their way to the front door. "How often do your parents come to visit?"

Family was such an integral part of Anna's life. It was probably impossible for her to fathom an existence that didn't revolve around it. "You'd be surprised." He opened the door and ushered her inside, placing their bags on a bench in the spacious foyer.

"A lot, then?"

He shook his head. "No. Not much at all. Especially not my dad. My mom will come for a weekend once a year, but she's antsy the whole time she's here. I think she probably learned that from my dad." As hard as Jacob liked to work, he had seen his dad take it too far. He made a point of relaxing when he came up here, but that almost exclusively involved getting his hands dirty. Very dirty. He'd have to show Anna his collection after he'd shown her the house.

Anna turned and frowned. "Don't you get lonely up here?"

Jacob was so accustomed to being alone that it didn't faze him at all, but he was smart enough to know that most people didn't live that way. Especially not a Langford. "I won't be lonely this weekend. That's all that matters right now." He chided himself the instant the words were out of his mouth. Why couldn't he answer, "no"? Why was flirtation and leading answers his inclination? He wasn't the guy who had trouble turning off this aspect of his personality. He was usually far more in control.

Anna flushed with the most gorgeous shade of pink. "That's a great way of thinking."

The urge to cup the side of her face and sweep his thumb across the swell of her cheek bubbled up inside him. Stuffing his hands in his pockets was the only way to stop himself. He wasn't about to cross that line. He needed to get a grip and wrap his head around everything he was fighting in his mind. When he'd been irate with Adam, it was easy to imagine getting back at him by seducing his sister. But then he'd picked her up at her apartment and he was quickly reminded of two things—Adam's sister was a woman he cared about, and a path that led to intimacy was not to be taken lightly. A smart man would insist that the risk was not worth the reward, even if the reward did look stunning in her blue sweater.

As in all business, detachment was the most proven tack. For the moment, it meant focusing on his head and ignoring his body. There was a very clear answer to the question of what his body wanted—Anna. He couldn't even fathom what might happen if he made a move. Would she cast away her brown eyes in shyness or would she have the courage to meet his gaze and tell him what she wanted? If he could have anything right then and there, he would've loved to know what she was thinking. Why was she here? What was driving her? Was it really as simple as wanting to broker a big deal? Or was there something else?

He cleared his throat. "Allow me to give you the tour."

Anna nodded and he led the way.

Anna had grown up amidst wealth and splendor, but Jacob's house was truly remarkable—beautifully refinished wood floors, a refined mix of modern furnishings and antiques, every surface impeccable and of the finest quality. Even her mother would've been a bit envious, and Evelyn Langford devoted an awful lot of time and resources to feathering her nest.

They returned to the front door, and Anna assumed they were going to go upstairs to see the bedrooms. Instead, Jacob handed over her coat. "I have something I want to show you in the garage."

The garage? He was aware she knew what a lawn mower looked like, wasn't he? "Okay. Sure."

They walked along a wide flagstone walkway, past the swimming pool and tennis courts. Beyond was an enormous outbuilding. Practically a warehouse, with a keypad entry and a security system Jacob had to disarm once they were inside. He flipped a succession of switches and the lights flickered on, one by one, across the massive room. Anna gasped.

It was an homage to motorized travel—seven or eight very expensive-looking cars, all black, and at least two dozen motorcycles. The entire room was spotless—polished concrete floors, not a speck of dust or dirt anywhere. Chrome gleamed. The aroma of motor oil and tooled leather swirled around her, a smell she'd never anticipated could be so appealing. She'd had men show off collections before—art, autographed baseballs. One guy owned what she'd thought was a dizzying array of antique chess sets. Talk about dizzying—Jacob's display of testosterone-fueled fascination was enough to make her head swim.

"Jacob, wow. I can't even…" Anna paced ahead slowly, Jacob right behind her. She was mesmerized, but afraid to touch the wrong thing. "They're incredible."

They stood before a bike with a worn but polished brown leather seat. "This is my hobby. Everything is vintage. Nothing built after 1958. Some of them I've bought from other collectors, but quite a few were falling apart when I got them. They were a lot of work, but I love it."

She folded her hands. Jacob loomed behind her, so close. She could feel the measured rhythm of his breaths even when she couldn't see him. "You do the actual repairs?"

"Is that hard to believe?"

She shrugged. "I don't know. I'm just surprised you know how to do it, that's all."

He let out a breathy laugh. "At first, it was the challenge of teaching myself how to do it. I was very motivated to learn. Now it's simply that I don't trust anyone with these. They're prized possessions and that means I keep them all to myself."

"Well, they're just incredible. Truly beautiful. I'm very impressed."

He stepped over to a bike in the center of the front row, swung his long leg over the seat and straddled it. "This one is my favorite. A Vincent Black Shadow. Very collectible." The motorcycle popped back off its kickstand, bounced in place a few times under his weight.

His hands—good God, his hands—gripped the handles in a way that said he didn't merely know how to care for the machinery. He knew how to ride.

"Take me out," she blurted.

He smirked, his eyes crinkling at the corner. "It's cold out there. You'll freeze."

"I'll live."

"Have you even been on a motorcycle?" His voice rumbled, low and gravelly.

She had most certainly *not* been on a motorcycle. She'd lived her entire life in Manhattan. Riding on a motorcycle was the sort of thing her parents never, ever would have allowed her to do. As an adult, she'd never had the chance. Nor had she put much thought into how all-out sexy the idea might be until confronted with it.

"No. I haven't. And that's why I want you to take me out." She shook her head slowly, their eyes connecting. His dark stare was like a tractor beam—he could have drawn her across the room with a single thought, not needing to utter a word or even curl a finger. He made her so damn nervous when he looked at her like that, as if he knew how easily he could mold her every vulnerability into something of his own. She didn't have a lot of weaknesses, but there were a few. Did he know that he was one? That look on his face made her think that he did.

"You know what they say about this particular motorcycle?" he asked.

"No clue."

"That if you ride on it fast, for long enough, you're bound to die."

Anna gnawed on her lower lip. What was it about being with Jacob, the man she wasn't supposed to be

with, that emboldened her? Because there was no deny-
ing that it did. He could've been about to push her over
the edge of a cliff and she would've jumped off herself
and figured out what to do on the way down. "I'm not
scared."

"You realize that if any part of you gets hurt, your
brother will have my head."

Anna wasn't much for pain, but she wouldn't mind
Jacob wearing her out a little. Or a lot. "So now you're
going to use Adam as your excuse?"

He sat back, tall and straight, brushing the side of the
bike's body with his hand. He granted her the smallest
fraction of a smile and it made her knees buckle. "When
you put it that way, I don't think I have a choice." He
pushed the kickstand back into place and climbed off
the bike, heading for a tall cabinet in the corner. "Let's
find you a helmet and a jacket."

Her mind was at war with itself. *What are you doing?
You came up here for a meeting. Shut up shut up shut
up. Forget work. Forget the meeting. Who turns down
a motorcycle ride with an insanely hot guy?*

"We just need to be back in time for our meeting,"
she said, as if it would make this sensible if she brought
up work.

"That's two hours from now. Plenty of time."

"Okay." Anna trailed over to him, wishing she'd had
something smart or sexy or at least sane to say. She
felt so overmatched, much as she had when Jacob had
come to stay with her family that Christmas. As if he
was guiding her, pulling her in, making her his. Except
that it had never materialized that time. Was it all in her
head? Would it actually happen now? If not, it would be

fantastic to know now so she could preserve her dignity by dodging another brush-off.

He turned, holding out a black leather jacket. "Allow me."

She made a one-eighty, her back to him, steeling herself to his touch, sliding her arms into the heavy garment, which weighed down her shoulders.

He patted her back gently. "A little big, but it'll work."

The sleeves were stiff, and she had to work at bending her arms to zip up the jacket. Boxy and clumsy for her frame, it made her feel like a child in a winter coat a size too big. She faced him and her brain sputtered, fixated on the image of him as he put on his own jacket. Dammit. It fit like he'd been born in it, adding a dangerous veneer to his admirable physique. Where did he get that thing? The Absurdly Tall and Broad-Shouldered Men's Warehouse?

He grabbed a shiny silver helmet, but instead of handing it to her, he curled his hand around her head and reached for her ponytail, gently tugging on it as he pulled out the hair tie. She was so shocked, it was as if he'd pulled her breath out of her lungs at the same time. Her tresses collapsed around her shoulders. He was close enough to kiss. His mouth was right there—lips as tempting as could be, the moment resembling the one that preceded her ill-fated attempt at seduction. They'd been standing in nearly the same posture and stance. Why couldn't he have taken her hair in his hands that night? Why couldn't he have decided that she was more important than Adam?

"One of my old girlfriends always complained that it hurt to wear a ponytail that high with a helmet."

Talk about ruining the moment. He *would* have to

bring up other women, wouldn't he? Of course he'd gone on with his life, including his romantic one, after they parted ways years ago. He was smart. He hadn't wasted untold amounts of time wishing for someone he couldn't have.

She nodded. "I never would've thought to take down my hair."

He zipped up his motorcycle jacket, which was the sexiest meeting of metal teeth in the history of apparel fasteners. "If you want to know the truth, it's just that I find that moment when a woman shakes out her hair after riding on the back of my bike particularly sexy."

Was that his way of throwing down the gauntlet? Issuing a dare? Because she sure as heck could whip around her hair. She might not be the purely confident seductress, but that much she could handle. The raw anticipation of the ride ahead returned to her veins, pumping blood from head to toe.

"Ready?" he asked, climbing onto the Black Shadow.

He pressed a button on a key fob and one of the wide garage bay doors began to open. The crisp air rolled inside, but she appreciated the cooling effect on her ragged nerves. Jacob put on his helmet, then his sunglasses. Lastly, he pulled on a pair of black leather gloves.

"Yep," she answered, sidling up to the bike. She realized then that it wasn't the idea of the ride making her nervous. It was the idea of touching him. Then again, this gave her the perfect excuse, and if this was as close as they got all weekend, she'd find a way to live with it and later weave it into a super hot fantasy. She pulled on her helmet, adjusted the chin strap, and grasped his shoulders as she straddled the bike behind him.

He started the engine. The bike rumbled beneath them. "Hold on tight," he yelled back to her.

She wrapped her hands around his waist tentatively. She didn't want to be so hopelessly obvious. Better to wait until their speed warranted a stronger grip. The next thing she knew, they were moving, albeit slowly, as he turned to close the garage door. Then he sped up, rounding the outbuildings, chugging down the gravel driveway to the road, opening the gate ahead of them with another click of the fob.

He came to a dead stop at the road, balancing them with his foot on the blacktop as the gate closed behind them.

"You can go a little faster, you know," she yelled.

"That was gravel," he called back. "You want fast?"

Anna gulped. "Yes."

"I'll show you fast."

He revved the gas, still keeping them in place. The power of the engine had her body trembling. The bike lurched and they hurtled ahead like a rocket. They flew down the narrow state road, picking up speed, much faster than they'd gone in his car. Maybe it only seemed that way because she no longer had the protection of a steel cage around her. The momentum of the bike pulled her away from him, and she tightened her grip around his waist, clamped her thighs to his hips. Her shoulders tensed, but at the same time, she felt freed. It was the oddest sensation. Laughter and elation bubbled out of her. The wind whipped at her jeans, but the jacket kept her warm. As did Jacob. Very warm.

The engine popped and roared whenever he changed gears. Masterfully, he handled the bike, leading them through a curve. She grabbed him even tighter as he leaned them into the turn, defying the laws of gravity. The way his shoulders shifted, maneuvering the bike through the treacherous bend, was unspeakably hot. She loved seeing him so in control. One wrong move and they'd both be gone. In that moment, she couldn't imagine wrong. He was infallible. Invincible.

They continued for miles, on narrow, serpentine roads. He took her through a small town with a round-about, the changing leaves fluttering around them, people milling about from a coffee shop to a farmer's market, bundled up in hats and scarves. She felt as cozy as could be, as if she was curled up in front of the fire. The fire of Jacob. Once they got back to the open stretches of rural road, he took off like a bat out of hell again. He got cocky on a long straightaway, weaving back and forth. If only he could have seen the mile-wide smile on her face. He'd earned his macho moment. And good for him for claiming it.

Much too soon, the road returned to where they'd started, only this time, from the opposite direction. He took the gravel drive leading to his house slowly again, expertly guiding them into the safety of the garage.

Anna was catching her breath, adrenaline coursing through her. She unclasped her hands from Jacob's waist, but her arms were heavy under the weight of the jacket and they dropped. Dead center. Between his legs. She yanked back her hands as if she'd touched a hot stove. In some ways, that was exactly what she'd done. She gripped his shoulders to climb off the motorcycle. Embarrassment flooded her. She could only imagine what he must be thinking. Was he wondering if that was her awkward attempt at a pass? Because she was wondering the same thing.

Five

Composure was no longer possible. Jacob gripped the motorcycle handlebars, but only to steady himself. Anna and her slender, feminine hands had just stirred primal urges from the depths of his gut. It had been building in the car. The motorcycle ride brought it closer to the boil—her arms coiled around him, her clasped hands pressing into his stomach when he went faster, her thighs pressing into his hips, squeezing him when he took the turns. And then there had been the noises she made—muffled shrieks and cries of excitement. How was a man supposed to live through that without his body responding?

And then she'd touched him there.

He closed his eyes to take the edge off, but the reality was that he wanted her, and he was fairly certain that she wanted him. Was that brush across his crotch her way of sending a message? It didn't seem at all like Anna's style—she was subtle and demure, rarely so bold, but she'd been testing limits of late, with her brother and her career. Was she testing Jacob? He had to find out. Every drop of blood circling below his waist was making it impossible to let the question go unanswered.

He dared to open his eyes. She'd removed her helmet. He'd missed the moment when she took it off, but the result was worth it. Her hair was mussed—tousled, nearly disheveled, not at all its usual glossy neatness. He liked it. He liked it a lot. He could picture the rich, dark color against the white sheets of his bed. Her cheeks were flushed and rosy; he hoped not from the brisk autumn air, but from the thrill of the ride, the rush of being close to each other.

He cleared his throat as he climbed off the motorcycle. Now to figure out a way to get the ten or so paces to the gear cabinet where she was standing—his jeans were too snug to make walking a casual affair. He used his helmet to shield himself.

"That was so much fun. Thank you," Anna said, breaking the silence.

He wasn't in the mood for skirting things anymore. No purely polite response to her gratitude would come from him. "Isn't that what a guy does?" He eased out of his jacket and hung it up in the cabinet.

"Does what?" Anna furrowed her brow, climbing out from under the pounds of leather she was wearing.

"Try to impress a woman by showing off." He placed his helmet on the shelf, then turned to face her square-on. It took considerable effort to obscure his edginess. His attraction to her hadn't manifested itself this strongly before. His mind was racing to keep up.

She cocked an eyebrow. Her warm brown eyes flashed. "Is that what that was?" Her lips remained parted after the question, the flirtation only provocation to the devil on his shoulder.

"Yes." He scanned her face, waiting for one more sign—something that said it was a good idea to do what he wanted to do.

A warmth washed across her face. "If that's you showing off, you can do that all you want."

And there it was. He sucked in a deep breath of resolve and erased the gap between them. He clasped both hands around her neck, pushing his fingers into the silky hair at her nape and lifting her mouth to his, collecting what he wanted with a tender, but insistent kiss. Her lips were even sweeter than he remembered, the kind of dessert that makes you lick the spoon over and over again, craving one more taste.

"Tell me to stop," he said, not relinquishing the grip he had on the back of her neck. His thumb caressed the smooth skin below her ear.

"What?" Her eyes were half open, breaths heavy enough to hear.

"Tell me you want me to stop." His heart raced, part of him begging her to say that she wanted him, part of him knowing that it would be easier on them both if she stopped this right now. Being with Anna, as badly as he wanted her, would be pouring fuel on the flame that had dogged him for too long. "Tell me that you don't want me to kiss you."

Her mouth went slack, eyes wide as the day was long. "I can't," she muttered.

His heart was fighting to pound its way out of his

chest. Whatever it was that she couldn't do, he wasn't sure he wanted to know what it was. "You can't what?"

"I can't tell you to stop because I don't want you to."

A wave of relief crashed over him. One hand went to her elbow, his fingers tracing the underside of her arm until he reached her palm. "Good. Because I don't think there's any way I can."

He snaked his hands around her waist and she popped up on to tiptoes, planting her arms on his shoulders. He didn't even have to kiss her—she was all over him. As if he'd told her she'd earn a million dollars for every second they didn't come up for air. Their tongues wound together in an endless circle. Their noses bumped as she tilted her head and came in for a different approach. She flattened her stomach against him, and he responded by lowering a hand to her bottom and tugging her hips closer to his.

The metal door of the cabinet clanged against the frame when she pushed him into it. He was still trying to keep up with what was happening, trying like hell not to fixate on where it was going. Would their first time be in the garage? That could be insanely hot. But where? Concrete floor? Tool bench? He tensed for a second. He wanted it to be better than that. If they were only going to have one night, one weekend, he wanted them both to remember it. He quieted his mind. This was not the time for overthinking. His body relaxed. That only made him more susceptible to Anna's fire.

She hitched her leg over his hip as if she knew exactly what she was doing. Either she had far more experience than he'd ever bargained on, or she was going on pure enthusiasm. He hoped for the second, that this was her response to him, not just another time with another man.

"Do you have any idea how long I've dreamed about this happening?" Anna asked. Her voice was all sweet desperation.

His body came to a complete halt. *Dreamed?* Did this mean more to her than he'd banked on? If they were going to have their fling, they couldn't make love in a car or on a tool bench. He needed to make this right, not merely salacious and reckless.

"Believe me, I thought about our kiss a few times over the years."

"Just a few?" she asked, seeking eye contact. Her eyes were clear and intent, searching his face.

He couldn't tell her it had been more than that. It would only make things more complicated. There were enough dangerous feelings between himself and one Langford. "Let's not talk about the past anymore. I'm tired of it."

"I don't want to talk anyway."

Jacob caught sight of the clock on the wall. *Oh, no.* "Anna. Our meeting is in ten minutes."

She blew out a deep breath. "It is?" She lowered her head and shook it. An adorable groan leaked from her mouth. "Okay. I guess it's time to get to work."

So much for Anna's resolve that this trip was going to be about business and absolutely nothing else. She'd had about as much self-restraint as a toddler in a toy store the minute Jacob kissed her. She still couldn't believe she'd pushed him up against the cabinet door. Then again, she'd waited a long time for Jacob.

But there was work to be done. She sat and smiled politely as Jacob and Mark got situated in the living room at Jacob's. A fire crackled in the fireplace, the late afternoon sun cast a warm golden glow through the windows. Jacob had his arm spread out along the back of the chocolate brown leather sofa, his leg crossed, his other hand playing with the stitching at the end of the sofa arm. He laughed quietly at something Mark said, and glanced over at Anna with a look that made any sound in the room turn to a low hum. It was a look born of recognition. He wanted her and he sure as hell knew that she wanted him. There were no more questions of that basic intent. The real question was who would be the first to break down. Was she sitting inside the fireplace? It sure felt that way.

Her entire body warmed, in exactly the way a fire builds—a spark, dead center in her chest, became dancing licks of flame in her shoulders and belly, and the heat rolled right through her, making her face hot and her toes just as naturally off temperature. That kiss—that single, brain-chemistry-altering kiss, was more gratifying than any physical encounter she'd had with a man in years. What if more happened? What if clothes started to come off? Would she pass out? She might.

"So, Mark," Jacob started, again sliding a shy smile to Anna. "I'd love it if you could give Anna an overview of what you envision for the future of Sunny Side. I think that'll be a good start and then we can see if partnering with a corporation like LangTel could be a good option."

Mark shifted in his seat, stroking his hipster beard, not looking entirely sold on the premise of corporate anything. He struck her as a man who'd be a stickler on the finer points of an arrangement between the two companies. This deal, if it happened, would require more than the right amount of money. A day ago, Mark's reticence would have unhinged Anna to no end. Today, it was more of an annoyance. If he didn't want to be here, why didn't he just say so? Then she and Jacob could get back to business of an entirely different nature.

Mark nodded and started on his song and dance about Sunny Side. Anna listened, taking notes on projections and plans for future products, ideas he had for the launch of the technology, product integrations and applications. Adam was a damn fool for letting his rift with Jacob stand in the way of this deal. Of course, the fact that he'd ignored the financial upside was testament to how much he hated the man she'd just kissed with reckless abandon in the garage.

"Anna? Do you have any questions for Mark?"

She was on deck. It was time to make her case. Jacob might be distracting the hell out of her, but she needed to focus. "I don't. I've had a chance to look over these numbers and if your projections hold true, I'd say that Sunny Side can pretty much write their own ticket. So the real question is, how do we make that work within the structure of LangTel?"

Mark leaned forward and set his elbows on his knees. "Look, Ms. Langford…"

"Please. Call me Anna."

"Anna. You have to understand that I run a company of two dozen employees. Our product has come to fruition so seamlessly because we're a tight-knit group. Our company culture is immensely important. My worry is that a giant like LangTel will swallow us whole or dismantle us until there's nothing left."

"Let me assure you. We have no interest in dismantling your company. The dynamic of your team is crucial to your success. We will absolutely keep it intact."

"How can you make promises like that? Isn't your brother CEO? I've heard he can be ruthless."

Jacob shot her a sideways glance, as if to remind her that Adam's reputation was of his own making, not Jacob's, and he wasn't wrong. Adam liked knowing that some people feared him.

"Actually, Adam's business thinking is very much inline with yours. He's started two immensely successful and innovative companies from the ground up…" She stopped herself. One of those two ventures was the one Jacob and Adam had started together, the very source of the rift that made everything such a mess. Her stomach sank. What must Jacob think of what she'd just said? That she was hopelessly callous? She had to recover from her gaffe. "At the end of the day, whether your company is big or small, everyone wants to retain the dynamic that brought you success. Nobody wants to see someone else come in and dismantle what you've worked so hard for."

Jacob cleared his throat and Anna felt horrible. Bringing up his history with Adam had been a mistake. He'd said it himself in the garage. The last thing he wanted to talk about was the past.

Six

Jacob and Anna bid their goodbyes to Mark as he walked out to his car. The brisk night air filtered into the foyer. With a quiet click, Jacob closed the door. They were alone.

"Well? What did you think of Mark?" he asked, bending over to pick up a stray leaf that had been tracked into the house.

Anna stifled a sigh of appreciation for his backside. The man knew how to work a pair of jeans. "I like him a lot. He seemed open to some of the things I suggested, so that's good." Considering where Anna's mind had been that whole time, it was a wonder she'd been able to glean that much from the meeting.

"Good. Definitely good." He nodded, holding the orange leaf by the stem as if he didn't know what to do with it.

"Yep." The air was charged with anticipation. They

both knew where this was going. But no one was doing anything about it. Should she throw herself at him? That was as close to formulating a plan as she could come. "Pretty color." She pointed to the foliar evidence of the fall weather, resorting to painful small talk.

Jacob opened the door again and tossed the leaf outside. A new rush of cool air caused her to shudder. Perhaps it was nature's way of punctuating the fact that this time, he didn't merely close the door. He locked the deadbolt.

"Are you cold?" He dropped his chin, stepping closer, working his way into her psyche with an intense flash of his eyes. His hand gripped her elbow. Energy zipped along her spine.

Finally—touching. Nothing skin-to-skin yet, but at least someone had given in. Anna was hyperaware of her breaths, her galloping heartbeat, the rotating sway of her body in his presence. This wasn't that different from the moment after the motorcycle ride, except then, they'd had to break the ice. She was glad to be done with breaking. Now on to melting. "I caught a chill. I'm okay."

He smiled. "You're so cute when you're deflecting."

"What do you mean?" Even perplexed, her heart flitted at the mention of cute.

"You'll do anything you can to take any and all focus off of you."

She twisted her lips, trying not to fixate on his—the swell, the color, the memory of the way it felt when they were on hers. Why wasn't he kissing her again? Was he going to wait until she started things? "If I do, I never noticed it. It must just be my personality." She wished she could've come up with a sexy answer to the question, but there were too many urges to manage, like the one that told her she'd be a lot happier if he wasn't wearing that sweater. Or those jeans.

"I just find it interesting. Your brother is the complete opposite."

If Anna knew anything, it was this—if he didn't kiss her in the next two seconds, she would go off like a grenade with the pin pulled. "Let's leave Adam out of this. In fact, let's pretend he doesn't even exist."

"Are you flirting with me by describing my Utopia?" His eyes toyed with her. He was reveling in every second of their game.

Her mouth went dry. That kiss in the garage hadn't quenched a six-year-old thirst. It left her wanting more. "And what if I am?" She popped up on to her toes, gripping his shoulders to steady herself. "What if I did this?"

She closed her eyes and went for it—her lips met his, in a kiss that made it feel as if she was no longer standing. There was a millisecond of hesitation from him before his tongue sought hers. Every atom of her body celebrated in a chorus of delight and relief. She shifted her forearms up on to his shoulders, dug her fingers into the back of his thick hair. His lips—soft and warm and wet, became more eager, seeking her jaw and neck. His arms wound tightly around her, pulling her against him, nearly lifting her off her toes.

His hand snaked under the back of her sweater, conveying what she'd been so eager to know—he wanted clothes to come off as badly as she did. His fingers fumbled with the bra clasp, which was so adorable. He was so smooth. It was nice to know he couldn't make the entire universe conform to his will.

"Here. Let me," she muttered. Now flat-footed, she lifted her sweater over her head then clutched it to her chest. "Everybody's gone for the day, right?" It would be so like her to undress while the gardener was watching.

He laughed, a flicker of appreciation crossing his face as he plucked the sweater from her hands and tossed it onto the foyer bench. "Yes." Leaning closer, he poked his finger under one of her black satin bra straps, popping it off her shoulder. "It's just you and me and this big house."

His words didn't merely prompt a rapid wave of goose bumps—they were about to become a permanent feature of her complexion. She bit down on her lip. If this was going to happen, it would be good. She reached behind and unhooked her bra, but left it for him to take off. "Tell me you want me to stop."

"Tell me you want *me* to stop." He kissed the curve of her neck—the most sensitive spot, the one that made her want to squeal with delight.

"No stopping. Please, no stopping."

He didn't tear his gaze from her as he slid the other strap from her shoulder. He dragged the garment down her arms slowly. His vision sank lower. "You are too beautiful to have anything less than exactly what you want. Tell me what you want." Gripping her rib cage with both hands, his thumbs caressed the tender underside of her breasts, as he lowered his head and gave one nipple a gentle lick.

The gasp that rose from the depths of her throat sounded like a lifetime of frustration being cut loose. She dropped her chin to her chest when he did it again. She loved watching him admire her this way, knowing that she turned him on. "I want you. Right now."

"Upstairs," he muttered.

Before she knew what he was doing, she was off her

feet and in his arms, feeling tiny, like she weighed nothing at all. He marched up the stairs and she clung to his neck, desperate to kiss him again.

The hall to his bedroom seemed to stretch for miles. Neither of them said a thing. Their heavy breaths carried the conversation instead. They reached their destination, a grand room with vaulted ceilings and windows overlooking the grounds. He set her down gently on the enormous four-poster bed, smiling.

He lifted his sweater over his head. The soft, evening light showed off the incredible contours and definition of his chest and abs—perfectly smooth, no hair except for a narrow trail below his belly button. His shoulders were far better than any item of clothing had ever suggested. Not even the motorcycle jacket did them justice—square and broad, begging for her touch.

She sat up and flattened her hands against his firm chest, his skin warming her palms. With her arms raised, he cupped her breasts with his hands. She would've dropped her head back in pure ecstasy if she wasn't so anxious to have his mouth on hers again. As if she'd spoken her wish, he bestowed a long, reckless kiss... hot and wet and magnificent.

She was dying of curiosity to know what the rest of him looked like. She unzipped his pants and pushed them to the floor. She dipped her fingers beneath the waistband of his gray boxer briefs, shimmying them down his trim hips. He kissed her again, and she wrapped her hand around his length, relishing the forceful groan that he made into her mouth.

He urged her to lie back, kissing her bare stomach. She watched as he unbuttoned her jeans and wiggled them south. His eyes were on her body as if he were entranced. Everything between her legs was eager for attention. Her entire body tensed with anticipation. "Touch me, Jacob. Please." The words had wandered out of her mouth, the thoughts in her head trickling out.

He tugged her panties down, casting his dark eyes up toward hers as his fingers met her apex. She couldn't let go of her grip on his head as he rocked his hand back and forth. It felt impossibly good to be at his mercy—wanted, desired. The pain of the past washed away like the tide erases writing in the sand. Their gazes locked, and it was as if she could see more of him, parts that he obscured, the vulnerable things he had hidden from her.

The pressure was building, the peak within her grasp too soon. "Make love to me," she said. How many times had she imagined this? Hundreds, and it hadn't come close to matching the real thing.

He dotted her stomach with soft, open-mouth kisses, firmly gripping her waist. When he rose to his feet, he opened the top drawer of a tall, dark-wood bureau. He ripped open the foil packet and handed her the condom. She wasn't about to ruin the moment with mention of the reasons they might not need one. Plus, she liked the idea of focusing on him, just as he had on her.

He stretched out next to her, the most magnificent creature she'd ever seen—strong and muscled, but graceful and lean. He dropped his head back when she wrapped her fingers around him and rolled on the condom. When he returned his sights to her, he looked as if he wanted to consume her, heart and soul.

She arched her back, welcoming him as he sank into her, slowly, carefully, with a reverence she'd never expected or experienced. Her mind was a swirling vortex of thoughts and sensations, the most powerful of which was that she'd suspected he would feel wonderful, but not like this. She couldn't have prepared herself for it feeling this good.

He rolled his hips when his body met hers. It built the pressure in her belly quickly, her breaths coming faster now. Her hands roved over the muscled contours of his back, trailing down to his glorious backside. His kisses were deep and long, matching the steady and satisfying rock of their bodies. She wrapped her ankles around his waist, wanting him closer. Deeper.

She placed her hands on the side of his face, keeping his lips to hers. She wanted to be connected with him like this when she unraveled. Her mind shuffled images—the motorcycle ride, the first real kiss, the moment when he looked at her in the front hall and she knew, with complete certainty, that he wanted her. Everything inside her began to uncoil. She was ready to let go of it all, even the past, and succumb to the bliss she'd waited so long for.

Anna was so close. Jacob could feel it, sense it in every fitful movement of her body. He was fighting to stem the tide, but it wasn't easy. Concentrating on her face was the only way to do it, a beautiful distraction from the energy doubling in his belly.

Her breaths came in frantic bursts. Every sound she made was sweet and sexy, but she nearly blew his mind when she called his name, clutching his back and digging her fingers into his skin. She tensed around him, her body grabbing on to his as if she might never let go.

Deliberate thought was gone. Tension clenched his legs and stomach, pure instinct took over. A blissful smile spread across her face. Breaths shallow, strokes longer and harder. Now faster. The pressure threatened to burst. Anna bucked against him. She fought for it just as eagerly, until finally his body gave in to the pleasure. It barreled through him like a freight train.

"Oh, no," he blurted, stilling himself on top of Anna as the swells ebbed in his body. He'd never had this happen before, but it wasn't hard to guess what it was. He'd felt it. "The condom broke. Don't move."

Anna wrapped her legs around him even tighter. "No. Keep moving. You feel so good." Her voice was catlike, a purr, a fitting match for her reaction. She didn't seem the slightest bit concerned about what he was now panicked about.

"Anna. The condom. It broke. And I just came. Did you not notice?" He pressed one hand into the mattress and slowly began to lift his hips away from hers. What now?

"Oh." She shook her head as he got up from the bed. "I guess I didn't notice."

"Yeah, this is a problem." He rushed off to the bathroom to clean up. "This is a huge problem," he muttered to himself, discarding it and washing his hands. It was one thing to exact revenge on Adam by taking his sister to bed. It was quite another to go and get her pregnant. Plus, a baby? No way. He was the last guy on the planet who had any business becoming a dad.

He stepped into his boxers and rushed back to the bedroom. He could make out Anna's gorgeous curves even in the dark. She'd climbed under the covers, partially covered, lying on her stomach and patting the spot on the bed next to her.

"I missed you," she murmured.

He blinked several times in complete confusion. "I

was gone for two minutes. And aren't you worried? There's a very good chance you and I just made a baby."

She shook her head as he eased back into bed next to her. "I'm almost entirely certain that we did not make a baby. Don't worry about it."

Even with the way things had just gone wrong, being that close to her completely naked form had everything in his body stirring again. "Care to fill me in? Maybe I missed that day in health class."

"Can't you just take my word for it?"

"What? You're on the pill? Then why did you let me use a condom?"

She took a breath and buried her face in the pillow.

He rolled to his side, placed his hand in the center of her back. Why did she not understand what a big deal this was? "Anna. What is going on? Will you talk to me, please?"

She finally turned to look at him. "I can't get pregnant."

"What?"

"Or at least not until I get some of my plumbing fixed."

"I'm sorry. You've lost me."

She rolled over, pulled the sheet up over her chest and sat up in bed. He hated the fact that something he'd said made her want to cover up, but he did need to know what in the world she was talking about.

"A fertility doctor told me I can't conceive. I'd gone to talk to him about artificial insemination."

"You're twenty-eight years old. Why would you think about doing something like that?" He watched a wave of embarrassment cross her face. It nearly took his breath away. He eased closer to her, craving her touch, her smell.

"Losing my dad really made me think about having a baby. About how much I want that in my life at some point."

"Oh." It was hard to imagine ever feeling that way, but lots of people did. Most people, in fact. Or so it seemed.

"All I could think was what if I never find the right guy? Being a female executive is tough. Most men let their ego get in the way."

He had to wonder what sorts of men she'd dated, but he wasn't about to ask. There was no point worrying about that particular obstacle. He'd never get past the barrier of Adam. "I hadn't considered that."

"I've never been serious enough about anyone to want to have a child. And losing my dad underscored how important my family is to me. My whole life revolves around them. Adam and Melanie are building a future together and…" Her voice wavered and she looked up at the ceiling. "This is the world's worst pillow talk. I'm sorry."

He hated seeing her upset. He tried to imagine a scenario in which he could share something like this, something so deeply personal, the sort of thing that left a human hopelessly vulnerable. He gave her a lot of credit for having the courage to be so open. "It's okay. You should tell me about it, if you want to."

"Really? Why?"

He took her hand in his. It wasn't meant as romance, but his inclination to comfort her was strong. "Because I care."

Anna explained everything her doctor had told her about scar tissue and surgery and how that affected her ability to get pregnant. He listened intently, saddened that she'd had to go through that. She clearly cared a lot about having a child. Why else would she have gone to a specialist about it?

"What did your mom say?" he asked.

"I never told her. I never told anyone." The wobble in her voice was back, the one he hated hearing.

If she'd never told anyone, that meant he was the first. The weight of that wasn't easy to bear. Here she was, in his bed, after giving him the most precious thing she could give to him, and now she was baring her soul. He never harbored guilt over a business decision, but his secret weighed on him. He was trying to engineer the takeover of her family's corporation, and she had no idea. What if that came to light? She would never, ever forgive him. And why should she? "Why didn't you tell anyone about what the doctor had said?"

"I wasn't sure I could talk about it without crying."

He was glad she'd been able to hold back tears. He didn't do well when a woman cried. He never knew what to do or say other than give a hug, which he knew didn't fix a damn thing. "But the doctor said it could be fixed, right? With surgery?"

"Yes, but the point was that I just wanted something to be right, to be easy. Everything over the last year has been a nightmare. This was supposed to be my way of looking to the future. I guess I felt a little defeated."

"So we didn't just make a baby."

"We didn't just make a baby."

Relief washed over him again. No baby. Good. Things were tangled enough. Now he just had to deal with his own internal conflict over the LangTel takeover plan, and that might require action on his part. He was excellent at keeping the business and personal separate, and in this case, he'd clearly allowed the two to commingle far too much.

"Are you feeling better now?" she asked. "You were pretty panicked there for a minute."

He laughed quietly. He had indeed let it get the better of him. "I'm fine. Although I wish you would've told me about this earlier. We could've skipped the condom all together. I'm clean. I get tested every year for my physical. Plus, I've never not used one, so it would be virtually impossible."

"You've never felt what it's like without one?"

He shook his head. "Never worked out that way. It can't really be that different, can it?"

A mischievous smile crossed Anna's face. It was so sexy. She scooted closer, until their thighs were touching. She kissed him, sending vibrations through this entire body, especially the parts they'd just been discussing. She took his hand, twined her fingers with his. "I've heard that it's very different."

"Very?" he asked between kisses. His body was ready to discern this for himself.

She climbed on top of him, straddling his hips. "Why don't we test the theory?"

Seven

Jacob finished off his third cup of coffee. Two was his limit, but he hadn't slept at all. It was difficult with a woman in his bed. It was partly sexual distraction, but there was another side to it. Something wouldn't allow him to relax enough to give in to real sleep.

He placed his mug in the sink and strode down the hall to the foyer, where Anna was waiting. "I'll be ready to go in a minute. I need to take care of something in the garage."

"Okay." Anna nodded, smiling thinly. Things were definitely awkward between them now that it was the morning after. How could they not be strained? They'd crossed a line that might've been better left uncrossed, however much they'd both wanted to do it.

He hurried out the door and around back to the garage. He'd deliberated about waiting and making his phone call after they returned to Manhattan, but he had to do it now. He couldn't sit in the car with her for five hours feeling even worse about his secret. He needed absolute privacy, and he wasn't about to kick Anna out of the house. That meant the garage.

He had to take steps to clear his conscience. Could he go through with a LangTel takeover at this point? Even if he and Anna never ended up taking this any further? The answer was a surprising, but decided "no." The guy with the killer instinct for business rarely changed his mind and he never undid his own work, but he was sure. He couldn't hurt Anna. Not after what they'd shared. Even if this weekend had to be the logical end, it wouldn't erase their most intimate moments, and he didn't want to forget them anyway. He wanted to keep them in his head for as long as possible.

He entered the garage and closed the door behind him. He wasted no time pulling out his cell to call Andre, his closest ally in the War Chest. He had to end the campaign against LangTel, even if it might be a tall order. His fellow investors were astute, shrewd, and skeptical to a fault. They would want to know why he was backing off, and he couldn't tell them the real reason. He couldn't tell them that he'd seduced a woman who'd gone and seduced him right back.

"Jacob. What's up?" Andre answered. "Not like you to call me on a Sunday."

"I know. I wanted to talk to you about the LangTel deal. I'm out." He held his breath, not offering any reasons. With his investment record, he could sometimes get away with only a mention that he was making a move and others would follow suit. The why wasn't always necessary.

"You're what? Are you insane? Why would you do that?"

Crap. So he would have to offer an explanation. The cult of personality would only get him so far today. "I don't think the upside is there like we thought it was. And it's such a huge undertaking. We could be knee-deep in this for a year. Or longer. Do we really want that? Do you want that much money tied up like that?"

"With that kind of payday? Yes. Don't forget, you aren't the only person Adam Langford has pissed off over the years. A few guys are eager to knock him down a peg or two."

Everything that had seemed so perfect a few months ago was now quite the opposite. "Isn't the notion of revenge a little outdated? Don't you have better things to do?"

"You seemed pretty damn motivated by revenge that night in Madrid when we first talked about this."

Jacob was skating very thin ice right now. Andre was absolutely right. Jacob had pushed them all. Hell, he'd not only rallied the troops, he'd riled them up. "I can't spend my life worrying about Langford. I'd rather wash my hands of it. And him." That much was the absolute truth, however much he was unsure of his feelings for Anna.

"I don't know what to tell you," Andre said. "You want out. I'm still in. I can't imagine the other members bailing."

Jacob pursed his lips. How could he have thought for even a second that he might get out of this easily? He'd put a nearly flawless master plan in place. All he could do now was control his own holdings, make a few more phone calls and try to convince some others. Otherwise, what could he do? This train he'd put on the tracks had momentum of its own. "Well, obviously I can't tell you guys what to do. All I can do is tell you that I'm out. I'm moving on to greener pastures. Greener pastures with less of a headache."

"Suit yourself, Lin. I don't see any way any of these guys are going to back down any time soon. Plus, there's talk of a new investor in the mix. A big hitter with very deep pockets."

His mind raced. This was news to him. "A new member? Nobody spoke to me about this. I have say over who joins the group."

"This guy apparently has no interest in joining the group. But he already has extensive holdings in the company and is keenly interested in a takeover. Probably just one more person who hates Adam Langford."

Jacob threaded his hand through his hair, the most colossal headache he'd ever had making his eyes burn. "And no idea who this guy is?"

"None. Right now, it's just talk. I have to ask why you would even care? Even if you pull your money out of the deal, you'll still get the fun of seeing LangTel and Adam Langford taken down. That's gotta be worth something."

Funny how the appeal of seeing Adam destroyed had taken on a pall, all because he'd given in to his desire for Anna. How could he even think about moving forward with Anna when this was all going on? He couldn't. It would be reckless and stupid and worst of all, unconscionable. Forget that her brother despised him—he couldn't begin things with an enormous secret hanging over his head. It would never work. That left him only one option. He had to back off with her. If she wanted to pursue things, she'd have to let him know, and then he'd make a decision. For now, he'd have to play it cool.

"Okay. Thanks. We'll talk soon." Jacob hung up and shoved his phone back into his pocket. So much for being a financial wizard. That wasn't going to keep him warm at night.

Anna couldn't sit in the house anymore. She needed fresh air, so she made her way outside to the driveway and set her overnight bag next to Jacob's car.

The notion of the end of their getaway was all too depressing. Last night had shattered her expectations. Just thinking about the things they had done together, his touch against her skin, every white-hot kiss, made her tingle. They'd flipped on a switch and completed a circuit, but that could be turned off just as easily, couldn't it?

She felt as if he'd answered the question mere moments ago, when he went out to the garage to spend some time with his beloved motorcycles. He'd patted her back on his way out the door, like a pal—as a buddy would do. He'd been distant all morning. It was hard not to take the hint. Last night was in the past. Today, he was moving forward.

She kicked a pebble into a puddle. It had rained at some point in the middle of the night, which left behind a grayish-blue sky with only the wispiest of white clouds. They would have a gloomy ride back to Manhattan, a fitting precursor to what was waiting for her when they got there—family, responsibilities that were more important than a fling. She didn't want to think about it too hard. She wanted to be back in Jacob's bed, curled up in the sheets, pillows cast aside, the rest of the world an afterthought.

So if this was a one-time occurrence, could she be content with that? She caught a glimpse of Jacob as he came out of the garage. The answer was clear as she watched the way he moved. One night would not be enough. In jeans and a gray sweater, clothes that were nothing special on any other man, he was stunning. He lowered his sunglasses, which had been nestled in his thick head of hair. Not being able to see more of him, in every sense of the word, would be such a disappointment. But was that realistic? Considering the circumstances, she feared it was not.

"I need to grab one more thing inside," he called to her from the flagstone walkway in front of the house.

"No problem. Take your time," she answered.

A muffled version of her cell phone ringtone sounded. *Who's calling me on a Sunday morning?* She fished it from the bottom of her bag, her stomach flip-flopping when she saw the name on the caller ID. Talk about an abrupt jerk back to reality. Adam. She walked away from the car with a finger jammed in her ear. "Adam. Hi. Everything okay?"

"Hey there, Anna Banana. How are you?"

Anna was about to ask if he was feeling well. He hadn't called her by that nickname in years. "I'm good. What's up?" Paranoid thoughts whirred through her brain. Did he have some way of knowing where she was? Of what she was up to? Every bold feeling she'd had yesterday about throwing caution to the wind was now haunting her; it enveloped her with a crushing sense of guilt. She wasn't the girl to sneak around, to hide things from her brother.

"I feel badly about our talk the other night. I was going to call you yesterday, but Mel and I were doing all sorts of wedding stuff. I'm really sorry about the way I spoke to you."

"That's nice, Adam, but you seemed pretty certain about what you were saying at the time."

"I know, but I was caught up in the heat of the moment. I don't want you to think that I don't want you in place as CEO. I do. I definitely do. And I believe in you. It's just…it's been hard. I think you know that."

Had he called to apologize or was he searching for validation? "I do know that. This has been hard for me, too."

He blew out a deep breath. "Look, Mel and I had a long talk last night. I swear, she's so good at figuring out what's going on with me. It's uncanny. I realize now that losing Dad has been much more difficult than I imagined. I knew it would be tough, but not this bad. And the pressure at work. Well, I think I just haven't been myself."

She hadn't quite expected he would come to this realization, ever. Adam had a real affinity for being detached when needed. The pain of losing her dad sat squarely in her chest. It was somehow more pronounced now, realizing that it weighed on Adam just as much. "I know it's been hard. I should've been more patient with you. I know you're doing your best."

"And I realized just how hard I'm being on you, which is so stupid on my part. You're my biggest ally. You're the one person I know I can trust with anything and I'm shutting you out. It's not only stupid, it's not fair to you."

The one person I can trust. The words echoed in her head. And here she was, hours away, with the man her brother had told her to stay away from. "Thank you for saying that."

"So, starting tomorrow morning, you and I need to get together our plan for moving you in as CEO."

It felt as if her heart had just stopped. Was he really saying that? Was he really willing to finally move forward? "We do?"

"Yes. You know, the board of directors is never going to be happy. If I sit around waiting for them to fall in line, you'll never get to take the job you want and I'll never get to return to what I want to do."

Jacob emerged from the house. The smile on his face was everything she wanted to see, while everything she wanted to hear was coming at her over the phone from her brother. She should've been happy, but she knew full well that these two things did not peacefully coexist in the real world. There was no having both.

"Does this mean you've changed your mind about Sunny Side?"

He groaned, making Anna regret even bringing it up. "I don't want to dismiss your idea again. Let's keep an eye on it. Maybe Jacob will take himself out of the mix. I refuse to touch it before then."

"Ready?" Jacob asked, walking around to her side of the car and opening her door.

"Did you say something?" Adam asked.

Inside, she was begging Jacob to please not say another word. Her heart pounded in her chest. This was far too messy. She had to get off the phone right away. "I have to go, but thanks for calling. I really appreciate it. A lot."

"I have confidence in you, kiddo. I really do. I just

had to pull my head out of my rear end for a few minutes."

She sighed. How she'd longed for this moment—to hear Adam say that she was right about something, about anything, that he had confidence in her. "Thank you. That means a lot."

"See you at work tomorrow."

"Yep. See you then."

Anna put her phone back in her purse. Was she the worst human being on the planet? It felt that way. At best, she was a rotten sister for taking up with Jacob and pursuing Sunny Side behind Adam's back.

"Everything okay?" Jacob asked.

"Yes. Just fine." She nodded and climbed into the car, her conversation with Adam replaying in her head. *You're the one person I can trust.* Was it time to climb out of her dream? To keep Jacob where he was—a fun, amazing fling that had come to an end? The answer seemed clear. She'd scratched the itch and now she had to remain loyal to her brother and her own dream job. She'd worked so hard, and it was presuming a lot to even wonder if Jacob was interested in more. He'd been withdrawn all morning.

He started the car and turned on a news talk station. "I want to get caught up on the financial news. Back to work tomorrow morning, you know."

Anna leaned her head against the car window. *Back to work.* "Yes. I know."

Five hours later, they were pulling up in front of her building. "Let me get your door," he said, reaching for the handle on his own.

"No. Hold on." She grabbed his forearm. "I feel like we should talk." She probably should've brought this up during the ride, but she'd chickened out every time. Maybe this was better. At least she had an escape.

Jacob shut off the radio and turned to her. "Yes. Of course."

"I had a really wonderful weekend," she started, already feeling remorseful about what she was about to say. It was the smart thing to do, the right thing to do. It was also the last thing she wanted to do.

"Good. I'm glad. I did, too."

"It's just that…" she sighed deeply. "I like you a lot, but we need to be honest with ourselves. It probably wasn't the smartest thing in the world, considering that we have my family to contend with. I don't see Adam changing his mind any time soon, possibly ever, and my family is really important to me. I just think it will cause a rift that won't be good for me. Or you, for that matter."

"I see." He took his sunglasses out of the cup holder and put them on. "Whatever you want, Anna. You won't get an argument from me."

Was he hurt? Disappointed? His voice was so cold, his tone so aloof, it was impossible to know, but she had a pretty good guess. The night before, everything she'd dreamed of all those years ago, had been nothing but a one-night stand to him. "Okay. Great. I guess I'll talk to you at some point? About Sunny Side?"

He nodded, looking straight ahead through the windshield. "I'll call you if I have any information to share."

"Perfect." She climbed out of the car, closed the door and didn't look back.

This was for the best, but it felt absolutely wretched.

Eight

Telling Jacob "thanks, but no thanks" was the hardest thing Anna had done in a very long time. Four days later and it felt downright stupid.

"Still nothing from, you know, him?" Holly asked, setting a salad down on Anna's desk. They'd taken to eating lunches together in Anna's office since the executive dining room was no fun. Rumors of a LangTel takeover were rampant, but if it was happening, the perpetrator hadn't come to light.

"Shhh," Anna admonished, leaping out of her seat and making sure her door was firmly closed.

"It's not like I said his name." Holly dug into her own salad as if they were discussing the five-day forecast.

"Sorry," Anna whispered, heading back to her desk. "It's just, you know. If Adam found out, he would not be happy. You're literally the only person on the planet who knows about it."

"I feel so privileged to have this information that could get me fired."

"I'm sorry. I hope this isn't bothering you to know. I just had to tell somebody or I was going to go insane. And like it or not, you're my best friend."

"Don't worry. I'm very good at keeping my mouth shut."

Anna sighed. "To answer your question, no, I haven't heard from him, and it's been four days. I don't know why, but I can't stop thinking about him." Of course she couldn't stop thinking about him. It'd been an aeon since she'd felt so alive. But she'd made the sensible decision, choosing to put her career and family at center stage. Those were things she could rely on. Those were things that couldn't be yanked out from under her. After the last year, she needed to know that she was standing on solid ground, even if this particular patch of land still left her wanting more of Jacob.

"Sex will do that to a person, you know," Holly quipped. "Especially if you've gone long enough without it."

It was more than sex, though. She couldn't bring herself to utter those words, especially not to Holly, the woman of zero filter, but it was the truth. Anna hadn't had that kind of connection with a man, well, ever. Perhaps it was the shared history between herself and Jacob, everything she'd spent years anticipating and thinking she'd never have, but it felt even more elemental than that. They fit together—shared dreams, similar mind-sets and aspirations. The physical fit was certainly impossible to ignore. In bed, the fit was mind-blowing. "I guess. Not much I can do about it, though.

The drama of my family is too much, and he seemed all too ready to agree."

"Men and their axes to grind. Two women would never allow it to get this bad. They'd smile to each other's faces and do that phony nice speak, then bad-mouth them the minute the other person turned their back. It's much more civilized if you think about it."

Talk about uncivilized—one of Anna's coworkers had uttered Jacob's name in a meeting the day before, and Adam literally kicked the guy out of the meeting. No explanation, just an invitation to get the hell out. He'd softened his approach with her, but he was still being extraordinarily hard on everyone else.

Anna was picking through her salad when her cell phone lit up. Jacob's name popped up on the screen. She dropped her fork into the bowl.

"Who is it?" Holly asked. "You look like you just saw a ghost."

"It's Jacob."

"What are you waiting for?" Her voice was at a near-panic. "Answer it."

Anna wiped her mouth with a napkin and picked up the phone. What in the world could he be calling about? Nothing about their circumstances had changed. She stifled the hope that rose in her chest, that he was calling because he had to see her.

"Jacob, hi." She brandished her hand at Holly to shoo her out of her office, but Holly just sat back in her chair. Anna bugged her eyes. "Please go," she mouthed.

"Fine." Holly feigned sadness by jutting out her lower lip and begrudgingly got up from the chair.

"Is this a good time?" Jacob asked. Even when he was

being entirely too businesslike, his voice was so sexy that it shook her to her core.

"Yes. Of course."

"I didn't want to assume, since you're at work, but it's important and I didn't want you to hear this from anyone else but me."

Her heart began to beat furiously in her chest. "Hear what?"

"Sunny Side is going to have to go on hold. The patent has been delayed and there's a design flaw they have to work through. It's pretty routine with a technology like this, but it could be another few months until a sale is in the mix. They want to put their best foot forward with whomever they partner with, and I've advised them that that's a sound strategy."

Anna took in a deep breath through her nose. She fought her disappointment that he hadn't called about something personal. At least he had what might end up being good news—a delay could be fantastic for her. By the time Sunny Side was ready to sell, she might be in place as CEO and she could make the call. "I see. Well, I appreciate you keeping me up to speed on things."

"I hope you don't feel like our weekend was a waste of time because of this."

A waste of time? Does he feel that way? "Of course I don't. It was an amazing trip." There were hundreds more things she wanted to say to him, but could she make that leap? Could she even hint just how badly she wished they could do it all over again? And should she even cross that line again? "It was great. Both personally and professionally."

"Good. I'm glad to hear that you still feel like that."

Her mind was whirring like a broken blender. Why

did it feel as if he was calling about more? And if he was, why wasn't he just getting to it? It wasn't like him to tiptoe about things. "You didn't really think that I only cared about Sunny Side, did you?"

"No, I didn't. I just wanted to be sure." He cleared his throat. "Anna, I have to tell you something else. I'm actually glad that the delay with Sunny Side happened because it gave me an excuse to call you."

"You don't need an excuse. We're friends, aren't we?"

"Friends with a very complicated set of circumstances."

That much was indeed true. It didn't change the fact that she was hopelessly drawn to him. "So just call me whenever. You don't need an excuse." A long silence played out on the other end of the line. Had she nudged things too far? Was he now trying to find a way out of this phone call?

"Okay, good. Because I'm calling you right now to tell you that I can't stop thinking about you."

She smiled so wide that she witnessed the rise of her own cheeks. Her heart had apparently gotten the memo—it sprang into action by thumping her pulse in her ears. "Really?" Anna dug the heel of her pump into the office carpet, wagging herself back and forth in her chair, ultimately propelling herself into a lazy spin.

"It's especially bothersome when I'm trying to go to sleep."

She dropped her foot, stopping the chair. "Oh. I see."

"I just keep thinking about what it was like to be with you. I keep thinking about touching you, kissing you. I want to be able to do that again."

"You do?" Her mind went there—a gloriously wild confusion of every sexy moment they shared together...

the way his butt looked when he walked away from her, the way his mouth went slack when she did something that pleased him. And then there was the dark, intense stare he gave her when he had her pinned beneath his bodyweight, taking his time, making sure she relished every subtle move he made.

"Yes, I do. I also would appreciate it if you would stop asking questions and give me some indication as to how you feel about this. Right now I feel like I'm having one-sided phone sex."

If she blurted out everything going through her head right now, he wouldn't get a word in edgewise for a week. "I can't stop thinking about you, either." Something about making the admission was so freeing, however vulnerable it made her.

"Go on." His voice rumbled over the line.

"And I'm having the same problem. I can't sleep. I just lie there in the dark and replay everything that happened last weekend."

"Good." His declaration had a confounding finality to it.

Anna furrowed her brow. "Good?"

"No more questions. I'm sending a car to pick you up at five."

"I have a meeting at four-thirty."

"Is it important?"

What was it about the velvety quality of his voice that made her want to not merely throw caution to the wind, but send it through a paper shredder? Taking directives from a man was not on the list of things she enjoyed doing. In fact, she usually went out of her way to avoid it, but this was different. She not only knew what he was implying, but precisely what he was capable of. "I'll reschedule."

"That's my girl."

My girl. The words sent electricity zinging through her body. "Where are we going?"

"We aren't going anywhere. You're coming here."

Oh crap. I'm going to have to run home and change.

"And, Anna. Bring a toothbrush."

Nine

Jacob had never done anything quite so weak, but all bets were apparently off when it came to Anna. He'd managed four whole days without calling her. Why give in now? He knew from experience that the first forty-eight hours were the worst, when you know it's in your own best interest to stay away from someone.

In the case of Anna, it had only gotten harder after those first two days. It was like he was being starved for air, which was disconcerting. He couldn't focus on his work. He needed more of her and he needed her now. Damn the consequences, however complicated. Damn the fallout, too. He needed her insistent hands grabbing his body, her strong and graceful legs wrapped around him. He needed to smell her and kiss her, hear her laugh. He needed his fix.

He had to temper the romance. This was a rabbit hole

for him emotionally. He didn't let many people into his life and when he did, he didn't want them to waltz right out. That wasn't the point of trust. If you believed in someone, if you wanted them in your life, they would stay. There was no telling how long Anna would be able to stay, or even if she would want to.

Tempering romance aside, he knew he couldn't start an ongoing no-strings-attached thing with Anna. Even when strings meant the Langfords on some level. This left him with a very narrow tightrope on which to balance, at least for the foreseeable future. The War Chest had closed ranks, forging ahead with the scheme he'd planted in their heads. He refused to regret doing it, but he sure as hell wished he could turn it around. If he could just find someone willing to back down, the rest of them might follow, and that would mean one less thing hanging over his head.

He glanced at his watch. Anna would be here any minute and that made his nerve endings stand up straight and tall, pinging electricity throughout his body. The anticipation brewed an unholy cocktail of adrenaline and testosterone in him. He could only imagine what it would be like when he finally saw her. When he could finally kiss her again, feel her come alive beneath his touch. That was the response he cherished—when she allowed herself to be vulnerable, when she surrendered to him and he could feel and see the tangible results— quivers, shakes and trembles.

He walked out into his kitchen and removed a bottle of champagne from the fridge. Cliché? Maybe. But Anna did deserve at least one or two trappings of romance. He wasn't about to let that go completely unaddressed.

The knock at his door sent his pulse embarking on

a similar staccato rhythm. He retained his composure, fairly certain that it was the smooth, in-control Jacob that she lusted after. The one she wanted to take to bed.

He opened the door and had to fight the impulses of his jaw. This was not the time to do nothing more than stand there, mouth agape, like an idiot.

"Hi." Her grin was equal parts flirtatious and shy. Her cheeks flushed with that gorgeous pink, a slightly paler shade than her lips, all of it hopelessly inviting.

"Hello yourself." He ushered her in, shutting the door.

He followed her into the living room just off the foyer and helped her with her coat. His eyes zeroed in on the view—her black, sleeveless dress was tailored within a whisper of her figure, hugging every gorgeous inch. Good God. Was he still standing? The thing he admired most about her in that dress was that a woman like Anna could get away with wearing something like that to a meeting. Granted, a meeting where every guy in the room might have an impossible time focusing. Her toned legs looked even more tempting in black sky-high heels. Note to self: bring Anna to an important meeting someday. She'll make the deal.

"You look absolutely gorgeous," he said, craving her touch. He tossed her coat over the back of a chair and gripped her elbow. The electricity between them was obscene, like an out-of-control Tesla experiment. He was surprised he couldn't see the sizzling current arcing between them.

"Thank you." Her head dropped to the side, only a fraction of an inch, but he loved to see her soften to him like that, to give him a subtle indication that he was on the right track. "You don't look half-bad yourself." She stepped closer, still needing to look up at him in killer heels. He might have to beg her to keep them on the whole night.

Her hand pressed against his chest, smoothing the fabric of his suit jacket. He watched her, smiling, their eyes connecting. It looked as if there was a fire blazing behind hers—hot and intense. Which one of them would give in first? He had no idea, only that for once in his life he knew that he'd still be the winner if he was the first to show his hand.

"I missed you, Anna. I know we said that this wasn't a good idea, but I missed you. It's as simple as that. I missed standing close to you and looking at you and thinking about all of the things I want to do with you. The things I want to do to you."

Her lips parted ever so slightly and a gentle rush of air passed them. It was the sound of pressure being released. "I couldn't stop thinking about you, either. Every time I thought of the reasons we should stay away from each other, I just kept coming back to that original thought…"

He was reasonably sure of what she might say next, but he wanted to hear her say it. "Thought of what?"

"Of you and everything I was missing by staying away."

Perfect. "So now what?"

Her hand hadn't left his chest. She bowed into him, placing her other hand opposite it. Her fingers played with the knot of his tie. "We have the whole night ahead of us. Maybe we just need to see what happens."

He smiled again, this time much wider. It was hard not to be incurably happy around her. "Like what happens when I do this?" He snaked his hand around her waist and settled it in the curve of her lower back.

"Mmm." Her lips traveled closer to his. "I think the

next thing that happens is this." She tugged his tie loose, watching his reaction. She flicked open the top button of his shirt, taking liberties again. "Oops. I took two turns in a row."

"Taking advantage, I see," he murmured. This game of undressing, however compelling and sexy, would need to be seen to a quick conclusion. He wanted her naked. Now. He reached up for the zipper, pulling it down the center of her back as she made quick work of his shirt buttons. He longed to see that stretch of her skin, the one he'd kissed a week ago. He turned her around, admiring her porcelain beauty as it contrasted with a black bra and as he lowered the zipper further, lacy panties. He eased the dress from her shoulders, savoring every sensory pleasure—her smell, the heat that radiated from her, her smooth skin as he dragged the back of his hand along the channel of her spine. Her presence didn't merely have him primed, he was already teetering on the brink.

The garment slumped to the floor and she cast a sexy look back at him, her eyes deep, warm, and craving. "You made a big jump ahead there."

Hell yes, he had. And he'd do it again in a heartbeat. He grasped her shoulders and pinned her back to his chest, wrapping his arms around her waist. She craned her neck and he kissed her, hard. He cupped one of her breasts, the silky fabric of her bra teasing his palm as she tightened beneath his touch, her nipple hard. Their tongues tangled and Anna righted herself, turning in his arms. He took off his jacket and tie as she unhooked his belt and unzipped his pants in a flurry. He wrangled himself out of the rest of his clothes with one hand while keeping her as close as possible with the other. He wouldn't let go of the kiss either—she'd cast aside sweet for an edge that he couldn't ignore.

With a pop, he unhooked her bra, and didn't bother with the seduction of teasing it from her body. He cupped her breasts, molding them in his hands, his mouth seeking one of her deep pink, firm nipples. The gasp that came from her when he flicked his tongue against her tight skin was music to his ears.

She kicked off one of her shoes and then the other and stepped out of her panties.

Her beautiful bare curves heightened his awareness of how badly his body was driven to claim hers. There was no way he'd make it to the bedroom. He sat on the couch next to them, half reclining, and reached out his hand. "Come here. I need you."

She smiled and cocked an eyebrow, taking his hand. "Are you that impatient?"

"Yes. And we have all night." The breath caught in his chest as he watched her carefully set her knee next to his hip and straddle him. The sky outside was quickly falling into darkness, but the light was just bright enough to show off the dips and hollows of her delicate collarbone. He traced his finger along the contours. "Calling you this morning was the best thing I've done in a long time."

"I couldn't agree more." She smiled, dropping her head to kiss him. Her silky hair brushed the sides of his face. He was almost sorry he didn't have the visual of the moment she took him in her hand, guided him inside, and began to sink down around him. A deep groan escaped his throat as her body molded around him, warm and inviting. He wanted to be nowhere else.

She settled her weight on his and they moved together in a dance he never wanted to end. It buoyed his senses, made him appreciate her beauty and essential nature even more than before. She rocked her hips into his, over and over again, as they kissed and his hands grasped the velvety skin of her perfect bottom. Her breaths quickened and before he knew what was happening, she was gathering around him in steady pulses. She sat back, their eyes connecting for an instant before she gave in to the sensation, closing her eyes and knocking her head back. He closed his own eyes and the relief shuddered out of him, each passing wave invisibly bringing them closer.

Anna collapsed back on the bed, her chest heaving with fast and heavy breaths. Jacob clutched her hand, struggling just as much for air. She glanced over at the clock. It was after midnight. They hadn't stopped for much more than a snack and a glass of champagne since she'd arrived a little after five. How much stamina could one man have? Was he trying to prove a point? Because he had. And then some.

She was spent. Wonderfully, gloriously spent. It struck her as a summertime kind of exhaustion, the kind she'd experienced as a kid, up at the Langford family beach house. After swimming all day, sun-soaked, stomach sore from laughing too hard, you were absolutely starving. You would take your first bite of food at dinner and be sure that nothing had ever tasted so good.

That was Jacob. Nothing had felt so good before him.

"Can I just take the chance now to apologize for what happened that first time we kissed?" he asked. "It's pretty clear that was the wrong decision."

She rolled to her side, smiling, despite the unpleasant nature of the topic he'd just chosen to introduce. "You don't have to pretend that you wished things had ended differently. It's okay. I'm a big girl. Plus, you made up for it tonight."

"Don't you think I regret it? What exactly did I turn you down for? A friendship that would ultimately turn into the worst thing in my entire life."

Had she gone through years of pain over the wrong decision? She didn't want to believe that. It would be more comforting to go with the theory that everything happens for a reason. "As much as it hurt to have you say no, I have to admire the reason you did it, even if it didn't turn out the way you would've liked."

He stared up at the ceiling, seeming immersed in thought. Was his rift with Adam something deeper than warring over a business decision? She'd always assumed that Jacob's side of things was about the embarrassment of being publicly shut out of his first major business deal, about losing his cut of a big payday. Was there something else?

"I'm a loyal person, Anna. You have to understand that. If I let someone into my life, they're there for a reason. I don't do it lightly."

And there was her answer. "So it's not just about business. It's about losing the friendship, too."

He was quiet again, but she didn't want to interrupt whatever was running through his head. The intensity of his reservation was one of the things that had first drawn her to him. She bristled with curiosity, wondering what exactly his brilliant mind was choosing to ruminate over. She placed her hand on his stomach—he tensed at first touch, but just as quickly she felt his muscles give in to her. He grasped her hand and raised it to his mouth, kissing her fingers tenderly.

Anna felt equal parts exposed and protected. Did he feel the same? Was it the power of the afterglow, or was there more? Even when her brother had insisted that she couldn't trust Jacob, Anna couldn't buy into it. Her gut told her that she could. Plus, she didn't want to believe that the man who'd once turned down sex out of respect for a friendship would do anything less than the right thing. She might be inching closer to the edge of a treacherous place, but she wanted to believe that Jacob would tug her back if she put herself in the path of true danger. He had to. She didn't want to think anything less of him.

"I don't want to burden you with the minutiae of what happened between Adam and me," he said, breaking the silence between them. "We're having such an amazing night. I don't dare mess with that."

She propped herself up on her elbow and gazed down into his face. He was so gorgeous that it boggled the mind sometimes, even more so at this moment, when he'd given her a glimpse of how deep the waters running through him really were. Would she ever fully know those depths? If she were to live in this instant for all eternity, she wanted nothing more than to drown in them, sink to the bottom and never come up for air. There was so much to learn—she hungered for it.

But was it the right thing to do? To dive in, knowing the repercussions? Was it her weakness for him that was making her so eager to do the foolhardy thing? Maybe. Probably. Did she care? Not really. There were no guarantees, regardless of the situation two people found themselves in. It was up to them to find a way. No one could do it for them.

He rolled toward her and placed the softest, sexiest, most intimate kiss on her lips, plunging her into the sea she longed to get lost in. His hand wound to the small of her back, fingers drawing delicate circles against her skin. She could do nothing more than press against him—the inches between them felt so absurd. Pointless. Of course they should be together. Even if it might bring everything crashing down.

Ten

Life quickly became a beautiful blur, weeks of weekend trysts and countless late-night rendezvous. Sneaking around wasn't Anna's preference, but she couldn't deny herself the glory of time with Jacob, so as difficult as it was, they took great care to keep things a secret.

It was working for the most part, although there were times when it was touch and go. One day in the office, Adam had asked why she was so tired. Was she coming down with something? She couldn't tell him the truth, that she and Jacob had been up until all hours making love, intermixed with eating ice cream in bed and watching bad reality television. So she'd said that she simply wasn't sleeping well. It wasn't a *real* lie, or at least not a big one, but the tiny untruths were beginning to hang over her like a dark cloud.

"What do you want to do tonight? What if we went

out for a change?" Jacob asked over the phone as Anna sat at her desk.

"You know we can't do that. What if someone sees us together?" It was the awful truth, but tonight it was more of a convenient excuse. She glanced at the clock on her laptop and began packing up her things. If she was going to beat Jacob back to his apartment, she needed to leave now. She'd scrambled to put together a small birthday surprise—nothing too elaborate, but she hoped he would enjoy it.

"Anna. We can't do this forever. We need to get out of the house now and then. Not that I don't want to leave you tied to my bed. I do."

She smiled. It was hard not to—he was so good at working in the comments that reminded her how much he wanted her. Her most girlish tendencies lived for those moments. "You're right. We'll talk about it tonight. Your place?" He *was* right. They couldn't do this forever. Something would have to give, and that something bore a remarkable resemblance to her brother.

"Yes," he answered, seeming a bit exasperated. "I'll be home by seven. You have your key?"

"I do." He'd given it to her a few days ago, as a "just in case." She wasn't entirely sure of what that meant, but it made a surprise dinner possible.

"Anna?" he asked, with a sexy, leading tone.

"Yes?" she replied, knowing full well what he was about to say.

"I miss you."

She smiled, absentmindedly trailing her fingers along her collarbone. *I miss you*—three silly words they'd been saying to each other for a few weeks. It was one of their many secrets, the things they hid from the rest of the world. Were they a placeholder for "I love you"? Those particular three words hadn't come yet, however much she hoped that they would. They'd sat on her lips several times, but would he return them? Just like the ill-fated kiss years ago, the thought of that kind of rejection was too much. Wait, she'd told herself. It would happen. They would find a way. She had to believe.

"Miss you, too. I'll see you tonight."

She told her assistant she had some errands to run and tried to ignore the guilty feelings that came along with ducking out of work early. After retrieving a carrot cake from the bakery around the corner from Jacob's building, she let herself into his apartment.

It was certainly strange to be in his place on her own. What would it feel like to come home here? Even with the spaciousness of her own apartment, it didn't have the sprawling splendor of Jacob's penthouse, nor did it have the magnificent Central Park view. She could be more than comfortable here. She could be happy. That would be a wonderful life, if she could ever get to that point. She sensed Jacob was proceeding with caution and how could he not be? Her brother hated him. That would scare even the most formidable man away.

A half hour later, she was making good progress with dinner. She wasn't the world's greatest cook, but she could hold her own with pasta and a salad, and it wouldn't be the same if she'd ordered takeout. Luckily, Jacob was easily pleased. A big guy who worked out five days a week, he'd eat virtually anything you put in front of him, especially if accompanied by a glass of good wine.

Even though the dining room table could easily accommodate ten, she set it for two, placing them side-by-side at one end. She found some candles in the buffet, dimmed the lights. Then she returned to the kitchen to finish the preparations. He was only a few minutes late when he strolled into the kitchen.

"What's all this?" He smiled, seeming genuinely perplexed.

Anna rushed over to kiss him—a surreal moment, for sure. Was that what it would feel like to be husband and wife? She might not have much time to get dinner on the table if and when she became CEO, but she enjoyed this glimpse of domesticity. It felt especially comfortable with Jacob. "It's a surprise. For your birthday."

His brow furrowed. He now seemed even more confused. "How did you know it was my birthday?"

"You had your passport out on the dresser the other day and I wanted to sneak a peek at the picture."

"So you were snooping." He smirked, suggesting he wasn't entirely disappointed in her.

"A little. But that's beside the point. I wanted to do something nice for you. Honestly, I'm a little surprised you never told me about it in the first place."

"I don't really celebrate my birthday." He loosened his tie. "I never have."

"Really? Why?"

"I spent a lot of time away from my parents as a kid. They were always doing their own thing, I was away at boarding school. It just doesn't mean much when you get money wired into your bank account and a phone call."

It was about the saddest thing she'd heard in a long time, but she didn't want to dwell on the negative. She took his hand and led him into the dining room, where she sat him down and poured him a glass of red. She held out her glass to clink with his. "Happy birthday."

Something about the sentiment fell short, like she was supposed to add something about their future or that she loved him.

As to what tomorrow held, or even a month from then, she didn't know. As to the question of love, she knew in her heart that she did. He understood her in ways that no one else seemed to—he appreciated her aspirations, he encouraged her, he commiserated when she'd had a difficult day at work. He was always so focused on her, everything she wanted and needed. No one had ever done that, and he made it seem so effortless. Even better, he accepted her affection unconditionally. He never had an agenda outside of being with her.

It was perfect. *He* was perfect, or at least he was perfect for her. But that made their situation all the more frustrating, stuck as she was between him and her family.

She served their salads and took the seat next to him. How could he have gone his whole life not celebrating his birthday? Her heart felt unusually heavy—birthdays had always been a big event in the Langford household. Always. She wanted him to have that, to have everything she'd had.

"Maybe today can be the start of a new birthday tradition."

He offered her the faintest of smiles. "That's a nice idea."

The start of a new tradition. Did Anna really mean that? Did she see a future for them? Because as incredible as it was to be with her, it felt as if the universe was conspiring against them. It was only a matter of time before the War Chest takeover surfaced.

He ate his salad, listening to Anna talk about her day, feeling more guilty with every bite. Hours before, the War Chest had staged their coup against him—ousting him from the group for daring to push them so hard, vowing to continue with their hostile takeover of Lang-Tel. They'd done to him what he'd once hoped they could do to Adam. Being on the receiving end of vengeance wasn't fun. These people were dangerous, all deep pockets and determination. Experience told him that it didn't take much else to be successful. Not even luck.

Anna served the pasta, which might've been one of the most delicious things he'd ever tasted—ziti with Italian sausage, white wine, saffron and arugula. She'd found the recipe online after having taken note of how much he loved those particular ingredients—so thoughtful of her, and yet he couldn't truly enjoy a single bite. Watching her, the sweet smile on her face, thinking about the effort she'd gone to. She'd planned this incredible evening for him, and he'd planned to destroy the company her father had built. What kind of a monster was he? Had getting back at Adam really been that damn important? Had his father messed him up so badly that his so-called business brilliance was capable of ruining lives?

He had to find a way to stop it—sell every asset he had, pull together a new group of investors to help him. Something. There had to be a way. Because the truth was that he was absolutely falling in love with Anna. He'd known it for weeks now. Hell, he was fairly sure he'd fallen for her during the motorcycle ride. But he couldn't confess his true feelings for her until the takeover was squashed. That was no way to start a life together, with a secret of epic proportions lurking in the shadows, about to reveal itself at any time.

After they finished Anna's meal, she brought in a cake and serenaded him with "Happy Birthday" in her slightly off-tune voice. It was corny and adorable and not at all the sort of attention he'd ever had before he'd met Anna—sweet, genuine and thoughtful. Then she gave him his gift—a gorgeous pair of perfect-fitting black leather gloves.

"They're handmade," she said, watching with excitement as he tried them on. "I called a motorcycle shop out in Queens and talked to the owner, so I knew what kind to get."

"Thank you. Thank you so much." His heart ached, so overwhelmed with this show of generosity from Anna.

"You forgot the card." She flipped over the gift box and removed a small envelope taped to the lid.

His eyes couldn't be torn from her as he opened it. Where had she come from? Was this all a dream?

For Jacob,
There's no one I'd rather be on a motorcycle with.
I'll be the one holding on tight.
Love, Anna

He nodded, struggling to manage the emotions welling inside him. *Love, Anna.* He loved her. She was so warm and giving, so beautiful, inside and out. He wasn't even sure he deserved to be in the same room with her, let alone ever have a place in her heart or her life. "Thank you so much, for everything." He set the gloves aside and took her hand. "Truly. I am so thankful for this evening. It's been wonderful." The card was sitting right there. He wasn't much for sentimentality, but he would cherish it forever, even if things didn't work out, even if the horrible things he'd done came to light. "The gloves are absolutely perfect and the card is just…" He nodded, swallowing back everything he wanted to tell her. *I love you.* "It's perfect, too. You have such a way with words."

She smiled sheepishly. "I have a fair amount of experience with writing you notes and letters."

"I don't ever remember you writing to me."

She downed the last of the wine in her glass and refilled it, topping off his as well. "After that Christmas you stayed with my family, I had a hard time. Writing to you was my outlet."

"A hard time?" What in the world was she talking about?

She shrugged. "I just couldn't stop thinking about you. A lot of it was just wondering if you'd said no when I kissed you because you didn't like me. It had definitely occurred to me that you might have used Adam as an excuse."

Could she really think that? After all this time? "He wasn't an excuse. I was completely honest with you, Anna. If it hadn't been for Adam, I would've kissed you all night long. Your Dartmouth sweatshirt would've been off in a heartbeat."

She dropped her chin and grinned. "Really?"

"Yes. Really." Just thinking about it filled him with equal measures of regret and gratitude. At least he'd gotten a second chance, but had he unwittingly thrown it away?

"So anyway, I wrote you letters. A lot of letters."

He narrowed his gaze. "But I never heard from you at all."

"I never mailed them. I kept them in a box. I threw them away right before I graduated from college. At that point, it felt pretty silly to still be pining for you, and I had a boyfriend. Although he didn't last for long."

"Why didn't you send them after my friendship with Adam went south?"

"You can't be serious. Didn't you hate my entire family at that point?"

He had to think hard about that. "I definitely told myself I hated all of you, but I never truly felt that way about you. Or your mom. You were both so kind to me."

"Would you have actually read them?"

He had to be honest. "Probably not. I was insanely angry those first few years. I probably would've just thrown them away." If only he could have thrown away that anger instead, he wouldn't be in this position right now. If only things with Adam hadn't ended the way they had. "Can you tell me what they said?"

Her face flushed with bright red. "You would ask that, wouldn't you?"

"I'm curious."

"Of course you are. They were all about you. Who doesn't want to hear about a bunch of love letters someone wrote about them?"

"Just tell me one thing." His curiosity was getting the better of him. It was difficult not to be fascinated by the idea of someone being that preoccupied with him. The thought of Anna feeling that way was nothing short of awe inspiring.

She laughed quietly and walked her fingers across the table until she took his hand. It covered his arm in goose bumps. What she could do with a single touch—it astounded him every time. "It depended on the day. If I was dealing with it okay, I would just write and tell you how much I missed you, but then I would write about normal things happening with me. If I was sad, then it was *a lot* about how much I missed you." She cast her eyes aside as if she was trying to summon her courage. "And then there were the times when I was feeling lonely in other ways. That's when I wrote to you about what I wished would've happened that night."

Now he was really kicking himself for having turned her down that night. "Dammit. Really? And you threw those away? I'd pay just about anything to read that."

"How about if I just show you instead?"

Her eyes glinted with mischief, warming him from head to toe. Was he the luckiest man on earth? Because it sure felt that way. He not only needed her at that moment, he needed to have her as his forever. He couldn't imagine a moment without what they had together. That meant he needed to double his efforts to stop the Lang-Tel takeover. Then he could tell her he loved her. Then he could find a way to smooth things over with Adam. Then he could go to Tiffany's, buy her a big fat ring, and have what he knew he couldn't live without—Anna.

Eleven

Anna could no longer tiptoe around Adam. Hiding her relationship with Jacob had become ridiculous. His birthday had illustrated that they were moving in a good direction, but they were both clearly holding back. She'd sensed it all night from him, that there was something he was dying to say. Was it that he loved her? If those were the words he wanted to say, the only thing she could imagine stopping him was Adam. There was no other explanation.

Could she persuade Adam to set aside the feud? The more she thought about it, the more convinced she was that it could be fixed. If she could get her two favorite guys to bury the hatchet, everything in her life would be better.

Anna buzzed her assistant, Carrie. "Can you let me know when my brother is out of his meeting? I need to speak to him this morning."

"Sure thing, Ms. Langford. Anything else?"

Anything else. *Maybe get Adam's secretary to slip a shot of bourbon into his coffee cup.* "No, Carrie. Thank you."

Twenty minutes later, Anna got the call. "Mr. Langford can see you now."

She strode down the hall, feigning the confidence that wavered inside her. Her relationship with Adam had improved so much since he'd had his revelation about how hard their father's death had hit him, but she still had no idea how he would react to this news. Would he feel betrayed? Would he be angry? He'd be entitled to either reaction. She only knew that the time had come to finally own up to everything. It was her only chance to have Jacob, for real.

"Hey. What's up?" Adam asked, glancing up from his computer screen.

His upbeat and affable tone convinced her she'd gotten the timing right. This was the morning for progress. "I was hoping to speak to you for a few minutes about something personal." She closed his office door behind her and took a seat opposite his desk.

He closed his laptop. "Of course. Is everything okay?"

"For the most part, everything is great, but it could be a lot better if I could just fix one thing."

"I'm listening."

"You and Jacob. I'd really like to see you two find a way to be civil to each other and stop the fighting. It's gone on for far too long."

He shook his head. "I thought you said this was personal. Sunny Side is not personal. And we agreed to table that."

"I'm not talking about that. I'm talking about me."

Did she have the courage to say what had to come next? She had to do it. Now or never. "Me and Jacob. Together. Personally. Very personally."

His eyebrows drew together. "I don't understand."

"Me and Jacob. You know…"

"Working together?"

"Do I have to draw you a map, Adam? Jacob and I are involved. Romantically. Not business. Personal."

He reared back his head as if she'd just told him that the world was flat. "How in the hell did that happen? You can't be serious."

She took a deep breath to steel herself. She'd worried this might be his reaction. "I don't want you to be angry, but I went away with him. To his house upstate. About six weeks ago. That's where things started."

"Why in the world would you do that? Did he kidnap you?"

"Will you stop? That's just mean."

"Anna, this is making zero sense."

It was time to come clean and she knew it. "I went behind your back and met with the founder of Sunny Side."

"You what?" The fury in his eyes surfaced, just as it had the night they'd first discussed this.

She thrust her finger into the air. "Hold on, Adam. Let me finish. I was certain that I could convince you to come around if I had a better sense of the numbers. We need a strong financial upside these days, don't we?"

"That's not the point…"

"Just answer the question. Yes or no."

"Yes. We do."

"Okay then. That's what I was trying to do. And things just sort of happened between Jacob and me. And then it continued when we got back to the city. I want to see where it can go. We mesh together really well."

He twisted his face. "I don't even want to think about you two, meshing."

"That's not what I'm talking about and you know it." She scooted to the edge of her seat, folding her hands before her and resting her elbows on her knees. It was no coincidence that she looked as if she was praying. "I can't be with Jacob if you two are at odds. Family is too important. I can't be torn between the two. I understand that there's bad blood between you, but I need you and Jacob to sit down and work it out. Once and for all. It's been six years, Adam. You were both new in business. You both made mistakes."

He shook his head so vigorously that his normally perfect hair went astray. "If I made any mistakes, I made them because I was reacting to the things Jacob did. He could've ruined a multi-million-dollar idea."

"But he didn't."

"It doesn't matter. Jacob was willing to put our business venture at risk to prove a point. That told me that he was unreliable as a business partner."

"I just feel like this whole thing has gotten blown completely out of proportion. You used to be friends."

"So what are you hoping for? That I apologize and we start playing golf together? That's not going to happen."

"I'm not asking you to be best friends. I'm just asking for enough of a truce that you two can be in the same room without trying to kill each other. That's it. Although I'd be lying if I said I wouldn't be happy if you rekindled your friendship. That would be nice to see."

"You're deluded." He leaned forward in his chair, his eyes pleading with her. "He's scum, Anna. I don't know what kind of line he fed you to get you into his bed, but I'm sure he was just trying to get back at me. You need to stop acting like a girl and walk away from him now, before you get hurt."

Anna was so offended on multiple levels that she wasn't even sure where to start. "Sometimes I think you just don't want me to be happy, Adam. You know, you and Melanie found a way. I don't see why you can't do one thing for me. For your sister."

"I'm not doing a damn thing to help my sister ruin her life. Believe me, some day you'll thank me." He opened up his laptop and stared at the screen.

She sat back, folded her arms across her chest, crossed her legs. She wagged her foot, brainstorming a new approach.

"Is there something else?" he asked.

"Nope." She shook her head with fierce determination. "I'm not leaving until we talk this out. I don't care if I have to sit here all day." She dug her phone out of her pocket. "I can do a remarkable amount of work sitting right here."

"Mr. Langford?" Adam's assistant's voice broke in over the intercom.

"Yes?"

"I'm so sorry to interrupt, but I have an urgent phone call from Samuel Haskins. He says it can't wait."

Anna grimaced. Sam Haskins had held a seat on the LangTel board of directors longer than anyone, even before Anna had been born. He was big on propriety and manners. He would never ask Adam to interrupt a meeting unless it were a life-or-death situation.

Adam picked up the phone. "Put the call through." He tapped his pen on the desk nervously, his forehead creasing. Right then she could see how much things weighed on him. It was the same sort of look her dad had when things at work were a bear. "Sam. What can I do for you?"

His sights darted to Anna after a few seconds. "So we were right all along."

What in the world could they be talking about? And did it have something to do with her? Why else would he look at her like that?

Adam nodded in agreement, but there was anger in his eyes. "Yes, of course. Whatever you think is the best course of action, but clearly we have to stop these guys. Now. I'll clear my schedule and we'll get on it right away. It's all hands on deck." He glanced at his watch. "Yes. I'll see you in an hour."

"What's going on?" she asked, trying to disguise the worry in her voice.

"Your boyfriend? Jacob? He's heading up a secret investment group. They're the ones buying up Lang-Tel stock."

Her heart felt as if it didn't know whether to leap to action or keel over. "What are you talking about? That can't be right. I just saw him last night." *I've been seeing him every night.* This couldn't be right.

"Jacob Lin and a bunch of guys with a lot of money are preparing for a hostile takeover of LangTel. He's trying to destroy the company our father built, Anna. He's trying to destroy our family's livelihood."

"That can't be right." Her eyes darted all over his office, desperate for some sign that this was all a bad dream. "I'll go talk to him. Right now. This must be a mistake."

"It's not a mistake. Sam has the evidence. And if you were looking for proof that Jacob is scum, here it is."

Anna had never just shown up at Jacob's office. Not once. But here she was, standing in front of his desk after storming in, eyes wild, chest heaving, looking as though she was about to explode. What a relief that he'd put the bag from Tiffany's in his desk drawer. From the look on Anna's face, this was not the time to propose marriage.

"I'm going to have to call you back," he said into the phone, not waiting for a response before he hung up.

"Please tell me it's not true," she blurted, a distinct tone of panic in her voice.

Oh, no. His stomach sank as if he'd just swallowed an anvil. "Tell you what's not true?"

"You and your investment group, Jacob. Please tell me it's not true. Please tell me that Adam got some bad information. Because right now I feel like I'm going to be sick."

He closed his eyes and took a deep breath. His worst nightmare had just come true, but he couldn't lie to her. He'd already endured the guilt of not coming out with it in the first place, or even better, not starting the endeavor at all. "Please let me explain."

All color drained from her face. "Oh, my God. It *is* true." Her voice was fragile and delicate, as if she'd just been broken in half. It killed him to hear her sound like that and he was responsible. "I can't even believe this. Did you sleep with me just so you could get information about LangTel? Because Adam thinks you did. Has this whole thing been a big lie?"

"No. Of course not. How could you think that?" He stepped out from behind his desk, but she shunned him with a quick turn of her shoulder. The physical pain of her rejection resonated deep in his body, but he couldn't deny that he had it coming. "Adam knows about us?"

"Yes, Jacob. I went to him this morning to tell him. Do you know why?"

He shook his head. He couldn't imagine what had finally prompted her to share the thing they'd been hiding all this time.

"Because I hated the sneaking around. I wanted to give us a chance, a real chance. And now I find out that you were trying to destroy my family's company all along." The pain of the betrayal was clear as day on her face. She was shaking like a leaf.

He wanted to pull her into his snug embrace and make everything okay, fix the massive problem he'd created, except he couldn't. It wouldn't help anything. He'd messed up, in tragic fashion. "Will you please sit down so I can explain everything?"

"What could you possibly say that's going to make me feel any better?"

Again, she was right. "Look. I know now that I shouldn't have started this, but the reality is that I never in a million years imagined that you and I would become involved the way we have. That came completely out of left field."

"And it would've been so awkward to roll over in bed and whisper in my ear that you were trying to take over the company my dad built from nothing. That definitely would've put a damper on the sex, huh?"

Every word out of her mouth drove the knife in his heart a little deeper, but he didn't dare flinch. He deserved it all. "I went on the counteroffensive the morning after we first made love. That's what I was doing out in the garage before we left. I called my closest friend in the group to try to convince them to back off."

"So what happened? Why are you guys still trying to do this?"

"*We* aren't trying to do anything. They ousted me. Yesterday. They were tired of me pushing so hard to end the LangTel takeover."

"Does that mean you have no more pull with them? They're really just going to go ahead and do it without you?" She sighed and stared out the window. "This is getting worse by the minute."

"They say they're going to. I don't really have a way of knowing. Believe me, I've been racking my brain, trying to come up with a way to stop them."

Her jaw tensed. She shook her head. "What was the plan, Jacob? Tell me the plan you had before I came along. If you want any chance of redeeming yourself in any way to me, tell me the plan."

"We planned to get enough stock to take over the board of directors and oust Adam as CEO."

"Oust Adam or oust the CEO?"

"Is there a difference?"

"In six months, there will be."

He almost wanted to laugh at his own short-sightedness. Of course. The board of directors was probably already trying to oust Adam. He hadn't thought about that. "Do they already have a successor picked?"

"You're looking at her."

It was as if all air in the room stopped moving. *Anna? CEO?* What had he done? "You?"

"Yes. Me. My dad gave his blessing before he died, but they had to put Adam in place first because that had always been the plan. I'm supposed to be the next

LangTel CEO. It's my dream job. Not that it's going to happen now."

No. Good God, no. He'd set a plan in motion to take away the dream job of the woman he loved. "Please let me try to find a way to fix this."

"You just said you've been trying to fix it for over a month. How are you going to magically make it happen now? And how am I supposed to trust you? We've been involved for weeks now, and the whole time you knew there were plans to dismantle my family's company. The company my dad spent decades building. You were best friends with my brother, Jacob. You stayed at our house. And now you want to destroy us?"

"I never wanted to destroy *you*. Never."

"Yeah, well, whether it was your intention or not, that's exactly what you're doing. You're destroying me and I can't sit around and watch it happen. Which is exactly why I never want to see you again. Ever." Her lip quivered. Was it because she was so angry? Or did it kill her to say those words as much as it killed him to hear them?

"I love you, Anna. I love you more than I ever thought it was possible to love someone. Please don't do this. I need you."

A single tear leaked from the corner of her eye. "You love me? Why do you decide to tell me that now? When you have to save your own hide? Why couldn't you tell me last night when I was making you dinner for your birthday or singing you a song or…" Her eyes clamped shut. "Or when I was telling you that stupid story about the ridiculous letters. Do you have any idea how betrayed I feel right now?"

Again he was overwhelmed by his need to touch her,

but everything in her body language said she would absolutely kill him if he took another step closer. "You have the right to feel all of this. I made a huge mistake and I'm so sorry. I just want the chance to make it better."

"I'm sorry, Jacob. I can't give you another chance at anything. Ever."

"But what about my feelings for you? Does that mean nothing?"

She stood a little straighter and looked him square in the eye. "Actually, it would have meant everything to me if you hadn't betrayed me. Because I love you too and now I have to figure out a way to fall out of love with you."

She loves me. The full repercussions of his one vengeful act came at him with full force. He was about to lose the one thing, the one person, he truly cared about—Anna. "Then don't do it. Give me the chance to make it right."

"I can't. You took my love and threw it away. And that means we're done."

Twelve

Optimism. Anna would've done nearly anything to cultivate a single optimistic thought as she stalked through the LangTel halls to her office. The satisfaction she'd once felt about working here was gone. LangTel was officially embroiled in a battle for survival, against a threat that was impossible to defeat because there was no real way to build a stronghold. No one knew who the mysterious big investor was, and as much digging as Adam and Anna did, they came up with virtually nothing.

The fact that Anna had slept with the enemy only made her life more miserable. Luckily, Adam had remained discreet about that fact, but it had made Thanksgiving especially tense. She prayed he wouldn't say something about it to their mother. It was bad enough that Evelyn Langford had to know about the threat of takeover—LangTel was the bulk of her sizable nest egg, after all.

For the moment, Anna's days were spent jumping through hoops for the board of directors, which had gotten her exactly nowhere, as they were likewise all consumed with the threat of a takeover. It all added up to one thing—her dream job felt more out of reach than ever.

And then there was her personal life, which in many ways felt more like her personal death. Having gone from the high of being with Jacob to the low of discovering what he'd been doing behind her back the entire time they were together had been far worse than jarring. It felt as if she'd been pushed off a cliff with no warning and most certainly nowhere soft to land.

Anna's assistant, Carrie, filed into her office with a cup of coffee. "Is there anything else I can get you this morning, Ms. Langford?"

"No, thank you." Anna settled in at her desk for the ten minutes of her day she actually looked forward to— reading the newspaper. At this point, she clung to the little things that made her happy. There weren't many.

"Oh, before I forget, Ms. Louis was looking for you this morning."

Anna glanced at her watch. "Can you buzz her and let her know that now is a good time?"

"Certainly." Carrie closed the door quietly behind her.

Anna unfolded the business section and was immediately sickened by the headline beneath the fold. Sunny Side had sold. To a rival telecom, no less.

She quickly scanned the article, her heart pounding, half out of shock and the other half out of anger. Somewhere in there was sadness, but she hadn't given in to that yet. It said that the sale was orchestrated by Jacob. So much for the big delay on their patent application. Was that another of his lies? Carefully crafted to lure her in? To what end, she did not know—seek revenge on Adam, get inside information on LangTel. Jacob had everything to gain and she'd had everything to lose. She simply hadn't known it because she'd trusted him— with business, with her heart and her body. *Bastard.* Just when he couldn't have possibly betrayed her in any worse a fashion, he had to go and twist the knife in her back. First he'd tried to destroy her family, then he yanked away her most promising business deal.

So that was it. Jacob really had moved on, in every way imaginable. The thought made tears sting her eyes, but she had to face the truth. There hadn't been so much as a peep from Jacob since they'd broken up. Not a single word. She'd spent nights wide awake, wondering why it had all gone so wrong. Why was the perfect guy also the one who most hated her family? Why was he the man who had so easily betrayed her? It felt like some cruel joke, a tragic twist of fate.

And Jacob? He apparently wasn't quite so torn up by what had happened, moving ahead with the Sunny Side deal. Nope. He'd gone right back to work, making his millions. Perfect.

Her eyes drifted to the picture accompanying the headline. Jacob had that smile on his face, the one he wasn't quick to share, the one you had to coax out of him because he played everything so close to the vest. She missed that smile so much that it made her ache. And it was a longing for more than just him, it was a longing for the way she'd been with him—happy. It was also a longing for the possibilities of "us." Between her dad's illness, death and the company's troubles, the future had seemed bleak and uncertain for over a year.

The notion of "us" had lifted her out of that state, but it hadn't lasted long.

Holly rapped on her office door. "Carrie said you have a minute."

Anna shuffled the newspaper aside and collected herself. "Yes. Of course. What's up?"

"I wanted to ask if you can sit in on my meeting tomorrow morning. Everybody seems to react more favorably to bad news when you're in the room, and there's a lot of bad news." Holly sidled in and plopped a muffin down on Anna's desk. "Here. I brought you some breakfast so you can't say no."

"Is that blueberry?" Anna scrunched her nose. The aroma had overtaken her office with an artificial, off-putting smell.

"Yes. Isn't it your favorite?"

Anna shook her head. "Usually. I guess I'm not very hungry this morning. Thank you, though. I appreciate it."

"Let me get this out of your way then." Holly reached for the offending pastry and marched it out of Anna's office. She returned seconds later. "Are you feeling okay today? You look a bit pale."

Anna hadn't been feeling well at all—tired and blah. Probably a bug of some sort. December was right about time for the first cold of the season. "I'm okay. Just a little run-down."

"Yeah, I hear that. I have the worst PMS right now."

PMS. A thought flashed through Anna's mind—when was the last time she'd had her period? Miami? That was two months ago. "I know how that goes."

"So you're in on this meeting? Please say yes." Holly smiled and batted her lashes.

"Sure thing," Anna agreed, now distracted by the new direction in which her malaise seemed to be pointing.

Holly left and Anna immediately pulled up the period tracker app on her phone. The notification was right in front of her seconds later. Forty-two days late.

"I'm never late," she muttered to herself, her brain slowly catching up. She pinched the bridge of her nose. *No. There's no way.*

She shook her head and dismissed it as silly. She couldn't be that. She couldn't be pregnant. It had to be stress. She hadn't just been under a lot of it, she'd been buried in it. Sucking in a deep breath, she ushered foolish thoughts out of her head and got to work.

A half hour later, her stomach rumbled and growled. The muffin might have been disgusting smelling, but she probably should've eaten it. She rolled her chair over to the office credenza where Carrie had stashed some snacks. A protein bar seemed like a good idea, but the moment she tore open the package and got a whiff of chocolate and peanut butter, her stomach lurched again.

It has to be the stomach flu. I should go home.

She packed up her laptop, put on her coat, and stepped out of her office. "You know, Carrie, I think I'm coming down with something. I'm going to work from home for the rest of the day, but it'd be great if you could run interference for me, at least a little. Just tell people to send me an email if they need me."

"And Mr. Langford? What do you want me to tell him if he asks?" Carrie cringed. Adam had bitten her head off last week. It was hard to blame him at this point.

"You're welcome to tell him I'm sick." No use sugarcoating it.

One of the company drivers took Anna back to her

apartment, but she asked him to stop by the pharmacy on the way there. She dashed in, grabbed some pain reliever and seltzer. The line at the register was long, which only gave her more time to think about the improbable. Was she? The doctor had told her it was a virtual impossibility. Virtual. That didn't mean an absolute zero.

She turned back for a pregnancy test, admonishing herself for giving in to these ridiculous thoughts. As if she could be pregnant by her brother's biggest enemy, the man who'd started the war on her family's corporation. The entire idea was ludicrous.

When she got home, she whipped off her coat. Sitting in the car thinking about it had only made her that much more eager to put the idea to rest so she could curl up on the couch, turn on an old movie and slip into a vegetative state.

The instructions seemed simple enough—pee on the stick and wait. She did exactly that, studying the clock on her phone until the five minutes were up. Time to check.

Two blue lines.

She scrambled for the instructions, taking several moments before it sank in that she was reading the Spanish directions. She ruffled the paper to the other side. "Two blue lines, two blue lines," she mumbled, scanning the page. Two blue lines. Pregnant.

Oh, no no no.

The room felt like it was spinning, while her head traveled in the opposite direction and twice as fast. Pregnant? *I can't be.* She stared at the lines, but they only darkened the longer she looked at them, as if they were defying her to question the results. She consulted the directions again. *A false negative is far more likely than a false positive.*

What do I do? Who do I tell? Definitely not her mother. Her mother would freak out, and Anna was ready to freak out enough for a dozen people. She couldn't call Melanie. She loved Melanie, but she would blab to Adam and that would be bad. Very, very bad. The only answer was Holly. Holly was her biggest ally at LangTel, and if she were being honest, the only female she ever did anything fun with, like going out for drinks.

Holly's phone seemed to ring for an eternity. "Anna? You're calling me from your cell? Why didn't you just walk down to my office?"

"I'm at home. Can you talk without anyone hearing?"

"Two secs. Let me close my office door." There was a rustle on the other end of the line. "Okay, talk. Wait. Did you hear from you-know-who?"

"No." Anna rubbed her head. Good thing she'd bought that pain reliever. "I'm pregnant." No reply came from the other end of the line. "Holly? Are you there?"

"I just saw you two hours ago. What in the heck happened after I threw away the blueberry muffin?"

"It wasn't until you said that thing about PMS that I realized I'd completely skipped my period. So I came home and took a pregnancy test."

"Why didn't you tell me? I could've come with you."

"Because I was sure it was a stupid idea, that's why." It was worse than stupid. If she hadn't done it, she could've been going about her normal miserable day. Now she had to go about her pregnant miserable day.

"Do you know who the father is?"

"You can't be serious."

"You weren't together for much more than six weeks. How many times could you possibly have had sex?"

Anna nearly snorted at the question. *You have no*

idea. She and Jacob had been like rabbits. There was no escaping their physical attraction. It had a life force all its own. It had been made even more carefree by the knowledge that she couldn't get pregnant. Or so she thought. "Let's just say that he has a very short recovery time."

"No wonder you were so bummed out to break up with him."

Anna sighed. She had indeed been sad to break up with him, although sex wasn't the reason. She'd fallen in love with the big jerk. "He's probably going to be the reason LangTel will go down the tubes. I couldn't exactly look beyond that." She could never forgive him for that. He not only knew *exactly* what her family meant to her, he'd known it all along.

"No, I suppose not."

"So what do I do?" Anna hadn't even thought beyond this phone call. Making plans was not in her skill set at the moment.

"You have to tell Jacob."

"What am I supposed to do? Just waltz into his office and announce that I'm sorry that the last time I was there I had to tell him what a bastard he is, and by the way, I'm pregnant with your baby?"

"Think of it this way. It'll be ten times more awkward when you run into him on the street a year from now and have to explain where you got your little Asian baby."

A year from now. She might as well have been talking about the abominable snowman. Nothing seemed real anymore, especially not the future. Perhaps that was because she'd grown immune to all of it. Holly had a point, too. There would eventually be a baby to explain, to everyone. There'd be a baby bump before that. "I have to tell my family, too, don't I?"

"At some point, yes. Nothing makes Christmas morning more uncomfortable than a baby nobody knew about."

Anna laughed quietly. At last she had Holly around to lighten the mood. "You know what's ridiculous about this situation? I should be happy right now. I should be jumping up and down in the streets. I really want to have a baby. You know, I went to a fertility doctor about it after my dad passed away."

"Oh, honey. You did?"

"That's when they told me that I had so much scar tissue from my appendectomy that it was impossible to conceive until I had it fixed. I never had a chance to have the surgery."

"This is a miracle baby, Anna. I'm not exactly the sentimental type, but think about that. That's pretty special. Maybe this was meant to be. For whatever reason, the universe decided that you need this baby."

Tears sprouted in her eyes, just right out of nowhere. A miracle baby. "I don't know what to think anymore, honestly, but maybe there is a reason this happened."

"So when are you going to tell Jacob?"

"Can't I wait until after I go to the doctor? Maybe wait until the end of the first trimester just in case something goes wrong? The doctor had said the scar tissue could make carrying a pregnancy difficult."

"You have to tell Jacob, honey. No two ways about that. He deserves to know and he deserves to know now. Every bad thing he did in the past doesn't change the fact that you and he made a child."

Thirteen

Jacob was drowning in the dead quiet of his apartment, but he didn't have the energy to go into the office. Life without Anna wasn't getting any easier. If anything, it was getting harder.

He sat back in his office chair, rubbing at his stiff neck, feeling sore and achy. He'd been working out too much, not sleeping at all, and eating too little. Self-inflicted discomfort seemed only fitting considering the damage he'd done.

It'd been two weeks now, and each day felt as if it stretched on for eternity, a never-ending dirge of meetings and deals and money. He'd once lived on the adrenaline of it. Now it all felt empty. Every night before he went to bed, he looked at the engagement ring he'd bought for Anna. All of his pain, both physical and emotional, served as a reminder of what he was still holding out hope for—that he would stop the LangTel takeover and win her back.

Jacob's phone vibrated on his desk. Did he even bother to look? Just another person wanting something from him, most likely, but he had to force himself to check. When he did, he stared at his phone in utter astonishment. *Anna.*

His heart did a double take, jerking into high gear. Why was she calling? Was it because of the Sunny Side deal? He didn't want to pin his hopes on anything, but he really hoped she was calling for some other, more personal reason. "Hey," he said, fumbling with the phone. Was that really the best he could come up with? He sounded like a teenaged boy.

"Hey," she replied. Her voice was sweet, but distressed, echoing in his mind throughout the most awkward silence Jacob had ever endured.

"How are you?" he asked, deciding the course of polite conversation was the only one to take at this time. He wasn't about to be defensive with her. Everything bad and ugly had already been said.

"I've been better. I need to talk to you and we probably shouldn't do it over the phone. In fact, I know we shouldn't."

"Okay. Do you want to give me a hint?" Honestly, even if she wanted to come over and yell at him some more, he would've agreed. He would've served refreshments. Anything to see her. Even if it would be painful. He was already hurting more than he could've ever imagined.

"Jacob, I just need to talk to you, okay? I can't bring myself to say it over the phone."

His heart went back to acting as if it didn't know what

sort of speed was advised. Had she decided she could forgive him? Could he really be that lucky? And how long would it last if he was? There was still one indisputable fact—somewhere in the world, a very big shark was circling LangTel, and Jacob had dumped the blood into the water. If she lost her dream job because of him, there would be no coming back from that. "Yes. Of course. I'll come to you. Are you at the office?"

"Home."

He frowned. Anna never missed work. Ever. Had she left her job? Another big blow-up with Adam? Neither of those things made sense. She'd made it clear this was between them. Maybe she really was ready to reconcile. Maybe she felt as he did, that the other things between them, although messy, didn't usurp feelings. "I'm leaving right now."

The entire car ride was a lesson in patience, his curiosity killing him and his hopes refusing to be tempered, however much he wanted them to go away. He couldn't help it. He hoped she'd reconsidered.

Anna had left word with the doorman and Jacob took the elevator up to her floor, walking double-time down the hall to her apartment.

"Hi," she said when she opened the door.

The vision of Anna hit him the way an avalanche throws a mountain of snow down to the foothills. Her cheeks were blanched and her eyes pink and puffy. She'd been crying. Whatever this was, it was bad. He filed in to her kitchen, immediately plunged back into the familiar comfort of being with Anna, the one that made him feel as though he never wanted to be anywhere else, even when she was standing before him with her arms crossed, leaving a barrier between them.

"I don't want to make this any more of a big deal than it already is," she said, sniffling. "I'm pregnant and you're the only person who can be the father."

"Pregnant?" He remained calm on the outside, but his mind raced so fast he didn't know which way was up. His brain was a jumble of contradictory thoughts. A baby?

"Yes, Jacob. Pregnant."

Was this some sort of trick? "But I thought you couldn't get pregnant."

"I thought the same thing. The doctor had said it was virtually impossible for me to conceive."

"Virtually? So not completely impossible? Because you told me it was flat-out impossible."

"Virtually, completely. Does it really make that big of a difference?" She rolled her eyes. "Maybe you have superhero sperm. I don't know. Don't assume this is my fault. And remember, we were both there. It's not like I went and did this on my own."

Superhero sperm. His male ego wasn't about to argue that point. He started to say something else, to continue the argument, but one thing that had made him success-ful in business was his ability to accept facts and deal with problems, rather than burying his head in the sand. A pregnancy—a baby. That was a fact.

He'd told himself he would never have children. Not after the way his parents raised him—moving him from boarding school to boarding school, depending on his father's opinion of whether or not Jacob was being chal-lenged enough with his studies. His dad pushed and pushed. There was no other speed and there was no nur-turing any skills beyond academic, except for maybe the years he'd been forced to play classical piano when what he'd really wanted to learn was how to play guitar.

Was it even in his DNA to be loving and caring the way a dad should be? His father had given him a mind for business and that was about it. Such was the legacy of Henry Lin—mold your child in your image and tell him hundreds of times that you expect him to stay that way. Jacob had done it for the most part. After all, he was exceptional at doing exactly what his father did—making money. He had homes and cars and bank accounts to prove it. He merely didn't want to repeat his father's mistake, which had been becoming a dad in the first place.

"Jacob? Are you even listening to me? Are you going to say something?" Anna asked.

He shook his head and ran his hand through his hair. "I'm sorry. It's just that I'd never thought I would ever become a dad. This is just a lot to deal with at one time."

Anna's jaw dropped. "This is a lot for *you* to deal with? Why don't you ask the person who had to pee on a plastic stick how she's feeling about all of this?" She wrapped her sweater around her tightly. "I should've known better than to think that you would even care about this. You care about money and your pride and your stupid motorcycles and that's about it. Obviously the man who decided it was perfectly fine to destroy my family wouldn't care at all about the fact that he was going to be a dad. Goodbye, Jacob. Have a nice life. Don't make me call the doorman and tell him to come up here." She whipped around and rushed out of the room.

He chased her down the hall, grabbing her arm just outside her bedroom door. "Anna, stop."

She turned, not making eye contact, her chest heaving. "Just let me go, Jacob. Just let me go."

Her words, broken and desperate, gnawed at his heart.

How could he let her go? He didn't want to. He'd spent the last several weeks missing her, desperately. "I'm sorry. Truly." The words about to roll off his tongue next, the ones about wanting to embrace her, wanting closeness with her just wouldn't come out. His feelings about Anna hadn't changed since the breakup, but being near her was a powerful reminder of how badly losing her had hurt in the first place. "Tell me what I can do."

She sucked in a deep breath. "I don't need you to do anything, okay? I'm a grown woman and I can handle this on my own. Obviously this is more than you're equipped to deal with, so don't worry about it. I'll have plenty of support from my family. The baby and I will be fine."

A vision materialized—Anna and a baby. *The* baby. *Their* baby. Could he go on with his everyday life knowing they were out there doing the same without him? And what kind of man would that make him? Not only no better than his father, he would be far worse. "No, Anna. You're not going to handle this on your own. I will help you with whatever you and the baby need."

"I don't want you to do this out of some sense of obligation. That's not what I want."

"Well, of course that's part of it. How can it not be? This is just as much my responsibility as it is yours. Just because you're carrying the child doesn't mean that I don't need to share the burden equally."

"Burden? Is that how you see this? Because if you're going to use words like that, I can't even have you around. I need support. My entire life has fallen apart in the last year. I lost my dad, I've probably lost my dream job, and don't forget that my family's corporation is in serious danger of being dismantled, in large part, thanks to you. How is this even going to work, Jacob? How will we ever find a happy medium when my family hates you and you hate them right back?"

When she had the nerve to be so blatant with their circumstances, it certainly did seem as though they were screwed. The weeks apart of wanting her back hadn't changed any of it. "I don't hate your family, Anna. Your brother and your family are not the same thing. I can see that much. I had very strong feelings for you. Much stronger than I ever anticipated. I told you I was in love with you and I meant it. That didn't go away."

"But it did go away. You lied to me."

"I kept the truth from you. To protect you. I couldn't put you in the middle of the mess I'd made. I don't know why you can't see that."

"I don't want to argue semantics. I'm just telling you how I feel. That hasn't changed."

"Okay. Fine. I get it. Regardless, I'm not going to walk away from you and this baby." Had he really just said that? A baby. It was far too surreal. "I'm all-in."

"You do realize this isn't a card game. We're not placing bets."

"Of course I know that. I'm not an idiot."

"And I need to know that you're sure. This is an all-or-nothing proposition. You don't get to change your mind later."

"I'm not going to change my mind."

"We don't even know what's going to happen. The doctor didn't just tell me that I couldn't conceive, he told me it would be nearly impossible for me to carry a pregnancy to term."

How much more harsh reality could there be between them? Not much. "I understand. It doesn't change the

fact that I'm half of this and that means I will partici-
pate and be there for whatever you need."

She sighed deeply and rewrapped her sweater around
her waist, binding it to her body tightly. It was hard to
believe there was a tiny person growing inside her—one
half her, one half him.

"Just so we're clear, this does not mean we're back
together," she said resolutely. "We'll have to work out
the specifics when the time comes, but this partnership
is about having a baby and that's it."

He fought the exasperated breath that wanted to leak
out of him. He deserved this, the universe's way of reminding him that every action brought a reaction. He'd
done the wrong thing, and atoning for that apparently
came in the form of partnering with the woman he loved
while under direct orders that there would be no reconciliation. "Clearly, you're calling the shots here."

She looked down at the floor, and when her eyes returned to his, he could see exactly how scared she was.
It brought back, with a vengeance, the all-too-familiar
ache for her. "Well, if you want to be involved, you can
start by coming with me to my first doctor's appointment. Thursday. Ten a.m."

Jacob had a huge meeting scheduled that morning—
a deal he'd been working on for months. "Of course. I'll
be there."

Fourteen

Hospitals. One step inside and Anna was reminded of her dad—the months he spent fighting, in and out of the cancer ward, receiving treatments that they'd pinned so much hope on, only to ultimately lose. She wasn't sure she could deal with another loss like that, and she was already so attached to the idea of the baby.

"We're going up to the sixth floor." Anna pointed to the bank of elevator doors straight ahead. When the doctors realized who Anna was and the serious straits she was in from the beginning, they'd moved her first prenatal appointment to the specialist's office at the hospital. They wanted her to see a physician well-acquainted with high-risk pregnancies. Having that extra care was a comfort, but she really wished she didn't need it at all.

Jacob held the elevator door for her, being as gentlemanly as could be. She shoved her hands into her coat pockets. How she would've loved to be able to take his hand, squeeze it, have a true partner in all of this. But she didn't. He was the obligated dad. It had taken the pregnancy announcement to bring him back into her life. She hadn't heard a word from him after they broke up. Of the many things she had to get past, that now felt like the most difficult.

They reached their floor and stepped out into a quiet hall. There were several clinics along the corridor, theirs a few doors down. A woman at the reception desk welcomed them and had them take a seat.

A man across from them opened a breakfast sandwich of some sort, even when there was a very clear sign inches from his head saying there was no food or drink allowed. Anna loved eggs and bacon, but this morning the smell made her want to hide her head in a trash basket. Why wasn't the receptionist doing something about it? She was just sitting there, shuffling paper.

Anna turned into Jacob's arm, pressing her cheek and nose to the black wool of his coat, closing her eyes and drawing in one of the few scents she found appealing— woodsy and warm and surprisingly calming.

"You okay?" he asked, lowering his head to hers. When she looked up, their noses were inches apart.

She was caught in the fierce intensity of his dark eyes, which left her lips quivering. She would've done anything to be where they were weeks ago. Why did she have to have such strong feelings for him? Things would be so much easier if she didn't still want him. "It's the smell of his sandwich," she whispered.

Jacob stood and took Anna's hand, urging her to join him. "Come on." He marched over to the receptionist's desk. "Yes, excuse me. My wife is feeling a little queasy.

I think she would feel more comfortable if we could be alone back in the examination room, if that's all right."

"Your wife?" Anna mumbled under her breath.

"The nurse will be out any moment now. It won't be much longer," the woman said.

"It's okay," Anna whispered. "You don't need to make a fuss."

"She's uncomfortable. You need to help me fix that." He cleared his throat.

The receptionist glared at him. "As I said, sir. One more moment."

He grasped Anna's hand. "I understand, but it's literally killing me to watch my pregnant wife suffer. So if you could please find us a place to get settled, that would be wonderful."

"Fine, Mr., uh…" She reached for a folder. "Mr. Langford."

Anna prepared for him to explode, but Jacob took it in stride.

"I'm Mr. Lin. She's Ms. Langford."

"Oh, yes. Of course." She picked up the phone. "Two seconds."

A nurse quickly emerged from the door next to reception and brought them back to a private room. "The doctor will want to speak to you and then do the pelvic exam. You can change into the gown after I take your vital signs." She took Anna's blood pressure and temperature, as well as her weight, then left them alone.

"You really didn't have to make a fuss about it, and I appreciate it, but please don't call me your wife," Anna said. There were enough gray areas. They didn't need more.

"Would you have preferred I identify you as the woman

I impregnated? And don't forget it's my job to take care of you." Jacob unbuttoned his coat and put it on the hook, then took hers from her.

"It's your job to help me with the baby, when and if the time arrives."

"You are the vessel carrying the baby, and I don't like seeing you suffer, anyway. It's physically painful for me."

Remarks like that made her wonder if she'd made a mistake by telling him. The baby was not supposed to be a way back in for him, at least not into her heart. She had to protect herself from him as much as she could, however much they were already tied for a lifetime now. Even if the baby never arrived, it would be impossible to escape the fact that they had once shared this. And it would make it unthinkable to ever forget him.

She caught sight of the examination gown. "I need to change. So you need to step out into the hall."

"Anna. I've seen every inch of you. I could probably tell the doctor a few things. Don't worry. I won't stare." He sat down, pulling his phone out of his pocket, quickly reading something, and turning it facedown on his leg. "Too much."

"Uh, no. Close your eyes right now."

"Why?"

"Because I said so."

"Fine." He twisted his lips and did as he was asked.

She shucked her clothes and put on the gown in record time, then climbed up on to the exam table, covering her bare legs with the paper drape they had provided. "You can open your eyes now."

He crossed his legs and gave her a look that was far too familiar. "Next time, I'm looking."

"Next time you're standing in the hall. And you'd better be on the other side of the room during the exam."

A knock came at the door and a trim woman with long, curly red hair entered the room wearing a white lab coat. "Ms. Langford." She shook Anna's hand. "I'm Dr. Wright. It's nice to meet you." She turned to Jacob. "I take it this is Dad."

Jacob cleared his throat, seeming uncomfortable. "Jacob. Lin."

Dr. Wright wheeled over a rolling stool and scanned Anna's chart, nodding and humming. Lord only knew what she was thinking. She didn't show a reaction of any kind. Was that a good thing? A bad thing? After a few minutes, she closed the folder and stood. "All right, Ms. Langford. Let's have a look at you."

Anna lay back as the doctor took out the stirrups. Luckily, Jacob was following orders and had retreated to the far corner of the room. In all actuality, he'd created as much distance between them as possible. This was likely not a comfortable scenario for him, and she did have to admire him for not complaining or excusing himself.

Dr. Wright completed the exam and helped Anna to sit up. "Well, I'll be honest with you both. This is a tricky situation you've gotten yourselves into. I've seen the ultrasound images from your appointment with the fertility doctor. As to how you two got pregnant, I'm mystified. You must've been trying very hard."

Anna's face flushed with heat. Jacob snickered.

"Now, our hope is that this is a big, strong baby like Dad and that as he or she grows, the scar tissue has no choice but to give way. The worst case is that the baby gets stuck in a bad spot and the umbilical cord is squeezed or the baby simply can't grow."

Anna sat frozen. Dr. Wright dealt with dire situations every day, so it all came out of her mouth as if it wasn't a big deal. For Anna, this was a very big deal, and she was trying so hard to keep it together.

"Either way," Dr. Wright continued, "we'll have to watch you very, very carefully. You're most likely to lose the pregnancy early on. I'm guessing from your chart that you're almost eight weeks along, which is great. I need you to watch for spotting. Call us right away if that happens."

Anna sucked in a deep breath. "Okay."

Jacob stepped closer. "Dr. Wright, I'd like to know how many cases you've handled like Anna's and what the outcomes were. I want to make sure that Anna and the baby have the best of the best."

The doctor looked down her nose at Jacob. "I don't know the exact numbers, Mr. Lin. I assure you that I've handled many cases like yours, and I know what I'm doing. If you'd like to seek a second opinion, my nurse can provide you with some referrals."

Embarrassment flooded Anna. How could he do this? "No. Jacob, Dr. Wright has exceptional credentials."

"And I'd be a bad dad if I didn't ask about them."

"If you have concerns, Mr. Lin, you and I can talk about them some other time." Dr. Wright's voice was calm—almost soothing, but there was no mistaking the firm hand she was using with him. "We don't want Anna upset or experiencing any undue stress. It's not good for her or the baby."

"Oh. Okay." He nodded. "Good to know. No stress."

"That's probably the most important thing you can

do, Anna. Avoid it at any cost. Jacob, you need to buffer her from it as much as possible. Sex can help, since it's such a good stress reliever."

Jacob coughed. "Did you hear that, honey?" he asked, wagging his eyebrows at her.

Anna pursed her lips. First he'd pulled the wife thing in the waiting room. Now this. "Is that really safe for the baby?"

"Actually, yes. The baby's so small right now." The doctor pulled a funny-looking instrument, like a tiny microphone, from a drawer near the exam room sink. "Let's see if we can find the baby's heartbeat."

Anna had read about hearing the heartbeat with the fetal Doppler monitor. The notion both thrilled and terrified her.

"Just lie back," Dr. Wright said, lifting up Anna's exam gown to reveal her bare belly. She squirted some liquid on to her skin. "Just a bit of gel. It'll help pick up the sound."

A crackling sound like an old transistor radio broke out in the room. Jacob inched closer to Anna, bewildered. "We'll actually hear the baby's heartbeat?"

The doctor nodded, moving the instrument over Anna's stomach. "The heart forms and starts beating from a very early stage."

More static came from the small speaker the doctor held in her hand. Pops. Snaps. A rapid, watery sound rang out—likes waves at the beach on fast-forward. *Whoosh whoosh whoosh.* A smile spread across Dr. Wright's face. She nodded, consulting the instrument. "There's your baby."

Jacob held his breath. *Whoosh whoosh whoosh.* He'd never been so overtaken by shock and wonder, both at the same time. The miracle of the moment began to sink in, but it wasn't a weight. Not as he'd worried it might be. The baby was not an idea or an abstract—the life that he and Anna had created, against all odds, was real. A tiny human, with a heart and everything. *Whoosh whoosh whoosh.* He'd never been so affected by a sound. That sound and the life force that created it needed him. Anna needed him. And he would not let either of them down.

Anna looked up at him, her eyes wide with astonishment. "Our baby," she muttered.

"It's absolutely incredible," he said, taking and gently squeezing her hand. Maybe it was the wrong thing to do, but he was acting on pure instinct. She didn't protest, which felt like such a gift. "It's so fast."

"It's a tiny heart, Mr. Lin. It doesn't know any other speed."

"And what does the baby look like right now? When can we see it?" *It?* That didn't sound right at all. "I mean him."

"Or her…" Anna added, smiling. It was the first truly light moment of the appointment or for that matter, since she'd told him she was pregnant. He was so grateful for it. Finally, some good news.

"Or her," Jacob agreed. "When can we see him or her?" He was no longer surprised by the excitement in his voice. It was impossible not to get caught up in the moment.

"We'll schedule an ultrasound for next week. I'd like to do some 3D imaging. For now, the baby looks like a peanut with a big forehead."

"Hmmm," Jacob said. Had his dad been this involved when his mother was pregnant with him? Had he gone to a single doctor's appointment? Jacob doubted it greatly.

It was too bad—he'd missed out on so much. Jacob wouldn't have traded this experience for anything. It was only made better by the fact that he was with Anna. Now if he could only convince her to stop tabling romance and let him back into her heart.

The doctor put away the monitor and wiped off Anna's stomach.

"Where can I buy one of those?" Jacob asked. Being able to listen to the baby's heartbeat any time they wanted would be amazing. His mind drifted to thoughts of him and Anna in bed, listening to their baby's whoosh. Certainly their baby had an exceptional whoosh, far better than other babies' whooshes.

"There are inexpensive ones, but they don't work very well. The quality ones are in the neighborhood of six or seven hundred dollars."

"Oh yeah. We need one of those. Can your nurse order one for me?"

"That's a big expense for something you'll only use for another six months."

"And you think I really care about that," Jacob replied. "Because I don't."

Anna shook her head, grinning at him. "He doesn't care about that. At all."

Dr. Wright left after a reminder to watch for spotting, and a promise that they would all talk after the ultrasound. It was a scary, but exciting proposition, the thought of actually seeing the baby. He could only imagine how he would feel then. Everything that had just become so real would be even more so.

Walking down the hospital hall, riding on the elevator, through the lobby and back outside into the cold, gray December day, Jacob could hear that peculiar whooshing in his head. He and Anna and the baby were in the most precarious of situations, and he was determined to hold on to it with both hands. That wasn't at all the way he'd expected he would feel after today, but the heartbeat had changed everything.

Fifteen

"Are you doing okay over there?" Jacob asked as the limo sped along Lexington Avenue to Anna's apartment.

Anna wasn't okay. She wanted to be okay, but her mind kept dwelling on the medical issues. She looked out the window, entranced by the city passing her by, the people bustling along the sidewalks, in a rush that never ended. Had any of them received life-or-death news today? Probably. She wasn't so foolish to think she was the only person with problems.

"Anna." Jacob placed his hand on her shoulder. "Talk to me. It's okay if you're upset after the appointment. It was a lot to take in. I understand."

She closed her eyes for a moment, trying not to fix-ate on his touch, which called to her, even through her winter coat. Being with him brought back a lot of won-derful feelings, but something tempered it. Could she count on him? For real? She turned back to him, fighting the tears that welled at the corners of her eyes. "Do you, Jacob? Do you really get it? Because our baby is inside me and you said yourself that you'd never planned on becoming a dad."

He nodded eagerly. "And I feel like a fool for even thinking it. I'm telling you, the second we heard the baby's heartbeat, everything changed. I get it. I do."

She sat back in the seat, picking at a spot on the leg of her pants. It was hard to look him in the eye—he was so upbeat and eager right now, but was that just the rush of the appointment? Would it wear off? She didn't have the luxury of worrying whether he would be there for her and the baby. "It felt different then for me, too. Except in some ways, it just made me more scared. I'm going to be crushed if we lose this baby. Absolutely crushed. And every minute that goes by with this child growing inside of me, I'm going to change. I'm going to become more attached."

"Come here," he said, pulling her into his embrace. He rubbed her back as her head settled on his shoulder. "It's going to be okay. I promise."

Part of her wanted to be able to accept everything he'd said at face value, the way a child does when they're worried about monsters under the bed. He rubbed her back and anger bubbled inside her because she loved being like this with him. She wanted things back to the way they'd been before—before the world came crashing down, before he'd betrayed her, except this time, with the baby. Could she find a way to forgive him?

She wanted to let the bad things go, but one thing wouldn't stop nagging at her. If he had truly wanted her back after the breakup, why didn't he reach out?

Why didn't he fight for her? It had taken the pregnancy announcement to bring him back into her life, but that didn't mean he actually wanted to stay. What would happen if she lost the baby? Would he walk away? Would the issues that came along with being with her be more than he wanted to deal with? "Don't promise that everything will be okay. No amount of money or planning or crossing our fingers is going to make everything fine. We have to wait and see what happens and that's going to kill me. It's going to be so hard."

"You have excellent medical care. You're in the best possible hands."

"Thanks a lot for raking my doctor over the coals. What in the hell were you thinking?" She pushed away from him and shook her head.

"I want the best for you and for the baby. You can't fault me for that. Someone has to ask the hard questions."

"I didn't pick a random doctor off the internet, you know. I swear. Sometimes you and Adam are so alike it's ridiculous. Neither one of you trusts me to do what's right."

"That's not true. I trust you implicitly, and I'm sure your brother trusts you, too. He's just gone through a particularly misguided phase since your father passed away."

"It almost sounds like you're defending him. Are you?" She narrowed her stare. It was the first nonvenomous thing that had come out of his mouth regarding Adam. "Because that would be truly weird."

"I'm only pointing out that Adam is a smart guy. He'd have to be an idiot not to see how amazing you are."

She rolled her eyes. "Lay it on thick, much?"

"Anna, come on. I'm just being honest. Can't we be

honest with each other? After everything we've been through and with everything we're about to go through, I think it's only wise that we're truthful in everything."

Truthful? Was he really going to throw that at her now? "Ironic, coming from you."

He choked back the growl in his throat. "I was protecting you."

Protecting me. Really? "Tell yourself whatever you need to. That's not how it felt." The driver pulled up to the curb in front of Anna's building, then got out of the car to open her door. She couldn't even look back at Jacob to say goodbye. That would be too difficult when she was busy grappling with too many emotions. It would be so easy for him to look at her a certain way and she would be hopelessly drawn in, wanting to curl up into him and let him do exactly what he'd promised, the impossible—protect her. "I'll call you when they schedule the ultrasound."

Jacob was saddled with the most uneasy feeling he'd ever had. Anna and their baby were about to leave him. And she was upset. She shouldn't go upstairs and stew for hours. "Let me come in for a minute. We should talk."

"I'm tired of talking. And don't you need to get into the office?"

He was thankful he'd left his phone on vibrate. It'd been going crazy all through the appointment and during the car ride, but she didn't need to know that his business world might be falling apart while he was out of pocket. "You're more important right now."

She shook her head, seeming even more annoyed. "Fine."

They walked into the building and took the elevator upstairs. He liked feeling like this, almost as if they were a couple again, even if she was mad at him. What would it take for her to want him back? A lot of things, most likely—an absolute guarantee that LangTel was safe from a corporate takeover, a reconciliation with her brother.

"You really want to come in?" she asked once they arrived at her door. She had that icy tone in her voice, as if she were trying to freeze him out.

"I do." As they walked inside, he couldn't escape the feeling that this was only half right. He might be clueless about the notion of becoming a father, but he knew that they should be doing this together. If at all possible, this child should arrive with two loving parents, not a mother and a father fighting to remain civil. He didn't want to upset her, but perhaps it was time to just let her say her piece so they could finally more forward. "Anna, will you please tell me what I can do to make this better? Right now I feel like I'm stepping through a minefield."

She pursed her lips. "I'm supposed to stay calm."

"You're supposed to avoid stress, and walking around with all of this anger welling up inside of you is not good. Just let it out. Let me have it."

"Right here? Right now?"

"No time like the present." He took off his coat and slung it over the back of a chair in the living room. He was ready for her to start yelling and he would sit there and take it until she got it all out. "Like I said, let me have it. Tell me every last thing."

"I don't want to rehash our problems. It's not like you don't already know how I feel. What bothers me more than anything is what happened after I broke up with you."

He furrowed his brow. "The Sunny Side deal? Mark found a buyer he wanted to work with. I never meant for that to hurt you."

"It's not that. It's that I never heard from you. You didn't fight it, you just accepted it and moved on. You didn't fight for me. That hurt more than anything."

Good God, if only she knew how much he had *not* moved on after she ended their relationship. He wasn't sure he could even own up to that. He'd never been so miserable, a shell of a man. He didn't want to think of himself like that, the hopeless sap ruminating over his litany of mistakes, staring at the engagement ring he wasn't sure he'd ever have the chance to give her without her throwing it back in his face. "I did fight for you, it was just behind the scenes. I've been busting my hump to figure out who the secret LangTel investor is."

"See? That would have been good information to have, to at least know that you were trying."

"What kind of man would it make me if I came to you with half-filled promises? Trying and doing are two different things. After everything I did, you deserve better than that."

Anna sat down on the sofa, seeming deep in thought, but not saying a thing. Was he finally getting somewhere? He had to keep going.

"Anna, darling, I want you back. I think you know that. My feelings for you didn't go away when you said you were done with me. I still love you." He drew in a deep breath as he sensed his voice was about to break. Just thinking about today, about the baby, made his heart ache. "Now more than ever."

She raised her head slowly, her forehead creased with worry. "Because of the baby."

He took the seat beside her. "Some of it is, of course. There's no separating the two. But my love for you was there before you got pregnant, and it will be there tomorrow. It's not going anywhere. I'm not going anywhere."

"You're on a high right now from hearing the baby's heartbeat, from the excitement of what's new. How are you going to feel when we're forced to deal with my family? How are you going to feel if we lose the baby?"

Indeed, the road ahead was not getting any easier. He simply needed to know one thing. "Do you have feelings for me?"

She looked at him, scanning his face for what felt like a lifetime. "Part of me does. Part of me wants to punch you for what you did. It's hard for me to trust you. When I look back at our time together, all I can think about is everything you were keeping from me. That's hard to get past."

"Then maybe you need to try harder. I'll tell you I'm sorry until I'm blue in the face, but we had good times, too. Spectacular times. We had moments where I wasn't sure another person existed on the planet. Don't give up on our good memories. We can make more." He took her hand, relieved that she didn't fight the gesture. Body warmth traveled so easily between them—why couldn't everything else between them be so simple? Why couldn't things go back to the way they'd been at the beginning? So elemental. "I can't change the past. All I can do is try to build a future, but you hold the key. I can't do it without you."

She dropped her sights to their hands, joined. A tear fell onto her lap, darkening the fabric of her pants. "I need time to think. Today was a lot to deal with."

He nodded. Not that he had much choice, but he could

accept that. He'd make do with a sliver of a chance. "I'll wait, but let me know if there's anything I can do to speed up the process."

"Right now, more than anything, I just need to know that you're not only in my corner, but that you're going to stay there."

"I am Anna. I am."

"I mean it, Jacob. For real."

He sucked in a deep breath of resolve. "I do, too. And I'll find a way to show you. I won't let you down."

Jacob rode the elevator to the lobby, deep in thought. So much had changed in the past few weeks. From the miserable depths of losing Anna, he had new hope. He couldn't afford to doubt the future—she was the one questioning what tomorrow held. He hated seeing that from her. She was the optimist, the sunniest part of his life.

He had to show her that there was more for them. It was the only way back into her heart. That meant showing her that he wasn't going anywhere.

When the doors slid open to the lobby, he was so immersed in his thoughts that he nearly flattened a man rushing on to the elevator.

"Sorry," the man said, holding up a blue Tiffany shopping bag. "Forgot the wedding anniversary yesterday. I'm in a hurry to get out of the doghouse."

"No problem," Jacob answered, turning and watching the elevator doors slide closed. That flash of Tiffany blue was still there in his head.

If he wanted to show Anna that he wasn't going anywhere, he needed to make his overture. The question was when he would find the right moment.

Sixteen

Disbelief choked Jacob as he read the email the next morning—the missing piece of the puzzle, the information he'd been waiting on, sent by one of his informants. The identity of the high roller joining the War Chest was now known. Aiden Langford. And to think he'd woken up wondering when the right time would come to propose to Anna. That would need to be put off for at least another day.

He slumped back in the chair in his home office, sucking in a deep breath through his nose. His brain needed oxygen and fast. This was a huge problem and it had to be solved before it was too late. He knew that each Langford sibling owned 5 percent of the company. With that amount of stock in the mix, it would absolutely be feasible for Aiden to take down LangTel. And with everything Anna had once told him, Aiden had an axe to grind.

He wandered into his bedroom. Fixing the situation

with Aiden wasn't a one-person job, and he couldn't go to Anna for help. It would expose her to far too much stress. He had to protect her and the baby. That left one person, the person he'd vowed to never trust again, especially when it came to business. He had to go to Adam.

He hopped in the shower and dressed quickly. It was time to find Adam, pronto, and there was no time for second-guessing what the outcome might be. The sooner they devised a plan to get Aiden under wraps, the better. Luckily, Adam was notorious for getting into the office absurdly early. Jacob asked his driver to take him to Lang-Tel headquarters, sending Adam a text along the way.

We need to talk. Important. On my way to your office. Don't ask questions.

Adam's response came quickly. I'll tell security.

Jacob could only hope that Adam meant he was instructing security to let him *into* the building, not escort him out of it. He arrived at LangTel in ten minutes and rushed into the lobby. A guard was indeed waiting for him, but only to issue a security badge and instruct him on which elevator to take for the executive floors.

Jacob's head was grinding, mulling over options, devising plans. Short of amassing a huge amount of money to buy Aiden out, how would they stop this? His heart pounded fiercely in his chest as he made his way down the hall to Adam's office.

Adam's assistant was waiting. "Mr. Lin?" She stepped out from behind her desk. "May I take your coat? Can I get you a coffee?"

Jacob mustered a polite smile and handed over his black wool coat. "No, thank you. I'm just fine."

"Mr. Langford is waiting for you."

"Actually, you can do one thing for me. Adam and I are discussing a surprise for his sister's birthday. If she comes by, make sure you don't let her in. Don't even let her know that I'm here." He raised his finger to his lips to encourage her compliance. He had to keep Anna away from this powder keg at any cost.

"Of course, Mr. Lin. Your secret is safe with me."

Jacob stood straighter and took extra-long strides into Adam's office. He tried to think of a time he'd had to swallow his pride any more than at this moment. He couldn't think of one, not even with his dad. Could he keep it together, stop himself from getting sidetracked by old problems?

Adam turned slowly in his massive leather executive chair like a villain in an action movie. "This is a surprise."

Jacob didn't wait for an invitation to sit, taking a seat opposite Adam's desk. "I'm as surprised as you are."

"Are you going to tell me why you're here or are we going to play twenty questions?" Adam tapped a pen on the desk blotter.

"It's the War Chest."

"The gang of thugs you put together to take down the corporation my father built from the ground up? I know all about that."

It was so like Adam to bring up the most damning details. "The investment group I was kicked out of when I pushed them to stop because I didn't want a takeover to ruin my chances at a relationship with Anna."

Adam cleared his throat. "Don't get me started on Anna."

You have no idea. Adam was going to blow up when

he found out that he and Anna were as involved as a man
and woman could possibly be, even if the romantic side
of things was fragile. "Please, Adam. I know I've done
some things you aren't happy about. You can't say that
you haven't done the same to me."

"I have a busy day ahead of me. Can you get to the
point?"

"Your brother Aiden has joined the War Chest."

"What?" Fury blazed in Adam's eyes.

"With his percentage of stock in the mix, they can
take over LangTel. Without much problem, I have to
point out. You need to do something about this now."

"Oh, my God. Aiden." Adam's skin blanched, his eyes
grew wide with disbelief. It was the first chink in Adam's
armor that Jacob had ever seen. "He's been estranged
from the family for years and it got worse when my dad
got sick, but I never imagined he would go this far."

"Well, he has."

Adam's elbows dropped to his desk, and he pushed
his hair back from his forehead. He twisted his lips. His
stare narrowed. "Why didn't you take this to Anna? Was
your breakup really that awful? I know she's not fun
when she's mad."

Jacob had already covered up an awful lot with Anna,
and the guilt from that might remain forever. He couldn't
take the lies any further. "No, Adam. Anna is pregnant
and I'm the father. I didn't want to tell her because stress
could jeopardize the baby."

Anna walked through the quiet reception area on the
executive floor, making her way to her office. She didn't
normally get in so early, but she hadn't been able to sleep
much. Perhaps the distraction of work would help clear

her head before she ultimately returned to her worries about the baby and whether or not Jacob was really going to stand by her, no matter what.

"Good morning, Ms. Langford. Will you be joining Mr. Langford and Mr. Lin in their meeting?" her assistant, Carrie, asked as she took Anna's coat.

Anna froze in place. "Mr. Langford and Mr. Lin? Meeting? With each other? Here?"

"They're in Mr. Langford's office right now. I just assumed you knew." Her voice trailed off.

What in the world? Confused, she composed herself. "Oh, uh, yes. Yes, I'm joining them." Anna marched down the hall to her brother's office as if this had been the plan all along. A flurry of thoughts was turning her mind into a snow globe of speculation. Was this Jacob's way of fighting for her? Of showing her that he would take the worst of it? She could only hope that this meeting didn't end up with fists flying.

Adam's assistant bolted from her seat when Anna breezed past her and lunged for the doorknob to Adam's office. "Ms. Langford, I'm sorry. Mr. Langford is in a very important meeting…"

"So I heard." Anna marched into her brother's office. She wasn't about to wait to be invited in. Somebody could be dead.

She first saw Adam's response—surprise and shock. Jacob turned and showed a similar horror.

"Well, you're both still alive. So I guess that's good. Anybody want to tell me what's going on?" She planted her hand on her hip, assessing the situation. *What are these two up to?*

Jacob shifted in his seat. "We, uh, had a few things we needed to discuss."

"Right," Adam said, unconvincingly.

"You two can't stand to be in the same zip code. How about we try again?" She glanced over at Jacob, eager to glean from his facial expressions what was going on.

"Maybe it's time to finally change that," Adam interjected.

Now she had to make eye contact with Jacob. She tapped her foot on the floor. Something about this was off and she could see it on Jacob's face.

Adam blew out an exasperated breath. "This is stupid. Nobody's going to believe that you and I can actually talk to each other. Especially not Anna." He pointed at her. "Look. I know everything. I can't believe you're pregnant and you didn't tell me? Your own brother? And Jacob's the dad? I don't even know where to start with all of this. It's like a bad dream."

Jacob stood and grasped Anna's elbow. "I had to tell him. I'm sorry."

She closed her eyes and shook her head, drawing in a deep breath through her nose. The fact that he'd had the guts to come out with it certainly earned him a few points. "We had to tell him eventually. I just can't believe you came here to do this and that you didn't want me here at the same time."

"Well, that's not the only thing we're talking about," Adam said.

Jacob turned to Adam quickly, and even though Anna couldn't see either of their faces head-on, she could tell they were having a conversation without words.

"Will somebody please just tell me what you're doing?" Anna asked. "I'm not leaving until one of you spills it."

"Well?" Adam asked, staring down Jacob. "Do you want to tell her, or should I?"

"Please. We have to stay calm. For the baby's sake," Jacob said, turning to her. "I found out who the War Chest brought in as their big investor. It's Aiden."

"What?" Anna asked. "Aiden? I don't understand."

Jacob looked at her thoughtfully, showing her his miraculous eyes. They were the only thing that calmed her in this unimaginable situation. He explained everything with Aiden as she struggled to keep up with the details. "It's very important that you don't get worked up about this. My first and only concern is for you and the baby."

Anna narrowed her focus on Adam.

"It's the one thing we didn't account for," Adam said flatly. "We're going to lose controlling interest in the company and I doubt there's much we can do about it. He's had a chip on his shoulder forever about LangTel, and you know how he feels about me in particular. Jacob and I were just strategizing on ways to raise the capital to fight this."

Anna sat down in the chair next to Jacob's. This was not the time for panic. There had to be a solution. "No. Adam, you have to reach out to him. Don't fight this with money. That's going to make things far worse. Send him an email. Tell him we know about it. But do it kindly. We don't want to scare him. Tell him that we want to talk, that we want to find out what would make him do this."

"How is that going to work?"

"You have any other bright ideas? He's our brother. If we do anything less than extend the olive branch, he'll never forgive us. Put yourself in his shoes."

"Maybe you should do it. He actually likes you." Adam's voice had an uncharacteristic wobble. Their father had left an awful lot on Adam's shoulders—the CEO position, now this. The root of the problem with Aiden was undoubtedly their father. He'd pitted the boys against each other from the very beginning.

"I think it will mean more from you, especially if you use a softer touch," she said. "He'll expect you to be all bravado, so don't do that. Be his brother."

"This is business. Do you really think that's advised? It sounds awfully girly."

Anna sat back in her chair and crossed her legs. "Then ask Jacob what he thinks."

Adam cocked both eyebrows at Jacob. Anna was amazed they'd managed this much without taking pot shots at each other.

"Anna's right," Jacob said, taking his seat next to her. "If your brother is feeling like he's on the outs with your family, it's going to take a softer approach. If you try to steamroller him, he'll steamroller you right back. Except he can flatten you with this one, Adam. Completely."

Adam looked as befuddled as Anna had ever seen him. "That's a surprising answer coming from you, Mr. Number Cruncher."

"I know exactly what it feels like to be on the outs with the Langford family. It's not a fun place to be."

Anna swallowed, hard. She couldn't argue that point. The good news was that as of now, Adam and Jacob had to be going on at least twenty minutes of being in the same room and everyone was still living and breathing.

Adam visibly tensed. "Okay. I'll do it. I'll play the nice guy and reach out to him." He went to his laptop and started typing. After a few keystrokes, he looked up at the two of them. "Are we done? I have work to do. I'll let you know when I hear back from Aiden."

Jacob cleared his throat and stood up. "Actually, there's one more thing."

"What?" Adam pushed back from his desk and crossed his arms.

"I need you to know that I love your sister more than anyone or anything on this entire planet. And I'm hoping that she and I can find a way to work things out, but we have some obstacles to get past and I want to get rid of one of them right now. You and I need to drop the fighting. It's stupid, and frankly, I have more important things to worry about."

"Do you really think it's as simple as that?" Adam retorted. "We decide to forget it? I can't believe that you, of all people, would think that you could just come in here and declare a truce and make it all go away. It's far more complicated than that."

"Actually, Adam, it's not. It's really very simple. Do we love Anna more than we hate each other?"

A puff of astonished air left Anna's lips. Six years of feuding and Jacob had boiled it down to one question.

"I know what my answer is," Jacob continued. "I love her far more than I ever hated you, which should tell you just how much I love her. Because I really, really hated you."

Adam sat back in his chair, his jaw slack. He was clearly letting this tumble around in his head, and they had to let him process it. "Wow. I guess you really can make it that simple." He looked at Anna, seeming to get a little choked up. "Anna Banana, I definitely love you more than I hate him. I don't know what I would've done during the last year without you."

"Then let's bury the hatchet, Adam. Please," Jacob added.

"If it will make Anna happy, I will give up the fight."

For the first time in a long time, she felt as if she could

breathe without worry. "It would make me insanely happy. There's enough trouble going around for all of us." She stood and walked over to her brother to give him a hug. Relief washed over her.

"I can't believe I'm going to be an uncle," Adam muttered into her ear, holding her close, not letting go.

It would've been so nice to agree that indeed he would, but they weren't out of the woods. "Fingers crossed that everything goes okay."

"Anything you need at all," Adam said, stepping back, but still holding on to her shoulders. "Just let me know."

"Of course. I will."

"As for you," Adam said, reaching out his hand to shake Jacob's. "I didn't really think this day would come. It'll be good to put it behind us."

Jacob smiled. "It's long overdue."

Anna led the way out of Adam's office. "That's not quite how I expected to start my day," Anna muttered to Jacob in the hall. One enormous problem had been resolved, even if another—Aiden—had cropped up.

"Can we talk?" he asked.

Her staff and coworkers were already milling about. The sight of Jacob Lin in the office was prompting hushed voices and sideways glances. "Of course, but not here. My office." She marched ahead, Jacob in her wake. They passed Holly when they rounded the corner to Anna's office. Holly bugged her eyes, but kept her mouth shut. Anna would have to fill her in later. She closed the door behind them, unsure where to start, only that she knew he deserved an awful lot of credit. "That must've been so hard for you to swallow your pride with Adam. I'm just floored that you would do that for me."

"It was for *us*, Anna. It had to end."

She found herself hopelessly drawn to him—his voice, his presence. When he stripped away her defenses, her reasons for being mad or doubtful, he could have whatever he wanted. She looked up at him, peering into his penetrating eyes, the ones that left her undone. She'd asked him to fight for her, and he'd done exactly that. Big time. "I really admire you for it. I don't know what else to say, other than thank you. I know that couldn't have been easy."

"It wasn't, but I don't care about what's easy anymore. I care about getting you back."

Tingles raced over her skin, her breath caught in her chest. That rumble in his voice was there, the one that made her knees threaten to buckle. "Now what?"

"Have dinner with me tonight. My place."

He'd convinced Adam to let bygones be bygones. Could she do the same? Was she ready for this? Because she was certain that if she wound up in his apartment again, she was going to end up in his bed. Was that the logical next step? If it was, she knew very well that it led to a place where it was nearly impossible to be angry with him. Maybe that was for the best—finally just give in to what she wanted, finally just trust that this was the way things were meant to be. "I'd love to."

His smile was warm and immediate. "Good."

He cupped her shoulder gently and leaned in for a kiss—Anna nearly had a heart attack, her pulse erratic and frantic. She closed her eyes, her lips waiting for the reward, and then it arrived, square on her cheek.

She might've been disappointed if it wasn't so sweet, so warm and comforting, telling her that he was still letting her dictate their speed, even after he'd just put on a commanding performance. "Playing it safe?" She couldn't hide her smile. The ways in which he'd figured her out were uncanny.

"Baby steps. Literally." He placed his hand on her stomach gingerly. She felt his hesitation radiate from his core—he was holding back, employing restraint. "I'll see you tonight."

Seventeen

Jacob hadn't even made it down to the lobby before he had a text from Anna. He did a double take when he saw the message.

Don't leave. I'm spotting.

Was this really happening? Just when everything was finally going well? On my way up. What happened?

He stayed put on the elevator when it dropped people at the lobby, having to wait for what felt like an eternity as a new load of people boarded. It was just before nine, everyone on their way to work, which meant that nearly every button, for every floor, was pressed.

He took a deep breath. *Stay calm.* His heart wasn't cooperating at all, nor was his stomach. Everything in his body was on edge. Why now? Why this?

Anna sent a reply. Went to the bathroom and saw the blood.

Good God. Just when things were getting better. Don't worry. Be there soon.

He sent a text to his driver, instructing him to be ready to get them to the hospital as quickly as possible. Jacob would have to wait until he got somewhere private to call Dr. Wright's office. He couldn't announce in a crowded elevator that Anna Langford was in danger of losing a pregnancy. Nobody but Adam even knew that she was pregnant.

On Anna's floor, he stormed past the receptionist and down the hall, rushing inside her office. "I'm here. Let's go. The car is downstairs." His heart was still pounding—seeing Anna and the panic on her face turned everything into an even harsher reality. They could lose the baby.

Anna nodded, putting on her coat. He put his arm around her shoulders, ushering her out of the office. They didn't stop to say a thing to anyone. There was no time for explanations.

"I called Dr. Wright," she whispered as they waited for the elevator. "They're expecting us. She told us to come up to her office. Not the emergency room."

"Good. Okay. It's going to be okay." He had no business guaranteeing anything, but he had to believe it. They were so close to putting things back together. He rubbed her shoulder—anything to calm her, let her know that he was there for her.

Jacob got Anna down to the car and they were quickly whisked through the city, his driver breaking a few traffic laws while dodging taxis, cyclists and buses. Jacob put his arm around Anna's shoulder, pulling her close. She sank against him, turned into his chest, wrapped her arm around his waist. It was the only comfort he could take in that moment. They had each other. Whatever the future held for the two of them as a couple, or the three of them as a family, they would get through it. They had to.

When they arrived at the hospital, Jacob wasted no time getting Anna through the lobby and up to the sixth floor. The nurse was waiting for them and quickly showed them back to an exam room. Anna changed into a gown. Dr. Wright was in moments later.

"Ms. Langford. Mr. Lin. Before I say anything, I want to tell you both to take a deep breath." She motioned with both hands for them to calm down. "I know you're worried, but this isn't always a bad thing. Let's see what's going on."

Anna leaned back on the exam table and Jacob took her hand. She tilted her head, looking up at him as if he held all of the answers. He'd never felt so helpless in his entire life—the two things he cherished most in the world were right here, Anna and the baby—and there was very little he could do to truly keep them safe. How he longed to tell Anna that everything was going to be okay and to be certain of it.

Dr. Wright wheeled back on her rolling stool. "The good news is that your cervix is closed up tight. Let's listen to the heartbeat and make sure there's no sign of fetal distress."

Fetal distress. Those two words felt like a death sentence. The thought of their child in distress brought the most sickening feeling up from the depths of his gut. He hoped to hear that beautiful whoosh. *Please God, let us hear the whoosh.*

"Before we do this," Dr. Wright started. "I want you

both to understand that this is very early days. If the baby is in trouble, there's not much we can do. I want to remind you that you're both so young. You have your entire lives ahead of you. Today doesn't have to be the end."

Jacob's gaze dropped to meet Anna's. Tears streamed down her cheeks. They welled in his as well. He couldn't even remember another time when he'd cried, but he couldn't have stopped it if he'd wanted to. His dream of a life with Anna could still happen, but it would be different if they lost the baby. Neither of them would ever be the same. He would still want her if the worst happened, but would she still want him? She'd worried that he might not be around for the long haul, but the reality was that the same could be wondered about her. Without this child binding them together, and with every mistake he'd made, would she want to walk away? He couldn't fathom how empty his life would be if that happened.

"We understand. Go ahead," Anna said to Dr. Wright.

Jacob nodded reluctantly. "Yes. Please. Go ahead."

The static and pops had a distinctly different tone to them this time—it was hope at odds with itself, a moment born of desperation while clinging to what you already have, not focused on what might be. He'd never piled so many wishes on a single moment before. Jacob looked right into Anna's eyes. If they were going to receive the worst of news, they would experience the pain of that instant together. She would not be alone. Anna clung to his hand, squeezing tight. Static buzzed. The speaker popped. Frantic crackles echoed.

And then the whoosh. *Whoosh whoosh whoosh.*

Anna's eyes sprang to life, quickly followed by her electric smile, jolting Jacob back to a state where he felt as if he could breathe again. Anna raised her head and looked down at her stomach. "The baby…"

"The heartbeat sounds perfect," Dr. Wright said.

"Thank God." The most profound relief Jacob had ever experienced threatened to knock him flat. He closed his eyes and his shoulders dropped from the solace of that perfect sound. He leaned down and cupped Anna's cheek then pressed a kiss to her forehead. His lips wanted to stay there, keep contact with her warm and wonderful-smelling skin.

Dr. Wright turned off the Doppler and sat back down on her stool. Jacob helped Anna back up to sitting.

"I'd like you on bed rest for the next twenty-four hours. Take it easy. It's very possible that this is just normal first trimester spotting and has nothing to do with any of your other issues."

"Normal?" Jacob asked.

"Yes, Mr. Lin. Normal. Possibly."

He'd never quite imagined his glee at hearing that anything was normal, possibly, but there it was. He was ecstatic.

"You aren't out of the woods. There are never any guarantees. But I'd say that everything, for the moment, looks good. Go home. Relax. Together. Dad, no going into work. Stay with her and call me if anything goes wrong."

"You don't have to worry about that. I'm not going anywhere."

Eighteen

Jacob and Anna arrived at Jacob's apartment around one, after running to Anna's place to get her a few things. He insisted they would be more comfortable at his place. She had to agree, and it was also much closer to the doctor's office if they had to return. Although, as Dr. Wright had said, there wasn't much they could do but wait for the bleeding to stop. At least they would be doing it together.

Anna changed into pajama pants and a tank top, unfortunately finding a similar amount of blood when she used the bathroom.

"Well?" Jacob asked, sounding hopeful when she walked into his bedroom.

"Still spotting. But it's not any worse than before, so that's good." It felt as though she was shouldering the weight of the moment. Intellectually, she knew she had no control over the bleeding, but it was hard not to feel responsible. Perhaps that was the burden of being the messenger. It was okay. She'd take it.

"I don't want you to worry about it." He pulled back the comforter and patted the bed. "Your throne, m'lady."

She grinned and shook her head. He could be so silly if he wanted to be, but she knew for a fact that he wasn't like that with anyone else. He reserved his most un-guarded moments for her. "Are those your PJs?"

"Of course. I'm not leaving you in this bed alone." He'd put on a T-shirt and basketball shorts. How she loved those glorious, lanky legs of his. "I figure we'll watch bad movies all afternoon. I haven't played hooky from work in well, forever, I guess."

"You know, I think I just want to talk for now. Maybe take a nap." She climbed into bed and he did the same, on his side. This was indeed an odd setup, not really knowing the state of things between them. She knew how she felt—he'd obliterated her doubts about whether he'd fight for her. And he'd been right there with her at the doctor's office, holding her hand. He'd even cried with her, at that moment when they were waiting to hear if the baby was still okay. She knew then that her love for him had never gone away. There had just been other things in the way and she could see now that she'd put a few of those things there herself, or at least allowed them to remain.

"This wasn't exactly what I had envisioned when I was hoping to get you back into my bed," he said, punch-ing his pillow a few times.

Anna laughed. "Right now, this is all the romance I can take." She watched as his expression became decidedly less jovial. "I didn't mean it like that, Jacob. Really. I didn't."

He nodded. "It's okay. I'm just trying to follow your cues. I'm waiting for the moment when you tell me that it's okay for me to love you again."

She rolled to her side and took his hand. Of course he was waiting for her. She'd been the guardian of every roadblock between them, making sure he knew the reasons they shouldn't be together. It felt as though the time had come for her to focus on the reasons they should. "Do you think you can? Love me again?"

"Anna, I never stopped loving you."

"Never? Not even for a minute? What about the day I barged into your office?"

He shook his head. "I still loved you that day. It simply hurt more then. That's all."

She thought of the awful things that had come out of her mouth that day—yes, he had done the unimaginable, but she shouldn't have been so determined to end things, no matter what. "I should have listened to you that day. I was hurt, but you were right about a few things. What you had done didn't change what was between us." She smiled when she noticed the way he was hanging on her every word. "In some ways, it was better that we fell in love in a vacuum, hiding our relationship from my family and the rest of the world. It was really the only way it could happen and be real. There was no outside influence."

"Just you and me, Anna. That's the way it should be. Just you and me." The smile that rolled across his face was so pure and unguarded, it took her breath away. "I love you more than you'll ever know. Forever." He leaned closer and brushed a strand of hair from her forehead. "I started to fall in love with you from that very first kiss, and my feelings have only gotten stronger."

His words floated around in her head—so beautiful, so lovely. She couldn't help but be swept up in the moment. "I'm sorry that being with me has been such a test."

He shrugged. "We tested each other. All couples do. We just got a lot of testing out of the way during those early days."

"In some ways, it's good. If we can survive all of that, we can definitely handle sleepless nights and diapers, the terrible twos and kindergarten."

"You make it sound so glamorous." He reached out and pressed his finger to the end of her nose.

"You know what I mean."

"But that's the baby, Anna. There's more than that ahead of us. If you want it. Do you want more?"

She suddenly found it difficult to breathe. Even if he was merely asking for them to spend more time together, the answer was yes, although she hoped for more. Much, much more. Even these few moments in bed together were enough to remind her that she didn't want anything other than him, at her side. "I do."

"Good, because I can't lose you again. You know that I'm a pragmatist. I deal with numbers all day long. I deal with absolutes. But the truth is that my love for you is an absolute."

The tears came. There was no stopping them. They rolled right down her cheeks. "That's the sweetest thing anyone has ever said to me."

"It's true. All true." Before she knew what was happening, he climbed out of bed and walked over to the dresser. When he turned, he held a blue Tiffany box in his hand.

Anna gasped. It was the most horrifically girly thing to do, but she couldn't help it. "Jacob. Are you?" She sat up in bed, wiping the tears from her face.

His eyes grew very serious. "Shhh. I only get one chance to get this right."

"I know. But I just want to make sure you're thinking about what's happening here. I might lose the baby. Will you still feel like this is the right thing to do if that happens?"

He perched on the edge of the bed. "Anna Langford, I love you with all of my heart and soul. If we lose the baby, that doesn't change my love for you. We will get through it together and we'll find a way to be stronger on the other side. In the end, all I want is you." He presented the box, which was dwarfed by the size of his hand. "If you'll do me the honor of becoming my wife, I promise to love you and put up with your family until my very last breath."

She smiled, staring down at everything he held in his hand—their future, happiness. This wasn't at all the way she'd ever dreamed this moment would transpire, but she wouldn't have traded it for anything. "I love you so much. I want nothing more than to have you as my husband."

He opened the box and plucked a gorgeous round solitaire in a platinum setting from the box. He slipped it onto her finger. It was a little big—in both band size and heft—but it was perfect.

She clasped her other hand over her mouth as she admired the ring and the way it sparkled. "It's absolutely beautiful. I couldn't ask for anything more. Literally. I'm not sure I could carry around a bigger diamond without some help."

He laughed quietly. "I swear it didn't look that big in the store."

"Of course it didn't. Your hands are huge."

"All I care about is seeing it on your hand. It couldn't make me any happier."

He leaned forward and kissed her, softly. It was the first time their lips had touched since the breakup, and it was as if she was being reborn. That gentle brush of a kiss told her just how much they were made for each other. If they weren't, they wouldn't have found a way. This was where she belonged, with him, on the other side of their troubles. Or at least a few of them.

"This would be the part where we tear off each other's clothes and make love all night. Sorry about that," she said sheepishly.

"Don't worry. I can hold off for a few nights until the spotting stops. Then I'll make you mine." He cozied up next to her, wrapping his arm around her, making her feel as protected as she could've imagined. "In the meantime, we wait for what comes, and we go through it together."

She took a deep breath, fighting the tears that fought to take over again. She wouldn't cry—there had been too many tears in the last year, and now was a time to be happy. She would focus on Jacob, the ring. She would focus on the baby, on her hope that everything would turn out okay for once. "It's raining," she said, looking out the bedroom windows, with the glorious view of the city.

"Just like that night upstate."

"I guess it did rain that night, didn't it? I remember the puddles the next morning."

"It rained like crazy and you slept right through it."

"I take it you didn't?"

"Not a wink. I was too busy wondering how I was going to get past your brother to get to you."

"Well, you did it. Big props for that."

"Now we just need to hope he can take care of your other brother."

She turned to shush him. "Let's not talk about the bad. Let's just think about the good."

He smiled and pulled her closer, kissing the top of her head and raking his hands through her hair. "I have all the good I'll ever need right here in my arms."

With morning came the sun. After the steady deluge of rain all night, Jacob could only hope this was a good sign. He hadn't slept at all—consumed with a mix of gratitude for Anna's answer to his proposal and hope that today would bring good things.

Anna was asleep on her side, his arm draped over her. He loved having her back against his chest where he could feel her breaths—that steady, measured reminder that she was here again and wasn't leaving any time soon. They hadn't slept in the same bed in weeks. He'd remembered it as being wonderful, but it was even better with the promise that they would be together. Forever.

Anna stirred. As happy as he was to be able to talk to her, that feeling faded as he realized that she would soon get up and go to the bathroom and they would have news—good or bad.

"You're up," he said, pushing his hair from his face.

"I am," she answered, sleepily, shifting her weight and swinging her legs out from under the covers.

"Are you?" He nodded toward the bathroom.

"I am. Fingers crossed."

He sat up in bed. "Do you need me to come with you?"

She sighed and managed half of a smile. "I'm okay. I'll let you know what happens."

"Whatever happens, Anna. I'm here. Good or bad."

Anna tiptoed off to the bathroom. Jacob climbed out of bed, wondering when it would be okay to ask how things were going. Luckily, the flush of the toilet gave him his cue. "Well?" he called from the other room, his heart threatening to pound its way out of his body.

"Nothing," she called back with an elated squeak. "No more spotting."

Jacob had never moved so fast, arriving at the bathroom door in a flash. "Really? Nothing?"

She nodded, going to the sink to wash her hands. *Thank God.* He came up behind her, wrapped his arms around her waist. She was so stunning in the morning—fresh-faced, simply beautiful. The fact that she was carrying his child and had his ring on her finger made her that much more irresistible. He was the luckiest man in creation. "I am so glad."

"I know. Me, too." She looked down and pressed the palm of her hand to her belly. "Me, too."

"You know, you and I are going to make really cute babies," he said, kissing the top of her head. It was the truth—their children would be absolutely gorgeous.

Turning in his arms, she looked up at him. "Babies? Plural?"

"Of course. I want a whole pack of little Lins running all over the penthouse."

She coughed so loud she practically sputtered. "A pack of Lins?"

"Yes, Anna. I had to swallow my pride with your brother. I have to beat him at something. Surely you'll grant me that much."

"Sorry. I don't get your point. Beat him at what, exactly?"

"How ever many kids he and Melanie have, we'll just have one more."

"So this is about being competitive with my brother. That's going to get expensive, you know. What with college and keeping them all outfitted in tiny baby motorcycle jackets."

He laughed. Never had he imagined he could ever be so happy. "Anna, darling. You just leave that to me."

Epilogue

After everything over the last year, Anna had very much looked forward to dancing with her brother Adam at his wedding. She'd imagined the grand hotel ballroom, the legion of happy guests, stunning centerpieces of purple tulips and white irises picked out by Melanie, and the enormous wedding cake that likely took more than a week to create. She'd just never imagined that she'd be watching her other brother, Aiden, dancing with their mother at the same time.

"Aiden seems so happy to be back in the family fold," she said to Adam as he twirled her around the dance floor. He'd just finished his own dance with their mother, during which Evelyn Langford had cried her eyes out. Between having all three of her children in the same place for the first time in years and having her first grandchild on the way, Evelyn had made a point of telling them all how happy she was. There was much to be thankful for on this chilly January day, even the tears that flowed because of it.

"Aiden does seem happy, doesn't he?" Adam countered. "I still can't believe what a number Dad did on him, but I'm glad he was able to see past it. I know for a fact that it hasn't been easy for him."

Anna didn't even want to think about the things that had come to light about their father and his volatile relationship with Aiden—years of misunderstandings, Aiden being passed over in favor of Adam. She only wanted to focus on the good, especially today. "I think it helped a lot that you two talked everything out. He needed to feel like you weren't just toeing the family line because of your loyalty to Dad."

"I loved Dad as much as anyone, but we both know that he could be stubborn and narrow-minded. It doesn't mean he wasn't a good man. It just means that he made mistakes. We've all made mistakes. I've made a lifetime of them and I'm not even thirty-five."

Anna smiled. She wasn't about to rub it in, even though she very easily could have as pertained to Jacob. Adam and Jacob's friendship had rebounded nicely in the weeks since Jacob had dared to demand a truce. They weren't best friends, but they'd come to enjoy time together, and that was as much as she could've ever hoped for. "We all goof up, Adam. It takes happy days like today to remind us that sometimes we have to let those things go." That lesson had been no more important for her than when it had come to Jacob. The minute she put the past behind them, the future had opened up beautifully.

"Speaking of letting things go, why didn't one of us

come up with the idea of running LangTel together as co-CEOs? It's a brilliant move."

She smiled. This had been Jacob's idea, since they were already doing some restructuring in the company in order to bring Aiden on board as a Senior VP of Marketing. "Jacob made an excellent point. No two people are capable of accomplishing as much as we are when we aren't fighting." It wasn't exactly the arrangement Anna had expected. A few months ago, she would have said absolutely not, that she wanted the sole position for herself. But with her pregnancy progressing well, and with an early June due date, taking over as CEO would not leave her the time to be the kind of mom she wanted to be. Her career was important, but not so much that she wanted their child raised by a nanny. That existence had been so difficult for Jacob. She didn't care to repeat the pattern and understandably, neither did he.

"You don't need to worry about any fighting from me. I promise. The co-CEO thing means I can go back to working on my own projects, as well. It's really perfect for me."

"It's perfect for both of us," Anna added.

The song faded to its end and Jacob came up behind Adam with a wide grin on his face. "Hey, Langford. I don't want to be a jerk about it, but I'd like to dance with my bride-to-be."

Adam kissed Anna on the cheek. "Sounds like somebody is tired of sharing you. I can't say I blame him." He clapped Jacob on the back. If anyone had said six months ago that this particular scene would be indicative of the new status quo, Anna never would've believed it. "I'll leave you two lovebirds to it. I have a date with my own bride." He excused himself and waved at Melanie, who was extricating herself from a dance with her uncle.

Jacob swept Anna into his arms, twirling her several times, making the eggplant purple bridesmaid's dress flutter around her. "Finally. I get you to myself."

Anna giggled, the swarm of wedding guests around them fading into the recesses as she became solely focused on Jacob. He really was her dream man. He really was perfect for her. And she couldn't have been any happier.

"We need to get in our time on the dance floor. Just a little more than a month until we're in this same spotlight." They did, in fact, need to clock a few hours of dancing, although their wedding would not be anywhere near as extravagant—fifty guests, at Jacob's house upstate. Neither one of them cared to deal with anything more elaborate. Jacob had actually said he was hoping for a blizzard so no one would be able to show up and he could keep Anna to himself for an entire week or more. She couldn't blame him. It sounded like the perfect plan.

He pulled her closer, his body heat enveloping her, or perhaps it was just his magnetism, the things about him that wouldn't allow her to stay away. He was especially difficult to resist in a tuxedo. "I can't believe you're going to be my wife. Honestly, I can't believe I'm going to be part of the Langford family. I'm having a hard time imagining what it's going to be like. Especially after spending six years in exile."

She reared her head back, looking deeply into his soulful eyes. "Things happen for a reason. I believe that. Maybe you and Adam will end up having an even stronger friendship one day. I certainly wasn't ready to run away with you and have a baby six years ago. So maybe this was for the best, as difficult as it was for you to go through."

He nodded, a slight smile crossing his face. "I'd go through it all for you. Every last minute of it."

She smirked and shook her head. "You're sweet."

"Really I'm just angling to get you out of that brides-maid's dress."

"You and me both. I can't wait to change. It's too tight on my belly." Anna wasn't showing much yet, but her tummy had pooched out a little. Jacob liked to lie in bed and talk to the tiny baby bump. Then he would get out his Doppler for listening to the heartbeat, which had arrived shortly after the spotting scare. He made quite the doting dad-to-be.

Jacob pulled her in tightly, moving her in time effortlessly to the music. "Are you happy?" he asked.

"What kind of question is that?" Anna whispered, leaning into him as she watched Adam and Melanie sway in the tiniest of circles, husband and wife. It wouldn't be long for Jacob and her. The thought warmed her from head to toe.

"It's a perfectly valid thing to ask, especially considering everything we've been through. I want to know that you're happy, Anna. It's the only thing I care about."

She looked up into his eyes, which shone down on her like sunshine on the first day of spring. She could get lost in those eyes for a lifetime and be deliriously giddy. "I don't think it's possible for me to be happier. Truly. Being with you is all I'll ever want."

"Good." He slowed their dance to the most imperceptible of movements, lowering his head and planting the sexiest, hottest kiss she could've imagined on her lips. It was slow and seductive, a subtle parting of lips and the most tasteful bit of tongue. It left her ready to pass out.

"Jacob. My family is watching," she said when she came up for air, making a mental note that they absolutely would need to continue this when they got home after the reception.

"I thought we agreed that your family had interfered in enough of our kisses."

"True, but it's still a wedding. We don't want to be *those* people, do we?"

He laughed and spun her around, then stopped and laid another steamy kiss on her, this time dipping her back in his arms. He left her breathless, ready to surrender in a ballroom filled with hundreds of people. "Tell me to stop."

She smiled, caught in his eyes and the echo of the enticing rumble in his voice. "Jacob Lin, I never want you to stop."

* * * * *

MILLS & BOON®

Desire™

PASSIONATE AND DRAMATIC LOVE STORIES

'The perfect Christmas read!' - Julia Williams

Jewellery designer Skylar loves living London, but when a surprise proposal goes wrong, she finds herself fleeing home to remote Puffin Island.

Burned by a terrible divorce, TV historian Alec is dazzled by Sky's beauty and so cynical that he assumes that's a bad thing! Luckily she's on the verge of getting engaged to someone else, so she won't be a constant source of temptation... but this Christmas, can Alec and Sky realise that they are what each other was looking for all along?

Order yours today at
www.millsandboon.co.uk

MILLS & BOON®

Man of the Year

Our winning cover star will be revealed next month!

**Don't miss out on your copy
– order from millsandboon.co.uk**

Read more about Man of the Year 2016 at

www.millsandboon.co.uk/moty2016

**Have you been following our
Man of the Year 2016 campaign?**
🐦 **#MOTY2016**